ELEMENTS OF QUANTITY SURVEYING

By the same Authors

MORE ADVANCED QUANTITY SURVEYING

PRACTICE AND PROCEDURE FOR THE QUANTITY SURVEYOR

SPECIFICATION WRITING FOR ARCHITECTS AND SURVEYORS

---

and in collaboration with W. N. B. George and H. P. Scher

THE ARCHITECT IN PRACTICE

Also by Arthur J. Willis

AN EXAMPLE IN QUANTITY SURVEYING

GENEALOGY FOR BEGINNERS

INTRODUCING GENEALOGY

Edited and published by Arthur J. Willis

HAMPSHIRE MARRIAGE LICENCES 1607–1640

HAMPSHIRE MARRIAGE LICENCES 1669–1680

WINCHESTER CONSISTORY COURT DEPOSITIONS (Selections 1561–1602)

WINCHESTER ORDINATIONS 1660–1829 *in two volumes*

CANTERBURY MARRIAGE LICENCES 1751–1837

WINCHESTER GUARDIANSHIPS AFTER 1700

WINCHESTER SETTLEMENT PAPERS 1667–1842

A HAMPSHIRE MISCELLANY *in four parts*

WILLS, ADMINISTRATIONS AND INVENTORIES WITH THE WINCHESTER DIOCESAN RECORDS

Arthur J Willis FRICS, HonFIQS
and
Christopher J Willis FRICS, FIArb

ELEMENTS OF QUANTITY SURVEYING

Seventh edition

CROSBY LOCKWOOD STAPLES
GRANADA PUBLISHING
London Toronto Sydney New York

Granada Publishing Limited

First published in Great Britain 1935 by Crosby Lockwood & Son Ltd
Second edition 1940
Third edition 1943, reprinted 1944, 1945, 1946, 1947
Fourth edition 1948, reprinted 1949, 1950, 1951, 1953, 1955, 1957, 1961, 1962
Fifth edition 1963, reprinted 1965
Sixth edition (metric) 1969

Reprinted 1974 and 1976 by Crosby Lockwood Staples
Seventh edition 1978
published by Granada Publishing Limited
in Crosby Lockwood Staples

Granada Publishing Limited
Frogmore, St Albans, Herts AL2 2NF
and
3 Upper James Street, London W1R 4BP
1221 Avenue of the Americas, New York, NY 10020 USA
117 York Street, Sydney, NSW 2000, Australia
100 Skyway Avenue, Toronto, Ontario, Canada M9W 3A6
Trio City, Coventry Street, Johannesburg 2001, South Africa
CML Centre, Queen & Wyndham Streets, Auckland 1, New Zealand

ISBN 0 258 97117 7 HB
0 258 97098 7 PB

Typeset by Preface Ltd, Salisbury, Wilts.
Printed in Great Britain by Richard Clay (The Chaucer Press), Bungay, Suffolk

PREFACE

The publication of the seventh edition of this book follows the introduction of the sixth edition of the *Standard Method of Measurement* and the *Practice Manual* which accompanies it. We have over the years tried to make this book a practical interpretation of the rules for taking off the main elements of a simple building, combined with our suggestions of what we consider good practice, in fact a practice manual of taking off.

The arrangement of this book follows closely that of previous editions. Metrication has now settled down and we feel is sufficiently familiar to allow us to drop the m and mm from the drawings, which are now figured in millimetres in line with current drawing office practice. The virtual disappearance of the traditional worker-up has meant that less emphasis has been put on the abstract than before, although the skill of the experienced abstractor is still sometimes called for, even in these days of slip sorting and computers. It may well be that chapters 22 and 23 appear for the last time in their present form.

We are conscious that in the years to come, perhaps sooner rather than later, quantity surveyors may not be producing bills of quantities in the form we know today. However, we are confident that measurement in some form or another will continue to be the basis of valuation in our industry, and that as long as there is a *Standard Method of Measurement* that basis will be a relatively detailed one and text books such as this will be required.

The main changes in the new SMM aim at satisfying the requirement for more drawn information to be made available and the measurement of more cost-significant items at the expense of some detail. This has resulted in the incorporation, where appropriate, of line diagrams in the dimensions, and reference in the text when information is required to be given on accompanying drawings. The less need now to give some of the more detailed information means that certain items formerly measured have disappeared.

The opportunity of a new edition has been taken to modernise the drawings and in consequence some of the more traditional items common in the past have been dropped. Some may question why this has not been taken further and why work which could be described as anachronistic, like the fireplace, has not gone too. What is or is not anachronistic is sometimes a matter of geography (coal fires are common enough in the North of England, outside 'smokeless zones') and sometimes a matter of relativity. We have not given an example of the measurement of thatching, and indeed this section was dropped from the new SMM for this very reason of anachronism, but to a thatcher it is far from anachronistic; it is what he is doing all his time. Why such examples do not appear here is that there is a limit to the subject matter and the less needed subjects must be dropped.

One may sometimes feel like Samuel Johnson

'Leave to Heaven the measure and the choice'

but that is certainly an example of the 'vanity of human wishes'.

We hope this revision will help those starting out on their careers in this profession as we hope previous editions have done.

January 1978

A.J.W.
C.J.W.

VALETE

I thought that I should like to take the opportunity of this revision to say a sort of goodbye to the profession. At the age of 83 my share in revisions of our books is mainly to edit the Preface and, perhaps, the Introduction.

The idea of this book came when I was myself working for the exam of 1921. There was then no SMM and only two voluminous text books trying to cover the whole work of the quantity surveyor, which were of little use to show a beginner how to take off. I had to rely on a correspondence course to show me how to take off stonework with all labours measured separately as the exam question required.

I must say thank you to all my readers over some 40 years, who have each (unless they borrowed from a library!) made a contribution to a welcome supplement to my professional income. I hope the present generation of students will find the book useful.

ARTHUR J. WILLIS

PREFACE TO THE FIRST EDITION

My experience as both lecturer and examiner has impressed on me the apparent need for a textbook on the *elements* of quantity surveying, a book which, giving everything in its simplest form, will assist a student to a good grounding in first principles (in nothing more important than in quantity surveying). I have therefore kept solely in mind the requirements for preparing the bill of a normal simple domestic or small industrial building, and have refrained from introducing such allied subjects as pricing, variation accounts and professional practice.

It seems to me that a textbook on this subject should not attempt to repeat in detail the rules laid down in the official *Standard Method of Measurement*, a volume which it is now recognised must be in the hands of every student. My aim has therefore been to concentrate on method and procedure and to give practical examples, leaving the student to study concurrently the appropriate sections of the official volume, to the new (1935) edition of which references are given at the head of each chapter on taking off. Such references will not all apply to every case, but are given as a guide to those clauses of the *Standard Method* which, having regard to the limits I have set myself, are most likely to be needed.

In preparing examples I have made a point of reproducing all drawings to one of the customary scales without any reduction, so that the student can use his scale on them—an essential to their proper study. The examples cannot comprise all possibilities in even the simplest building, and are intended only as a first step in the understanding of the general principles involved. The dimensions and abstract are reproduced from handwriting to illustrate the proper method of setting out the sheets, which cannot be conveyed in print. I had hoped to include the complete dimensions, abstract and bill of a small building to which the student could refer after studying the isolated examples, but practical limitations do not allow it to be incorporated in this volume, and such an example must therefore await a later opportunity.

In deciding the scope of this book I have generally limited myself to the current syllabus of the Intermediate Examination Part II (Quantities sub-division) of the Chartered Surveyors' Institution, except that I considered that Internal Plumbing, as one of the integral parts of every domestic building, should be dealt with. It is hoped that the book will also be found of use for the examinations of the Institute of Builders and City and Guilds of London Institute.

My thanks are due to The Architectural Press Ltd. for permission to reproduce from my book, *Working Up a Bill of Quantities*, my suggested rules of order. I am also very grateful to Mr. R. H. Stevens, F.S.I., and Mr. C. E. Kenney, F.S.I., for kindly reading the proofs and making a number of valuable suggestions. I cannot but add a word of thanks to all those who as my principals, assistants, examinees, or students have by their ideas (and mistakes) contributed directly or indirectly to the subject-matter of the book.

July, 1935 A.J.W.

ACKNOWLEDGEMENTS

We are most grateful to our partners and staff for the valuable help and comment they have given in interpreting the implications of the sixth edition of the *Standard Method of Measurement* in the preparation of this edition of the *Elements of Quantity Surveying.*

A.J.W.
C.J.W.

CONTENTS

TABLE OF EXAMPLES

Example page

CHAPTER 1

INTRODUCTION

The Purpose of a Bill of Quantities.—Just as one asks before having a suit made what it will cost, so a prospective building owner naturally wants to know before placing the order what the cost of his building will be. The architect can prepare drawings and a specification which define exactly what is wanted, but the builder obviously cannot quote a price simply by looking at these documents. The tailor could estimate that the suit requires so many yards or metres of cloth and lining and so many hours of labour at known costs, to which he would add a certain amount to cover his profit and overhead charges. He does not work this out every time a customer asks, because he deals in a limited number of types with all of which he is familiar. In the case of buildings, each has its own characteristics and different conditions of site, and, except in the rare case of repeat orders, the builder must work out the probable cost to him in detail in each case, and the detail of labour and material necessary for a building is very much more complicated than that necessary for a suit of clothes.

Method of Analysing Cost.—It is evident that if the building is split up into its constituent parts and the cost of each part can be estimated, an estimate can be compiled of the whole work. It has been found in practice that a schedule can be made setting out the quantity of each type of work in recognised units of measurement, and that estimated prices can be built up for the labour and material involved in each unit. This schedule is the bill of quantities, the prices in which can be added up to arrive at a total sum. It must not be forgotten that the bill of quantities in its normal use produces only an estimate. It is prepared and priced before the erection of the building and gives the builder's estimated cost. Such estimated cost, however, becomes under the normal building contract a definite price to which the builder agrees for the work as set out in the bill. The bill must, therefore, completely represent the proposed work if the builder is not to find a serious discrepancy between his actual and estimated costs.

Origin of the Independent Quantity Surveyor.—Competitive tendering is one of the basic principles of most classes of business, and if competitors are given full information of the requirements of the case it should be fair to all concerned. Builders tendering, however, found that a lot of work was involved in making detailed calculations and measurements to arrive at the tender, and realised that by coming together and employing one man to make these calculations for them all in a particular case a considerable saving would be made in their overhead charges. They therefore began to arrange for this to be done, each including the surveyor's fee, and the successful competitor paying him. He provided each competing builder with a bill of quantities which the builder could price himself in a comparatively short space of time. Such was the origin of the independent quantity surveyor, and it was not long before the position was realised by architect and building owner. Here was the building owner indirectly paying for the surveyor through the builder, when by employing him directly he could make use of him as a consultant in his own special branch. In this way the quantity surveyor began to get the authority of the employer, and, being trusted by both sides, attained the independent position which he normally holds after the signing of the contract to measure and value variations as between building owner and builder. A relic of the earlier system remained in the practice, now almost obsolete, of adding quantity surveyor's fees to the end of the bill of quantities and the payment of such fees through the builder.

Essentials in a Good Quantity Surveyor.—What, then, are the essentials in a good quantity surveyor? He must be able to describe clearly, fully and precisely the requirements of the architect and so arrange his bill that the builder's estimator can quickly, easily and accurately arrive at the estimated cost of the work. This being so, it is obviously important that the surveyor should be able to express himself clearly in language that will not be misunderstood, and to do this he must have a sound knowledge of building materials and construction and of customs prevailing in the trade. He must, moreover, be careful and accurate in his calculations, have a systematic and orderly mind and be able to visualise the drawings and details with which he has to deal.

Divisions of Quantity Surveying.—The traditional preparation of a bill of quantities divides itself into three distinct stages:

(1) The measurement of the dimensions from the drawings by the 'taker-off'.

(2) The working out of the volumes, areas, etc. (known as squaring the dimensions), the casting up of their totals and the entering of all the results on the abstract, which collects and classifies them in a recognised order preparatory to the writing of the bill.

(3) The casting up of the abstract, the reducing of totals to recognised units, and transfer of the results to a schedule or bill having money columns ready for pricing out.

The stages (2) and (3) above are known as 'working up'. All calculations in these stages and every entry transferred should be checked by a second person to ensure that no mathematical or copying error occurs.

With the disappearance of the traditional worker-up and the introduction of electronic calculators for squaring and checking dimensions, the abstracting stage has in many cases given way to a system of slip sorting known as 'cut and shuffle' whereby the original dimensions, having been copied, are cut and resorted into bill order.

One stage from this is the use of the computer, when the working up is eliminated completely. The dimensions and descriptions are fed into the computer which does all the calculations and produces a print-out for the bill of quantities in the correct order.

Quantities as Part of the Contract.—The bill of quantities usually forms one of the contract documents, the contract providing that the quantity of work comprised in the contract shall be that set out in the bill of quantities. In such a case the builder is expected to do and the employer to pay for neither more nor less than the quantities given, an arrangement which is fair to both parties. It will thus be seen how important accuracy is in the preparation of the bill, and how a substantial error might lead a building owner to enter into a contract which involved a sum considerably beyond what he contemplated. It may be, however, that the quantities are not part of the contract, as is usual when a builder prepares his own from drawings and specification only, but which is rarely done when an architect or independent surveyor prepares the bill. In such a case the risk of errors in the quantities is thrown on the builder, which if he is preparing his own quantities he would naturally expect to bear, but which when the quantities are prepared by the architect or an independent surveyor it is hardly fair should fall on him.

Builders' Estimates.—The subject of quantity surveying is being dealt with here chiefly from the professional quantity surveyor's point of view, but the preparation of quantities is, of course, very necessary to the builder for the making up of estimates where quantities are not supplied, which is common in small contracts. The builder's estimate in such cases may, on the face of it, look a rough affair: it is, perhaps, written in pencil with shortened descriptions, it takes short cuts in measurement which the quantity surveyor dare not take, and has pricing worked out against the dimensions; there is no separate abstract, and no long preamble to each trade describing materials and workmanship. But it must not be judged by appearances: it needs every bit as much care and system as does the quantity surveyor's bill. The essential difference is that the quantity surveyor's bill will be interpreted by a number of firms tendering in competition, and must therefore be complete in its information and a suitable basis for a contract. The builder's estimate is solely for his own pricing. If he takes short cuts, he does so at his own risk; if he makes mistakes, he alone suffers. He can take as obvious what the quantity surveyor must describe in detail. The same general principles of measurement will apply in both cases, but the builder is free to adapt them to his own taste, where the quantity surveyor is bound by standard rules in the interests of all builders tendering. Nevertheless, the builder's surveyor must be able to check the quantity surveyor's bill and measure up variations on the basis of that bill. It is therefore essential that he should understand how it is prepared, and he should have no difficulty in adapting this knowledge to suit the somewhat different conditions when preparing his own quantities for a builder's estimate.

Differences of Custom.—It must be understood that, as a good deal of the subject-matter of this book is concerned with method and procedure, suggestions made must not be taken as invariable rules. Surveyors will have in many cases their own customs and methods of setting about their work which may differ from those given here, and which may be equally good, or in their view better. The procedure advocated is put forward as being reasonable and based on practice. Every effort has been made to explain reasons for suggestions, so that they can be balanced against any alternative proposed. Furthermore, all rules must be adapted to suit any particular circumstances which may specially apply to the work in hand, as the wide range of possibilities cannot all be provided for in advance.

Method of Study.—The student is advised in the first place to study Chapter 2 in order to grasp thoroughly the form in which dimensions are usually written. He is assumed to have knowledge of elementary building construction and simple mensuration and trigonometry, but if he feels weak on these subjects he should concentrate on them before proceeding further with Quantities. Chapter 3 will give him some information on and examples of the practical applications of mensuration as most commonly met with in quantity surveying. In Chapter 4 are collected a number of notes on general procedure which he should read before attempting to study actual examples of measurement, but to which he may find it useful to turn again after having made some study of taking off. Chapters 5—19 represent the clear-cut sections into which the taking off of a small building might be divided, and these should be taken one at a time. The principal clauses of the *Standard Method of Measurement** (abbreviated to S.M.M.) and the *Practice Manual* (abbreviated to P.M.) applicable are referred to at the head of the chapter and should be studied first. The chapter should then be read and the examples at the end studied, in which the student should find himself able to follow every measurement by reference to the relative drawing. Chapter 20 introduces a number of practical points for consideration in dealing with a complete building.

The examples of taking off in this book are all isolated small parts of what would be the dimensions of a complete building. When they have been mastered in their isolation it will be much easier to see how they are expanded and fitted together to make up the dimensions of a complete building. The traditional processes in preparing the bill have been outlined, and something is also said of the short cuts which are taken in some offices, but which are often not adaptable to every kind of building.

Chapters 21—26 deal with 'working up', which, though usually the work of the junior, is more logically dealt with after the taking off as being a subsequent process. The student may, however, study these chapters simultaneously with those on taking off. The various steps are fully described, and the student should follow each in turn with the examples at the end of the chapters.

Examples.—It must be realised that the examples are small detached parts of dimensions to illustrate the methods of measurement of a small unit of a building. They are not a connected series. They assume that full specification clauses would be set out in preambles to the bill (see page 229), and that clauses would be inserted, such as those required by the S.M.M. for keeping excavation free from water or for protection.

Metrication.—The use of metres and millimetres as the units of measurement results in many cases in the use of three places of decimals in side casts to the dimensions. This is necessary, although the resulting dimension set down in the dimension column would be restricted to two places in accordance with the guidance given by the S.M.M.

In line with current drawing office practice the dimensions of the drawings are figured in millimetres.

The unit symbols recommended in the B.S. *Guide for the Use of the Metric System in the Construction Industry* have been used throughout.†

**The Standard Method of Measurement of Building Works*, 6th Edition, May 1978 and the *Practice Manual*, April 1978. The Royal Institution of Chartered Surveyors and The National Federation of Building Trades Employers.

†PD 6031.

TAKING OFF

The examples in the chapters that follow are written on traditional dimension paper. It is recognised, however, that the majority of taking off today, when not coded for a computer, will be on some form of cut and shuffle paper and that the bill will be typed direct from the descriptions. The use of abbreviations, except where repeating a description already written, is little practised, therefore, as this would entail someone writing them out before typing. Thus, although the examples are written on traditional paper, this being considered the best system for a text book and indeed what the candidate will be faced with in the examination room, they are phrased as if they were on cut and shuffle paper, without abbreviations.

CHAPTER 2

SETTING DOWN OF DIMENSIONS

Traditional Dimension Paper.—The dimensions are measured from the drawings by the taker-off, who uses paper ruled thus:-

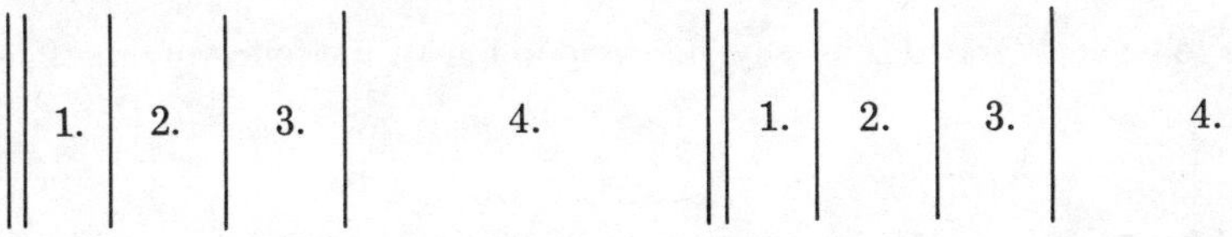

1.	2.	3.	4.	1.	2.	3.	4.

The columns (not of course normally numbered) have been numbered here for identification. Column 1 is called the timesing column, and its use will be described later. Column 2 is the dimension column, in which the measurements are set down as taken. Column 3 is the squaring column, in which are set out the calculated volumes, areas, etc., of the measurements in column 2. Column 4 is the description column, in which is written the description of the work to which the dimensions apply, and on the extreme right-hand side of which (known as 'waste') preliminary calculations and collections are made. There are two sets of columns in the width of a single foolscap or A4 sheet. There is usually a narrow binding margin (not shown above) on the left of the sheets so that they can be bound up when finished.

Some surveyors use dimension paper in single sheets, others in double, the choice really depending on the method of tying up or binding. Some prefer single sheets ruled on one side only. If the sheets are to be bound, double sheets should be used and all writing kept out of the binding margin.

Each sheet should have the name of the job written on or, better, stamped on, a stamp being easily made up from an office printing outfit or specially made commercially at no great cost.

Cut and Shuffle Dimension Paper.—An example of a sheet of cut and shuffle dimension paper is shown on page 198 and a full description of how it is used is included in Chapter 21 where the principle of slip sorting is described.

Form of Dimensions.—Before going any further it is necessary to understand the dimensions as set down by the taker-off. All dimensions are in one of four forms, viz.:

(a) Cubic measurements.

(b) Square or superficial measurements.

(c) Lineal measurements.

(d) 'Numbers' or enumerated items.

These are expressed in the first three cases by setting down the measurements immediately under each other in the dimension column, each separate item being divided from the text by a line, e.g.:

3.00 2.00 4.00		indicating a cubic measurement 3.00 m long, 2.00 m wide and 4.00 m deep.
3.00 2.00		indicating a superficial measurement 3.00 m long and 2.00 m wide.
3.00		indicating a lineal measurement of 3.00 m.

An item to be enumerated is usually indicated in one of the following ways:

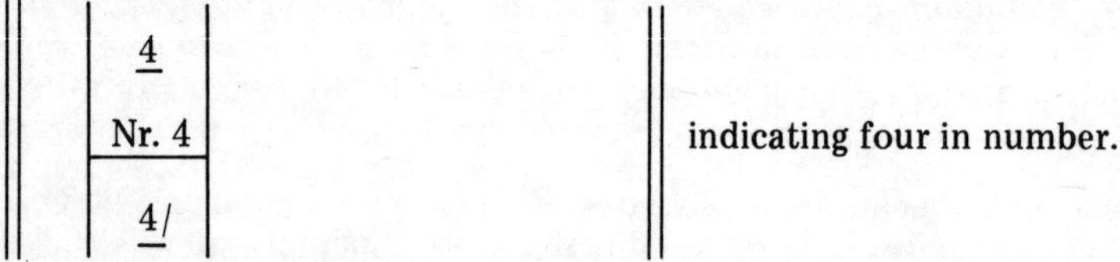

In the Building Industry all dimensions (except in the case of numbered items) are assumed to be in metres, unless otherwise particularly stated. There is no need to label dimensions cube, sq, lin, etc., as, if a rule is made always to draw a line under each measurement, it is obvious from the number of dimensions in the measurement under which category it comes.

It is usual to set down the dimensions in the following order:

(1) Horizontal length.

(2) Horizontal width.

(3) Vertical depth or height.

Although the order will not affect the calculation of the cubic or square measurement, it is very valuable in tracing measurements after they are written if a consistent order is maintained, and, as will be explained later, an incorrect order may even sometimes mislead an estimator in pricing.

'Timesing'.—It often happens that when the taker-off has written his dimension he finds that there are several similar items, and to indicate that he wants the measurement multiplied he will 'times' it, thus:

3/	3.00 2.00 4.00		indicating that the cubic measurement is to be multiplied by 3.
5/	3.00 2.00		indicating that the square measurement is to be multiplied by 5.

The 'timesing' figure is kept in the first column and separated from the dimension by a diagonal stroke. An item 'timesed' can be 'timesed' again, each multiplier multiplying everything to the right of it, thus:

5/			
3/	3.00		indicating that the cubic measurement having been multiplied by 3 the result is to be multiplied by 5, i.e. the original measurement is multiplied by 15.
	2.00		
	4.00		
2/			
5/			
3/	3.00		indicating that the cubic measurement is to be multiplied by 30.
	2.00		
	4.00		

The timesing is done to a lineal or numbered item in just the same way as shown above for a cube or square.

Dotting On.—In repeating a dimension the taker-off may find that he cannot multiply, but needs to add. For instance, having measured three items as follows:

3/	3.00		
	2.00		
	4.00		

suppose he finds two more. He could times by multiplying by $1\frac{2}{3}$, thus:

$1\frac{2}{3}$/			
3/	3.00		
	2.00		
	4.00		

but to avoid fractions and make his train of thought clearer he resorts to what is called 'dotting on', thus:

·3/	3.00		indicating that the cubic measurement is to be multiplied by 3 + 2, i.e. by 5.
2	2.00		
	4.00		

The dot is placed either in line with the top of the figures or half-way down. In practice there is a tendency for each figure dotted on to be lower than the last just as each one 'timesed' is usually higher, more space being thus available than if they were all written in a horizontal line.

'Timesing' and 'dotting on' can be combined, thus:

Timesing	Dimensions		Description
2/			
3/			
2 (dotted on)	3.00		indicating that the cubic measurement
	2.00		is to be multiplied by (3 + 2) x 2, i.e.
	4.00		by 10
2/			
3 (dotted on) 3/	3.00		indicating that the cubic measurement
	2.00		is to be multiplied by 3 x (2 + 3). i.e.
	4.00		by 15

or the last could again be timesed, thus:

Timesing	Dimensions		Description
2/			
2/			
3 (dotted on) 3/	3.00		indicating a multiplier of 30.
	2.00		
	4.00		

Irregular Figures.—So far only regular figures have been dealt with, but the taker-off often has to set down dimensions for triangles, circles and other such figures. Various examples are given below:

Timesing	Dimensions		Description
$\frac{1}{2}$/	3.00		Area of triangle with base 3.00 m and
	2.00		height 2.00 m, in accordance with the formula for the area of a triangle, viz. $\frac{1}{2}$(base x height).
	(circle) 3.00		Area of a circle 3.00 m diameter.
	(semicircle) 3.00		Area of a semicircle 3.00 m diameter.
	(circle) 3.00		Volume of a cylinder 3.00 m diameter
	5.00		and 5 m high.
$\frac{1}{2}$/			
$3\frac{1}{7}$/	3.00		Circumference of a semicircle 3.00 m diameter, i.e. $\frac{\pi}{2}$ x 3.00.
			This is sometimes expressed more directly as $1\frac{4}{7}$/.
x 1.25 x	(segment) 3.00		Area of a segment of a circle with 3.00 m chord and 1.25 m rise.

The above are the most usual figures, and other irregular ones will probably mostly be measured by building up in triangles or portions of circles.

Collections.—Except in very simple cases, dimensions should not be added together in the head. Not only will risk of error be reduced if they are written down, because the written calculation will be checked, but the process by which the figures were arrived at will be made clear if referred to at a later date, when some of the circumstances may be forgotten, or the dimensions are being dealt with by a different person. These preliminary calculations, known as 'collections,' are made on the right-hand side of the description column. They must be written definitely and clearly, and not scribbled as if they were a sum worked out on scrap paper, which the term 'waste' used for this part of the column might be thought to imply. In fact, every effort must be made to commit to writing the train of thought of the taker-off. Waste calculations should be limited to those necessary for the clear setting down of the dimensions by the taker-off, and not take the place of squaring out, which is properly left to the worker-up. See page 12 for an example of waste collection.

Alterations in Dimensions.—Where a dimension has been set down incorrectly and is to be altered it should either be neatly crossed out and the new dimension written in, or the word 'nil' should be written against it in the squaring column to indicate that it is to be taken as cancelled. Where a number of measurements in the dimension column are bracketed together care must be taken to indicate clearly how far the 'nil' applies, and this may be done thus:

	3.00 4.00	
	6.00 2.00	
	7.00 3.00	↑
	2.60 5.00	nil ↓

No attempt should be made to alter figures, e.g. a 2 into a 3 or a 3 into an 8. The figure may appear to have been altered satisfactorily, but may look quite different when the ink is dry or when the dimensions are photocopied. Every figure must be absolutely clear, a page a little untidy but with umistakable figures being far preferable to one where the figures give rise to uncertainties and consequent waste of time. Nor should erasures with penknife or rubber be made. It is often of value to know what was written in the first instance, and an erasure is at the best of times obvious. It is best to nil entirely and write out again such dimensions as are getting too confused by alterations, but great care is needed in copying dimensions, or an important mistake may be made, it being particularly easy to miss copying the timesing. Where, therefore, any dimensions are rewritten they should be very carefully checked through with the originals.

The Descriptions.—The description of the item measured is set down opposite the measurement in the description column, thus (the 'waste' collection being also shown):

		Ground level 15.05	34.00
		12.00	16.00
		13.50	50.00
		11.70	2/ = 100.00
		4)52.25	4/215 0.86
		av. = 13.06	99.14
		bott. of conc. 12.05	
		1.01	
	99.14 1.00 1.01	Exc. tr. exc. 0.50 m wide n.e. 2.00 m dp.	

Some surveyors prefer to write the item description first and put down their 'waste' calculations below it. The writers prefer to make their calculations first and think out the description afterwards.

It will be seen that descriptions are abbreviated*, and the subject of abbreviations as well as the framing of descriptions is dealt with in a later chapter. If two or more measurements are to be attached to one description they are bracketed, thus:

	99.14 1.00 0.60	Conc. in fdns.
	3.05 0.76 0.45	

the bracket being placed on the outside of the squaring column. As the worked-out results of each measurement have to be collected in groups according to the brackets, it is essential that a clear indication should be made to show where the bracket ends, the bracket in fact usually being a vertical line with a little cross mark to indicate top and bottom.

*For interpretation of abbreviations used here see Appendix 1.

Where two or more descriptions are to be applied to one measurement they are written thus:

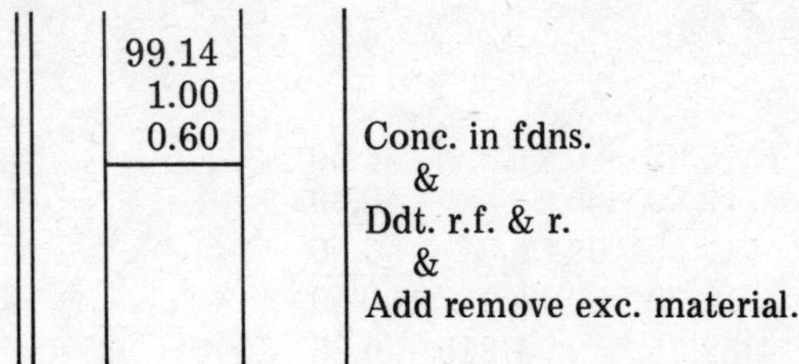

each description in this case being separated by '&' *on a line by itself*. The isolated '&' always indicates a separate item in the descriptions. No bracket is necessary in this case. Care must be taken when coupling in this way a square with a lineal item. It sometimes happens that it is very convenient to do so, but the distiction must be made quite clear to the worker-up, so that the lineal quantity is not entered in the abstract instead of the square. For example:

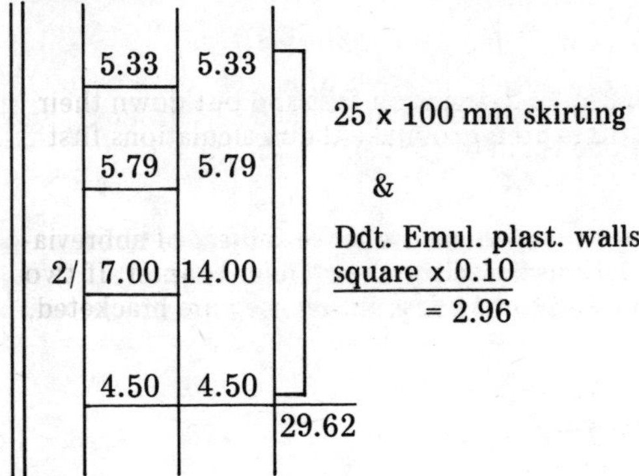

5.33 5.33
5.79 5.79
2/ 7.00 14.00
4.50 4.50
29.62
25 x 100 mm skirting
&
Ddt. Emul. plast. walls
square x 0.10
= 2.96

To measure the deduction of the emulsion paint in this way saves setting down all the dimensions again as square items (exactly the same lengths being used). Similarly a square item might be marked to be multiplied by a third demension to make a cube, e.g.:

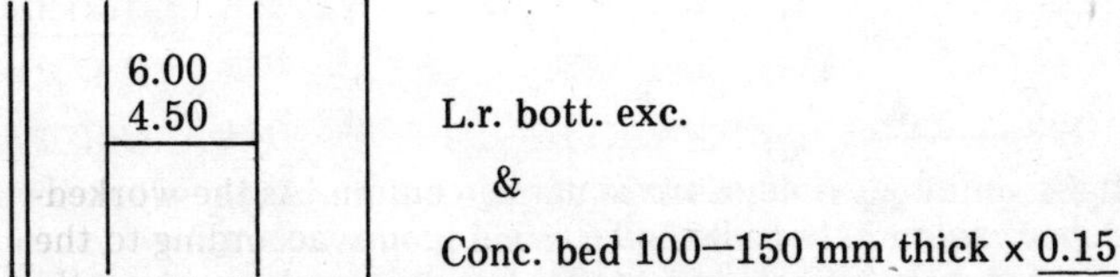

6.00
4.50
L.r. bott. exc.
&
Conc. bed 100—150 mm thick x 0.15

Deductions.—Where a deduction is to be made, the description is preceded by the abbreviation 'Ddt.' or 'Ded.', and it is of course important to be quite clear whether a measurement is to be added or deducted. Some surveyors put the word 'Add' always to any description immediately following a deduction, others only when a following addition is coupled to the deduction by '&', as in the specimen example given above. In taking off on traditional paper it will be seen from the method described in Chapter 22 how important it is that all deductions in a series of coupled descriptions are clearly marked 'Ddt.', all doubt whether any description is an 'add' or 'deduct' thus being removed. With cut and shuffle taking off it is not necessary, each slip being separately sorted, e.g.:

1.00 2.10		Ddt. $1\frac{1}{2}$ B. wall. & Ddt. fcgs. & Ddt. f. & s. walls & Ddt. emul. walls.
1.00 1.20		Ddt. ③ walls. & Add emul. walls.

It sometimes happens that after such an adjustment as the last it is required to reverse the deduction and addition. Supposing the walls of a room have been measured with others as emulsion painted and deductions made accordingly, and it is required to adjust them in this one room to gloss paint, the gross area of walls will be taken as:

15.00 3.00		Ddt. emul. walls. & Add ③ gloss walls

The areas of openings in these walls will then be taken and simply described as:

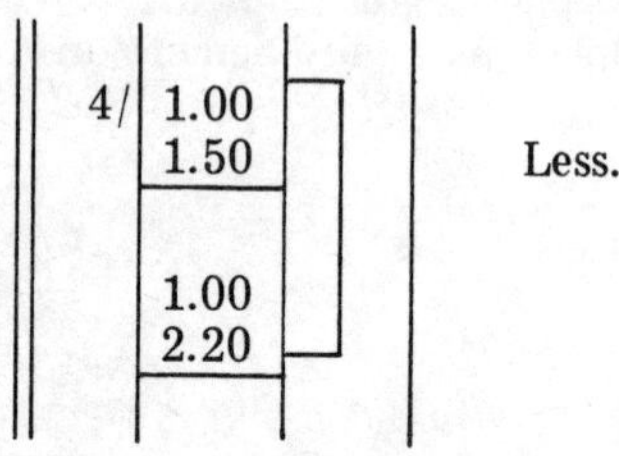

4/ 1.00 1.50		Less.
1.00 2.20		

and reveals to these openings then added, as:

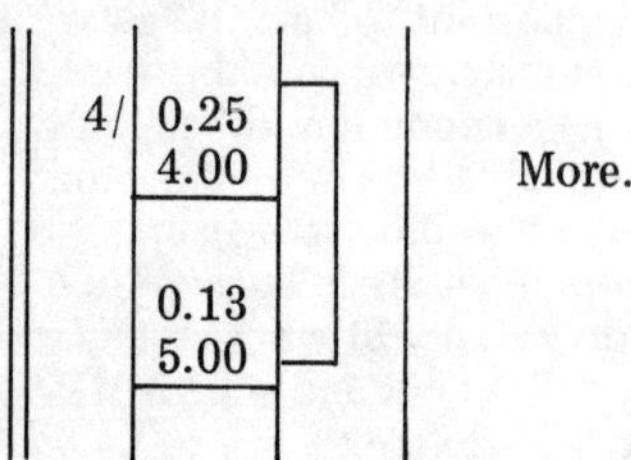

4/ 0.25 4.00		More.
0.13 5.00		

when 'Less' will mean 'deduct paint and add emulsion', and 'More' will mean 'Deduct emulsion and add paint'. The totals of each group will be carried forward as is described in Chapter 22, so that one net measurement will be arrived at of 'deduct emulsion' and 'add paint'.

Spacing of Dimensions.—One of the commonest faults found with beginners taking-off is the crowded state of their dimensions. All measurements and descriptions should be spaced well apart, so that it is quite clear where one begins and the other ends, As will be explained later, the taker-off's measurements are run through with a vertical line when they are abstracted, and if the measurements are crowded confusion may arise as to what has and what has not been abstracted. Moreover, it is not unusual for a taker-off to realise after he has written down the measurements that he has overlooked some item, and to want to insert it in its proper place. If dimensions are well spaced out, he will be able to squeeze it in, but otherwise he will have to insert it elsewhere and resort to cross-references, which only complicate his work. The use of a few extra sheets of paper will be found well worth while.

Cut and Shuffle.—The same rules apply for setting down dimensions in a cut and shuffle system of taking off as for the traditional system, apart from the different arrangement of descriptions (see the specimen sheet in Chapter 21).*

---

*Page 199.

CHAPTER 3

APPLIED MENSURATION

Mathematical Knowledge.—It is assumed that the reader is acquainted with the mathematical side of mensuration, a distinct subject, knowledge of which, as of building construction, is an essential preliminary to a study of quantity surveying. In actual fact it is comparatively rarely that knowledge is required more abstruse than of the properties of the rectangle, triangle and circle. When a case does arise needing some less known formula, it can always in practice be looked up in the appropriate mathematical reference book. The properties of the rectangle, triangle and circle must, however, be thoroughly understood, and if a student is not acquainted with them and with elementary trigonometry, he should study these before going any further. It is proposed in this chapter to give one or two examples of how the theoretical knowledge of mensuration is applied to building work.

Perimeter of Buildings.—The most common practical difficulty in dealing with the line and rectangle is the calculation of the perimeter of a building, the mean length of the external walls being required for the measurement of foundations and brickwork. This must be calculated from figured dimensions where given. Figured dimensions may be given internally or externally, and either can be worked from. In a plain rectangular building such as this with one brick walls (215 mm thick):

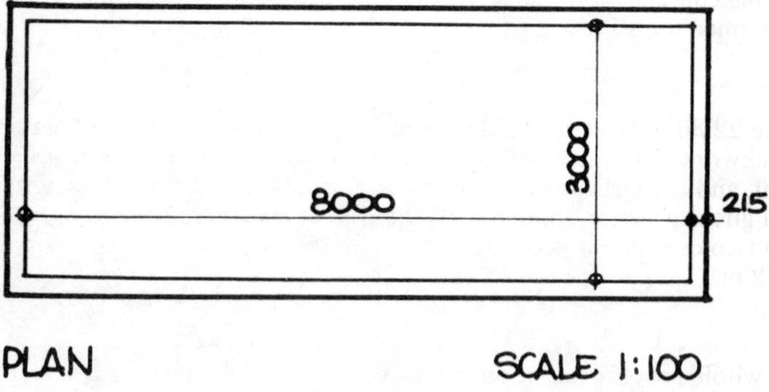

Fig. 1

the length required is the length along the centre line of the walls. The length on the inside face of the walls will obviously be

2/ 8.00 =	16.00
2/ 3.00 =	6.00
	22.00

To arrive at the mean length it is necessary to add once the thickness of the wall for each corner, i.e. 4/ 0.215 m = 0.86 m, making a total girth of 22.86 m. The reason for adding once the thickness will be seen from the following enlarged plan of the corner:

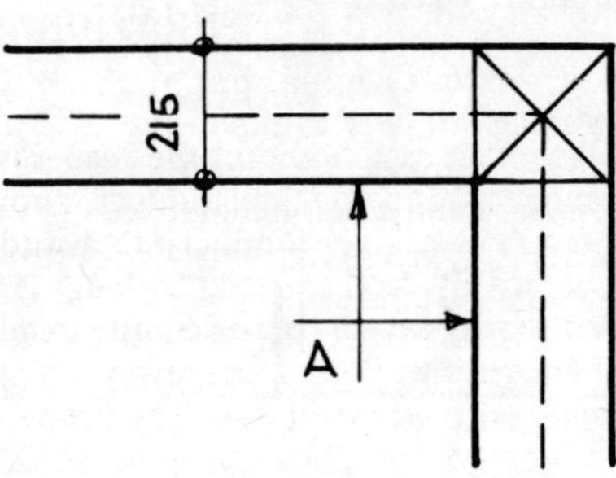

Fig. 2

The first collection of 22.0 m being measured to the faces A marked with arrows, the piece in the corner (marked with a cross) has not been included in that total. That piece, it will be seen, is the same width as the wall and of a length equal to that width (0.215 m). Or, looking at it another way, the centre line has been measured in the 22.00 m only up to the arrows marked thereon, and there remains the length of centre line within the space marked with a cross. This consists of two pieces obviously each equal to half the width of the wall, i.e. once the width in all.

While 22.86 m is the mean length used for the measurement of foundations and brickwork, the finish to inside wall face would be measured from a girth of 22.00 m, and the girth for external facings would be calculated by adding to the internal girth *twice* the thickness of the wall at each corner, it being necessary to add the two outside faces of the portion marked with a cross, thus giving a total of 23.72 m.

The whole process can of course be reversed, if outside measurements are given instead of inside, by deducting instead of adding, the mean length of the wall being obtained thus:

2/ 8.43	16.86
2/ 3.43	6.86
	23.72
Less 4/ 0.215	0.86
	22.86

Where the walls have breaks the calculation is a little more complicated. In the following example:

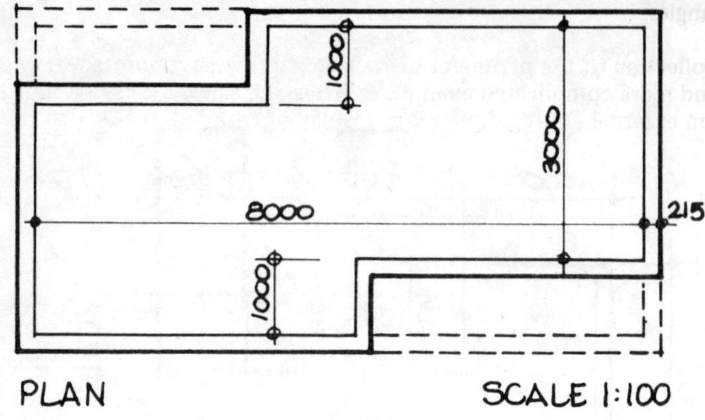

Fig. 3

the length on the centre line of the walls may be calculated on the same principle, based on the extreme internal dimensions, i.e. 4.00 m and 8.00 m. The length would be

2/ 4.00	8.00
2/ 8.00	16.00
	24.00
4/ 0.215	0.86
	24.86

Where the wall breaks back it will be seen from the following enlarged plan that the internal and external angles balance each other.

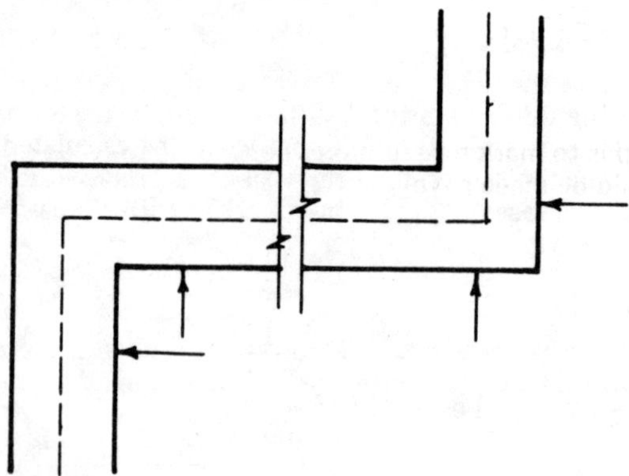

Fig. 4

As before, the inside face having been measured, the external angle needs once the thickness of the wall added to give the length on the centre line, whereas in the case of the internal angle once the thickness of the wall must be deducted. In fact the perimeter of the building is the same as if the corners were as dotted on fig. 3. In short, to arrive at the mean length once the thickness of the wall must be added for every external angle in excess of the number of internal angles.

This collection of the perimeter of walls being of great importance, one further and more complicated example is given, the calculations this time being made from external figured dimensions instead of from internal.

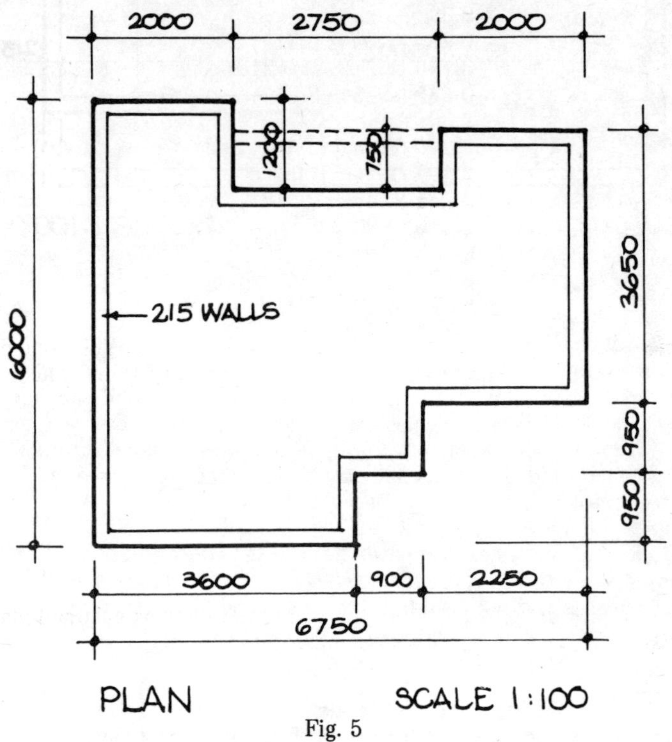

Fig. 5

The first step is to mark overall dimensions, if not already given, and the calculation would be made as follows:

2/ 6.75	13.50
2/ 6.00	12.00
	25.50
2/ 0.75	1.50
	27.00
Less 4/ 0.215	0.86
	26.14

If the reader will imagine himself making a circuit of the walls, the breaks in the previous example are, so to speak, on the way round, but in this case it will be seen that at the top of the plan there is a re-entrant portion, the break of 1.20 m being only partly on the way round, as the next break of 0.75 m goes back again and takes the walker out of his way. If the wall were as dotted, then no addition would be necessary for the re-entrant portion, and the mean perimeter would be 24.64 m, but as it is the two lengths of the 0.75 m re-entrant breaks must be added. A check of the above calculation can be made by collecting up each length of wall, starting, say, at the top left-hand corner and working round clockwise. In order to calculate the passings at angles correctly the usual method is to measure all horizontal lengths to extreme length, i.e. across the return wall, and all vertical walls between the horizontal ones only. By horizontal and vertical walls are here meant walls depicted by lines drawn horizontally or vertically on the paper. The check would be as follows:

2.00
0.985 (1.20 − 0.215)
3.180 (2.75 + 2/ 0.215)
0.535 (0.75 − 0.215)
2.00
3.22 (3.65 − 2/ 0.215)
2.465 (2.25 + 0.215)
0.735 (0.95 − 0.215)
1.115 (0.90 + 0.215)
0.735 (0.95 − 0.215)
3.60
5.57 (6.00 − 2/ 0.215)
26.14

This method of collection would in any case be used if the building were of irregular shape, but where its angles are all right angles the length can usually be calculated from overall dimensions, though such piecemeal collection as this is useful as a check. In difficult cases it may be found convenient to mark by pencil lines on the plan the limits of each dimension.

A good deal of space has been given here to the collection of walls. but it will be appreciated that this calculation is a most important one, as, having once been made, it is often used not only for foundations but also for brickwork and facings, with possibly copings, string courses, etc.

Irregular Areas.—The triangle is constantly in use. Any irregular-shaped area to be measured is divided up into triangles, each triangle being measured individually, and the sum of the areas being the area of the whole. If one of the sides, as for instance in the case of yard paving, is irregular or curved, the area

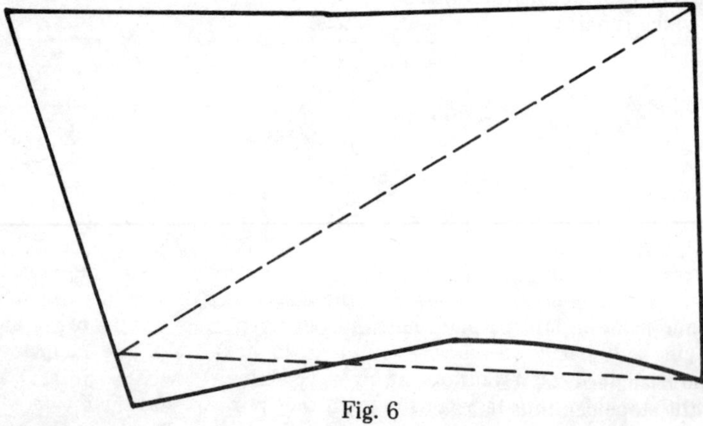

Fig. 6

can still be divided into triangles by the use of a ‘compensating line’, i.e. a line is drawn along the irregular or curved boundary in such a position that so far as can be judged the area of paving excluded by this line is equal to the area included beyond the boundary.

In the above example the area of paving to be measured is enclosed by firm lines, the method of forming two triangles (the sum of the areas of which equals the whole area) being shown dotted.

Where two sides of such a four-sided figure are parallel it will not be necessary to divide into triangles, as the area of such a figure (a trapezoid) is the length of a perpendicular between tha parallel sides multiplied by the mean length between

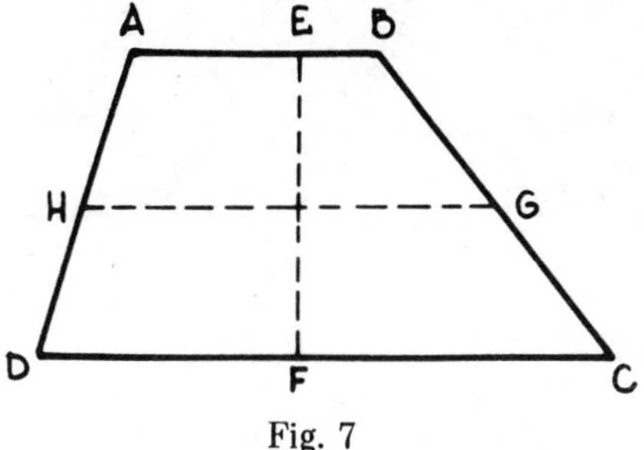

Fig. 7

the diverging sides. Thus, in this figure the area is EF x GH, GH of course being drawn half-way between AB and CD and being equal to $\frac{AB + CD}{2}$, i.e. the average between AB and CD.

Another irregular figure which often puzzles the beginner is the additional area to be measured where two roads meet with the corners rounded off to a quadrant. This is most easily calculated as a square on the radius with a quarter circle deducted.

Roof Slopes.—The length of a roof slope too can be calculated from the triangle either for measurement or as a check where the length is scaled on a small drawing. The roof slope of a pitched roof is the hypotenuse of a triangle the base of which is half the roof span and the height the height of the roof.

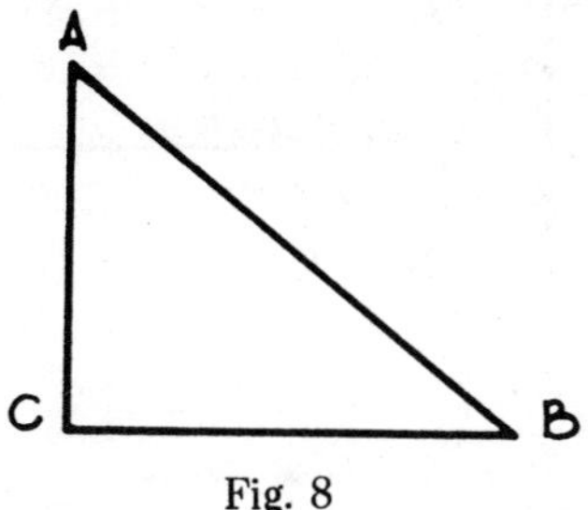

Fig. 8

In the triangle ABC, AB = BC x sec. B, and if the angle of the pitch of roof is known the slope can thus be calculated. For example, in the following:

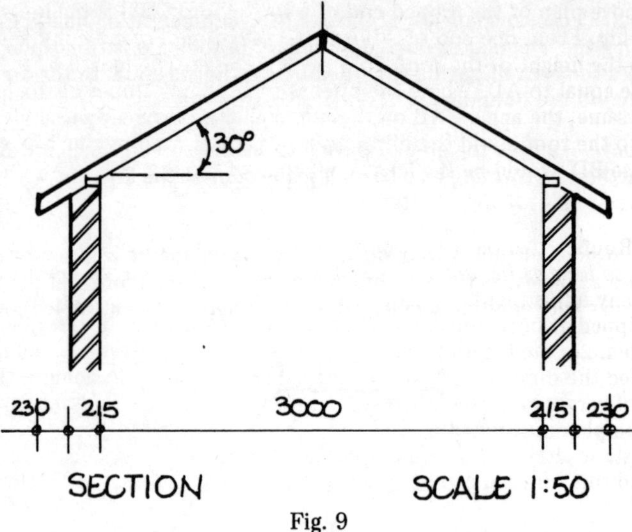

Fig. 9

half the roof span must of course be calculated to the extreme projection of the eaves. The span inside walls being 3.00 m, half the span for this purpose will be 1.50 + 0.215 + 0.23, i.e. 1.95 m. The angle of pitch being 30°, the length of the slope will be

$$\begin{aligned} & 1.95 \times \sec. 30^\circ \\ = & 1.95 \times 1.1547 \\ = & 2.25 \text{ m} \end{aligned}$$

and this can be checked by scaling.

Hips and Valleys.—The length of a hip or valley in a pitched roof must be calculated from a triangle, there usually being no true section through it from which it can be scaled. It will be seen that its length is the hypotenuse of a triangle, the base of which is the horizontal length on the roof plan of hip or valley, and the height of the roof. The usual way of finding the length of the hip is as follows:

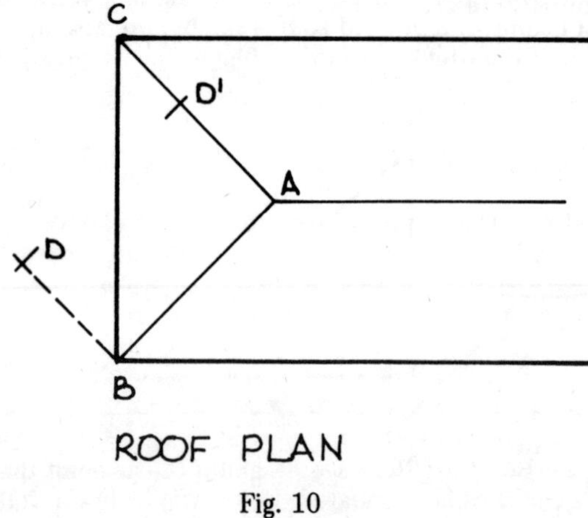

Fig. 10

In the above plan of the hipped end of a roof AB (or AC) is the length on plan of the hip. From one end of AB (or AC) set off a perpendicular as BD equal in length to the height of the roof from eaves to ridge. The length of the hip on slope will be equal to AD. Where the pitches of the three slopes of the hipped end are the same, the angle CAB on the plan will always be a right angle, and the height to the roof could therefore be set off from A along one hip, e.g. to D′, in which case BD′ would be the length on slope of the hip.

Broken-up Roofs.—It should be noted that however a roof is broken up by hips and valleys, *so long as the angle of pitch is constant* the area will be the same, apart from any adjustments of projections of eaves, verge, etc. The area of tiling on a roof hipped at both ends may therefore be measured in the same way as if it were gabled, i.e. the length × twice the slope, the only difference being that if it were gabled the dimension of the length would probably be smaller, the projection of verges being less than that of eaves. Just as the length of slope is the length on plan multiplied by the secant of the angle of pitch, so the area of a roof of constant pitch is the area on plan multiplied by the secant of the angle of pitch, and this formula can be a useful check on the measurements when worked out.

Circular Openings and Arches.—The most common use of the circle in quantity surveying is perhaps in the measurement of arches and the accompanying deduction of brickwork. Where semicircular arches are being dealt with this is fairly straightforward. In the case of segmental arches the deduction above the springing line and the girth of the arch are not usually calculated precisely, as they can in ordinary work be judged sufficiently accurately, in the first case by a triangle with compensating lines or by taking an average height, and in the latter case by stepping the girth round with dividers. Special care is necessary in the case of expensive work, such as rubbed and gauged or glazed brick arches, to be as accurate as possible, the measurements being worked out by precise calculation if necessary. A rough method of measuring the area of a segment is to take $\frac{11}{16}$ times the area of the rectangle formed by the chord and the height of segment. This is obviously not mathematically correct, and the margin of error will vary with the radius and length of chord, but when dealing with small areas this method will often be found sufficiently accurate. Another way is to take first the inscribed isosceles triangle based on the chord, leaving two much smaller segments each of which may be scaled and set down as base × $\frac{2}{3}$height. The error is then very small only. In dealing with large areas of expensive materials a more accurate method would be necessary using the formula

$$\frac{H^3}{2C} + (\tfrac{2}{3}C \times H)$$

where C is the length of chord and H the height.

Excavation to Banks.—The volume of excavation necessary on a level site to

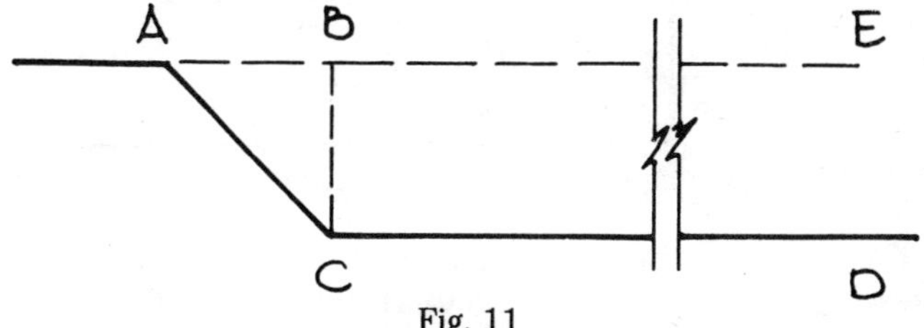

Fig. 11

leave a regular sloping bank is naturally the sectional area of the part displaced (triangle ABC above) multiplied by the length, the volume of the remaining excavation being the sectional area of the rectangle BCDE also multiplied by the length. It may be, however, that the natural ground level is falling in the length of the bank as shown on the following diagram:

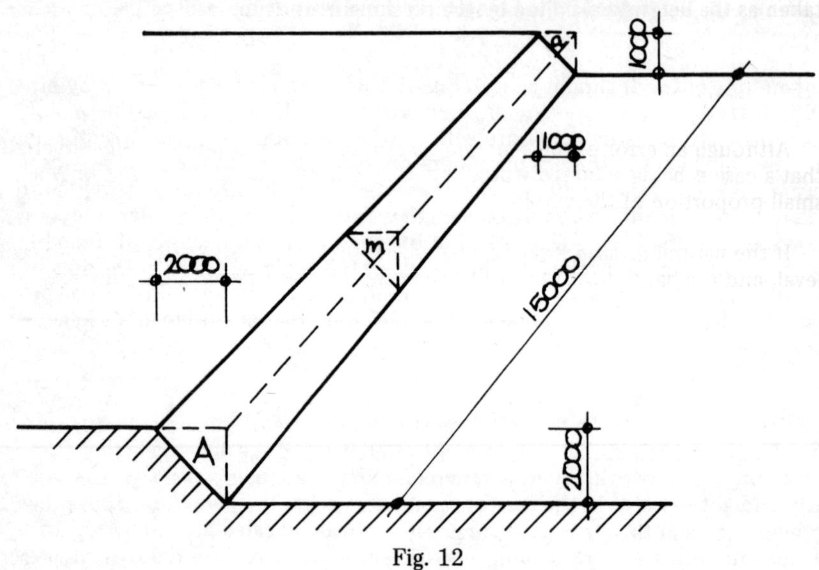

Fig. 12

The volume of earth to be displaced should then theoretically be calculated by the prismoidal formula

$$V = \frac{L(A + a + 4m)}{6}$$

where A is the sectional area at one end,
a ,, ,, ,, the other end,
m ,, ,, ,, the centre.

If AB and BC in fig. 11 are both 2. 00 at the higher end and 1. 00 at the lower end they would, assuming a regular slope, be 1. 50 at the centre. The volume of the prismoid in fig. 12 in cubic m would therefore be

$$\frac{15\left(\frac{2 \times 2}{2} + \frac{1 \times 1}{2} + 4 \times \frac{1.5 \times 1.5}{2}\right)}{6}$$

$$= \frac{15(2 + 0.50 + 4.50)}{6} = \frac{105}{6}$$

$$= 17.50 \text{ m}^3$$

In practice, however, it will often be found that so precise a calculation is not made in such cases. The surface of ground, whether level or sloping, is not like billiard cloth, and the natural irregularities prevent calculation from being exact. Moreover, in dealing with normal building sites the excavation for banks is a comparatively small proportion of the whole excavation involved (unlike, say, the case of a railway cutting), and any departure from strict mathematical accuracy due to the use of less precise methods would only involve an error comparatively small. In the example above given the volume might in practice be taken as the length multiplied by the sectional area at the centre, i.e.

$$15 \times \frac{1.50 \times 1.50}{2} = 16.88 \text{ m}^3$$

Although an error of 0.62 m^3 may be thought high, it must be remembered that a case is being assumed where the excavation to the bank is itself only a small proportion of the whole.

If the natural ground level falls to such an extent that it reaches the reduced level, and the bank shown in fig. 12 therefore dies out to nothing, thus:-

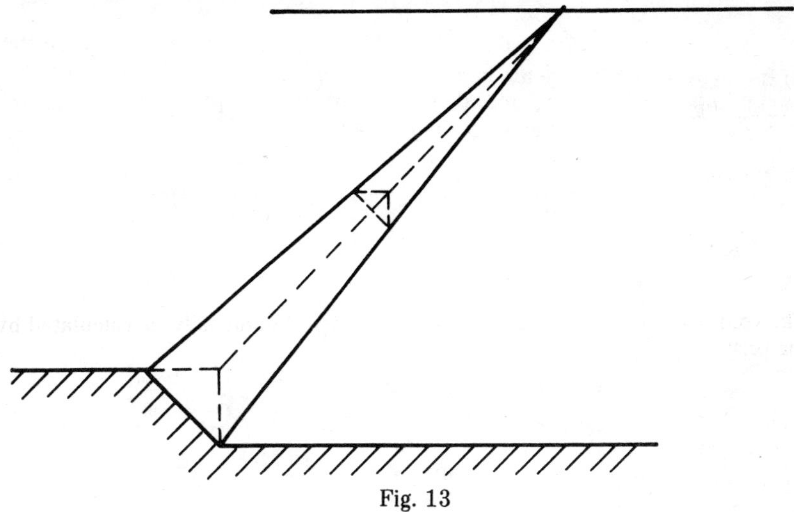

Fig. 13

the formula will be found to simplify itself.

a becomes zero,

m becomes by simple geometry $\frac{A}{4}$, because the triangles at A and m are right-angled triangles, that at m having two sides enclosing the right angle each half the length of the corresponding sides of the triangle at A.

$$V = L\,\frac{\left(A + 0 + 4 \times \frac{A}{4}\right)}{6} = \frac{L \times A}{3}$$

which is the formula for volume of a prism.

Excavation to Sloping Sites.—The theoretical principle for measuring the volume of excavation in cutting for a sloping bank may be extended to a sloping site.

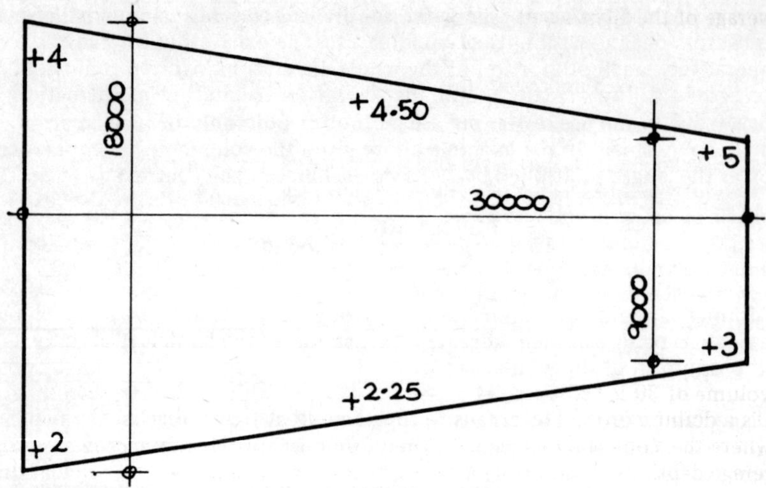

Fig. 14

If the figures given above are natural levels and it is required to excavate to a general level of +1 (the end boundaries of the area being parallel), the volume of excavation may be calculated by the formula

already given of $V = \dfrac{L(A + a + 4m)}{6}$.

When $\quad L = 30$

$$A = 18 \times \frac{3 + 1}{2} = 36$$

$$a = 9 \times \frac{4 + 2}{2} = 27$$

$$m = 13.50 \times \frac{3\frac{1}{2} + 1\frac{1}{4}}{2} = 13.50 \times \frac{19}{4} \times \tfrac{1}{2} = \frac{256.50}{8}$$

then $$V = \frac{30\left(36 + 27 + \frac{256.50 \times 4}{8}\right)}{6} = \frac{30(36 + 27 + 128.25)}{6}$$

$$= 5 \times 191.25 = 956.25 \text{ m}^3$$

If only a simple average of the four corners were taken the result would be:

	4
	5
	3
	2
	4)14
Average ground level	3.50
Reduced level	1.00
Average depth	2.50

$30 \times 13.50 \times 2.50 = 1012.5 \text{ m}^3$

An average of the eight levels (giving the centre levels double value) would be

	4
2/ 4.50	9
	5
	3
2/ 2.25	4.50
	2
	8)27.50
	3.44
	1.00
	2.44

or a volume of 30 x 13.50 x 2.44 = 988.2 m^3, from which it will be seen that there is a definite error. The error would vary with the regularity of the slope, and where the slope is fairly regular it may often be sufficiently accurate to take an average depth over the whole area. For an ordinary building site, calculation would probably be made in this way in practice.

If it is required to apply the formula where end boundaries are not parallel it will be necessary to draw parallel compensating lines along these two boundaries. It is of course assumed that slopes between the levels given are regular. If a line of intermediate levels were given between the upper and lower line in the diagram above, it would be necessary to treat the two portions separately.

CHAPTER 4

GENERAL RULES FOR TAKING OFF

In this chapter are given such general rules of measurement and other information as are considered necessary for the study of the examples which follow. The general organisation and procedure in taking off dimensions of a complete building are dealt with in Chapter 20, but they need not keep the reader from proceeding with the examples.

Sections of Taking off.—The taking off of dimensions is usually divided into sections under two main subdivisions:

(a) Carcase. (b) Finishings.

The sections found in a normal building, in the order in which they will be dealt with in this book, are as follows:-

(a) Carcase.

(1) Foundations.
(2) Brickword.
(3) Facings.
(4) Fires and Vents.
(5) Floors.
(6) Roofs.

(b) Finishings.

(7) Internal Finishings.
(8) Windows.
(9) Doors, including openings without joinery.
(10) Fittings and Sundries.
(11) Stairs.
(12) Internal Plumbing.
(13) Drainage.
(14) Engineering Services.
(15) Roads, Paths and Layout of Grounds.
(16) 'Spot' Items.

The terms 'carcase' and 'finishings' cannot be taken in an absolutely literal sense, as there must necessarily be a certain amount of overlapping. Some might consider external facings and roof coverings as 'finishings', but, being part of the structure, they are usually included in the carcase. Floor finishings may be measured with the floor construction, but some surveyors prefer to take them with the Internal Finishings. The order of sections too may follow the particular taste of the surveyor, but it is best, having decided on a definite order, to follow it always. It must be understood that the special requirements of any building may require additional or subdivided sections, and the list given above must therefore be regarded as elastic.

Taking off by Trades.—Some surveyors make a practice of taking off by trades instead of by sections of the building as above described. As the final bill will be arranged by trades, this method can eliminate the intermediate abstract, which, when measuring by sections of the building, is necessary to collect and classify the items into trades. Such a system may present difficulties in some cases, and would seem to increase the risk of overlapping or of something forgotten. In measuring by sections of the building the taker-off mentally erects the building step by step and is less likely to miss something. Although the abstract is eliminated, a certain amount of collecting and reducing must be done on the dimension sheets.*

'Cut and Shuffle'.—The system of taking off known as 'cut and shuffle' is fully described in Chapter 21.

Over-all Measurements.—It is usual in measuring to ignore in the first instance openings, recesses and other features which can be dealt with by adjustment. Brickwork, for instance, is measured as if there were no openings at all, and deductions are made when the windows, doors or other openings are dealt with in their proper section. Plastering and similar finishings are measured in the same way. It simplifies the work to measure in this way, as when, for instance, windows are being considered the sizes will be to hand, and openings will be measured to correspond. Moreover, it may happen that, say, internal plastering and windows are being dealt with by different takers-off, when it is obvious that the man who measures the windows is better able to make the deductions and adjustments. Measuring over all with adjustment is at all times preferable to piecemeal measuring. This principle will further be found of value if a window should be forgotten. The extra cost of window over solid wall would alone be involved by the error, a much less serious matter than if nothing at all had been measured over the area of window.

Use of Scales.—A warning should be given of the possibility of using the scale wrongly in measuring. If possible, each side of the scale used should not have more than one variety of marking on each edge, but this is not always practicable. The scale most easily available for general use is a standard metric scale having 1:5, 1:50, 1:10, 1:100, 1:20, 1:200, 1:250, and 1:2500 markings. Some surveyors prefer to have a separate scale for each variety, or one marked on one face only, but when working on two different drawings, e.g. 1:100 and 1:20, at the same time—as is quite common, it is a great convenience to have both markings on the same scale. In any case special care is necessary when measuring from different drawings to see that readings are taken from the correct markings of the scale. It may seem unnecessary to emphasise this, but mistakes on this account are not unknown.

Abbreviations.—When using traditional dimension paper everything should be done to reduce as far as possible the space occupied by a description without leaving out essentials. A certain number of abbreviations are in common use, and a list of these is set out in Appendix I, but this list is in practice considerably extended by the shortening of words generally and by other abbreviations understood in the particular office. In the case of cut and shuffle taking off such abbreviations are restricted to slave sheet descriptions (see Chapter 21).

A special note might perhaps be made here of the abbreviation 'a.b.' for 'as before'. Where this is used and might refer to more than one item it always refers to the last such item. For instance, a description '40 mm door a.b.' would refer to the last type of 40 mm door measured, if there have been several

---

*See 'Principles of the Trade-by-Trade System of Taking Off', by G. D. Walford, *R.I.C.S. Journal*, February 1958, page 448.

different varieties. If, however, there is any doubt it is best to say definitely '40 mm door a.b. col. 146', the reference to the column number being a definite guide. The abbreviation 'ditto', which also needs careful use, is dealt with in Chapter 24.

Descriptions.—The framing of descriptions so that they are both clear and concise is an art not easily acquired, but one which is of the utmost value. The builder's estimator, always working at high pressure, will waste much of his time if he is faced with long-winded and rambling descriptions, or has to make up his mind as to what the surveyor intended to convey by a confused sentence. The surveyor, therefore, must always aim at expressing himself clearly, being careful in his choice of words, and using the various technical terms in their proper sense.

The wording of descriptions is dealt with in Chapter 24 on writing the bill, but descriptions well drafted on the dimensions in the first instance will simplify considerably the work of the biller or editor. The taker-off must also be careful to see that he uses the same wording when referring to the same thing in different parts of his dimensions, as inconsistency in his descriptions may puzzle the worker-up, making him think that there must be some distinction intended by the different phraseology. For instance, if the taker-off, describing paint on bolts, writes '③ bolts', and then after several such items writes later '③ small bolts', the worker-up, especially if he is inexperienced, will wonder whether the difference in description is intentional, and, if so, why. Therefore, when the same item appears in different places it should be written in exactly the same form, or after the first time abbreviated with the letters a.b. to indicate that exactly the same as before is intended. It is important to confine the description to what is actually to appear in the bill, and not to add to it particulars of location or other notes which are merely put for reference and not intended to go any further. Any side notes should be written clear of the description and separated by a bracket as shown, for example, on page 43.

The descriptions written on the dimensions should be in the form intended to appear in the bill, such parts as would normally be covered by a preamble (see Chapter 25) being omitted, if there is no fear of their being missed. In practice, certain items which are constantly met with may have the description curtailed, being described by reference to the bill for some other job; the taker-off's time in writing out a long description is thus saved.

In some cases there will be added to the description of a superficial or lineal item a note of the number included in the item so that the estimator can judge the average size of each, e.g.:

Timesing	Dimensions	Squaring	Description
3/	0.22 0.40		4 mm c.s. glass to wood wi. beads in panes n.e. 0.10 m^2 (In Nr. 1 each).
	2.50		10 mm c.i. dr. in tr. in run n.e. 3.00 m (In Nr. 1).

The number given in brackets will indicate the number included in the measurement without the timesing, the word 'each' making this clear.

The tendency to subdivide items too much should be avoided, the general rule being that where parts of an item properly belong to different trades the item should be divided. For instance, the work to an asphalt skirting consists of two separate parts:-

(a) the asphalt work,

(b) the raking out of joints and pointing top edge,

and these two sections must be measured as separate items. The asphalt work itself will consist of angle fillet at bottom, vertical portion and tucking in of top edge. These, however, being all lineal items in the same trade and of the same quantity, can be coupled together in one description. So, too, the raking-out joints and pointing top edge, though distinct operations, will again be both lineal items of the same length in the same trade, and can therefore be described in one item. On the other hand, as a general rule a square item should not include with it something which can only be valued from a lineal dimension. There are, however, exceptions to this rule, especially where the lineal item is of comparatively small value, e.g. a square item of crosstongued shelving will include the crosstongued joints, but a moulded edge must be measured as a separate item.

Some of the requirements of the S.M.M. as to descriptions may be covered by general clauses, preambles to each Trade.* For example, S.M.M. M 48.3 says that the lap in joints of flashings shall be given in the description. A general clause saying that all flashings are to be lapped 100 mm at joints would be sufficient and probably save repetition.

Bill Sketches.—The sixth edition of the S.M.M. calls for more drawn information to be made available than in previous editions and the implications of these requirements are brought out in S.M.M. A 5 and in section A of the *Practice Manual.* Most of this drawn information will be available from the drawings used for the taking off and it will only mean ensuring that the information required by the S.M.M. is included and that the requisite number of copies of the various drawings accompany the tender documents. However in certain cases the S.M.M. suggests bill diagrams or bill sketches to elaborate a description. These diagrams or sketches can either be produced separately for inclusion in the text of the bill of quantities or drawn by the taker-off with his dimensions to be processed as a separate operation. How these sketches will appear in the bill of quantities is a matter for the individual surveyor to decide. Many years ago bills of quantities were full of annotated sketches for such things as mouldings and special features, and the introduction of these bill sketches is therefore nothing new.

'Extra Over'.—Certain items are measured as 'extra over' others, that is they are not to be priced at the full value of all their labour and materials, as these have to a greater or less extent already been measured. For instance, the external facing of a solid wall is usually measured 'extra over' the common brickwork, i.e. the estimator will have to price for the extra cost only of the facing bricks over common bricks, and the extra cost only of labour and any special mortar used for pointing. Some items treated similarly are brickwork in cement in lieu of lime, bends and junctions in drain or other pipes, valley or bonnet hip tiles, angles and other fittings to eaves gutters, and many 'labour only' items representing the extra cost of a special labour over the ordinary labour. Such items are simply described as 'extra for' where it is obvious what they are extra over, e.g., 'Extra for bend' following immediately after an item of pipe obviously means 'extra over the cost of the pipe in question for a bend'. The measurement of an

*See page 238.

item as 'extra over' something already measured as 'extra over' should be avoided. For example, a splayed brick plinth course in facings could be measured as extra over common brickwork, facings being deducted for its height, and thus not measured as 'extra over facings'.

The Standard Method of Measurement.—The different methods of measuring used by surveyors were found to be a serious difficulty to estimators and to be a standing cause of disputes. An effort was made by surveyors and builders to produce a standard method representing the generally accepted practice. As a result *The Standard Method of Measurement* (referred to below as S.M.M.) was published in 1922, and was republished in 1935 in a revised form after a very thorough examination of a large number of suggestions for revision. Further substantial revision was made in the 1948 edition and again in 1963. In 1968 a version with the units converted to the metric system was published and in 1978 the sixth edition accompanied by a *Practice Manual* was published.

The form of contract settled by the Joint Contracts Tribunal* provides that measurements shall be made in accordance with the principles of this standard method, and it is therefore of the utmost importance, where this form of contract is used, that the standard method should be adhered to. It should, however, be understood that unless so referred to in the contract it has no legal sanction and need not be adopted. However, this document has now been so long established that it could be produced as evidence of custom in the profession, and it is therefore advisable to study it and to follow its recommendations in all cases, or make quite clear where such recommendations have not been adopted.

The student should study clauses A 1—9 of the S.M.M., applicable to all sections of a bill and not always included in the references at the head of each chapter on taking off. These references must not be considered an exhaustive list, but only as indicating the principal clauses that should be studied in each case.

Measurements for Analysis of Price.—A distinction must sometimes be made between the measurements necessary for the preparation of a bill of quantities and those necessary for the analysis of the price of a particular item. This distinction is often not realised, especially by trade students. It has been found by experience that in certain cases a price can be built up for a unit of measurement without pressing the analysis of the item to its extreme limit, with all the additional work so involved. Stonework is in many cases measured per cubic metre of stone fixed, to include various labours the extent of which in proportion to the cubic contents may vary on each stone. If the item is one with which the estimator is constantly dealing he will have an accurate idea of the price of the unit given; if not, he can analyse the item further himself to arrive at its value.

Measurement of Waste.—It may be taken as a general rule (though like all rules it has exceptions) that measurements of work are made to ascertain the net quantities as fixed or erected in the finished building. Waste generally is

**Agreement and Schedule of Conditions of Building Contract* 1963, July 1977 revision (R.I.B.A. Publications Ltd.,). Separate forms are provided for use with or without quantities, and in each case there is a separate Local Authorities' edition. Copies are obtainable from the R.I.C.S., R.I.B.A. and the N.F.B.T.E.

allowed for by the builder in his prices, though sometimes a measurement is made to guide him as to the amount of waste, and in a few cases the gross quantity is measured. The exceptions to the general rule will be pointed out as they occur.

Averaging.—Where items are similar and differ only in one dimension they may generally be taken together, the varying dimension being averaged. It is important to note that an average cannot strictly be taken in more than one dimension. This will be plainly seen in comparing the following:

	Dimensions	Squaring	
	2.50		
	1.80	4.50	
	1.50		
	1.20	1.80	
			6.30

which it might appear could be averaged as:

	Dimensions	Squaring
2/	2.00	
	1.50	6.00

The difference in the above results shows the amount of error, which is not inconsiderable, and would be much increased if a third dimension were added, as say in the case of the excavation for two manholes 1.50 m deep:

	Dimensions	Squaring	
	2.50		
	1.80		
	1.50	6.75	
	1.50		
	1.20		
	1.50	2.70	
			9.45

	Dimensions	Squaring
2/	2.00	
	1.50	
	1.50	9.00

where the error is nearly ½ cubic metre for two manholes alone.

Suitable items to average are trench excavation (in depth), asphalt skirtings (in height), gutter boards (in width), etc.

CHAPTER 5

EXCAVATION AND FOUNDATIONS

References to S.M.M.

D 1–4, 10–45
F 1–4, 6–14

Particulars of the Site.—Before beginning the measurement of foundation work the drawings must be examined to ascertain that the natural ground levels are sufficiently shown for calculating average depths of digging. The nature of the ground surface must also be known, e.g. whether grass-covered, paved, or covered with buildings in whole or in part. The surveyor will almost invariably pay a visit to the site, when this information can be noted. At the same time it will be noted whether any trees have to be felled, fences or boundary walls altered or repaired, and particulars will be taken of 'spot items' of alteration work or the connection of new buildings with old. The visit to the site is perhaps best left till the general taking off is done, so that notes can be made during the taking off of what must be looked at on the site, and a second visit thus obviated. Where, of course, the proposed work consists mainly of alterations, an early visit to the site will be necessary, and most of the taking off may even have to be done there. The measurement of 'spot items' and the methods of dealing with this class of work are dealt with in Chapter 19.

Removing Surface Soil.—Where new buildings are to be erected on natural ground it is usual to measure separately the stripping of the surface or vegetable soil. This is measured over the area of the whole building including the projection of concrete foundations beyond external walls. Any further excavation for trenches, basement, etc., would then be measured from the underside of such surface excavation. If there were some existing gravel paths, tar paving, etc., over portions of the area to be stripped, an item must be taken for breaking up of paths, etc., and the surface excavation deducted from that area. Alternatively, this item can be measured as 'extra over' the excavation item.

Where the site is covered by existing buildings, the pulling down and taking up of floors would be dealt with as described in Chapter 19, no item of stripping surface being necessary. The excavation would be measured from the underside of the floors removed.

It often happens that part of the site is covered with good turf which is worth preserving, and in such cases an item should be taken for stripping it and a separate item for relaying any to be reused. (S.M.M. D 8)

Excavation Over Site.—Where a site is sloping it is often most economical to fix the ground-floor level so that one end of the site must be dug into, i.e. the underside of the site concrete will be below the level of the ground after surface soil is stripped. Where this is the case, a cube measurement is made of the digging necessary from the underside of the stripping of surface soil already measured to the underside of the concrete bed or hardcore under (if any). The depth for this item must be averaged, and it will generally be found that this digging is only necessary over part of the site, the level of the rest being made up with hardcore or otherwise. In fig. 15 it will be seen that the ground level must be reduced to 44.00 (300 mm below top of floor slab). The contour of 44.00 is

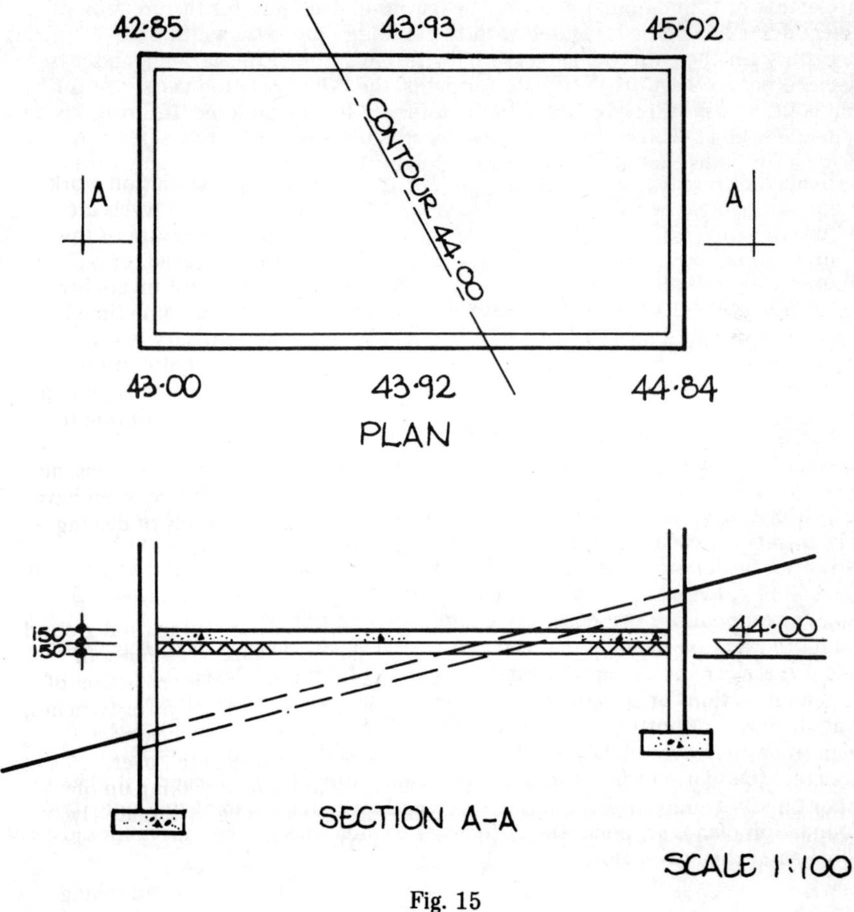

Fig. 15

therefore plotted on the plan as accurately as possible from the levels given; the area on the right hand side of this contour is measured for excavation, that on the left hand side for filling.

The excavation over the site must be measured before any trench digging, as it brings the surface to the 'reduced level' from which the trench digging is measured, and, like the stripping of surface soil, it must be measured to the extreme projection of concrete foundations. It will often be necessary, where the floor level of the building is below the ground outside, to slope off the excavation away from the building, and possibly to have a space round the building excavated to below the floor level. In such circumstances the additional excavation must be measured and a superficial item taken for trimming the bank.

Digging for Paths.—Stripping of surface soil and excavation to reduce levels may also be required for formation of paths, paved spaces, etc. External work of this nature is best measured all together after the building is dealt with, in fact it sometimes must be, when a separate estimate is required for this work. When this is so, and paths, etc., abut against the building (thus overlapping the projection of foundations), the whole excavation necessary for the erection of the building should be measured with the building, the extra width only necessary for the paths being measured with the paths. If this is done, and it is decided not to accept the estimate for paths, the full excavation necessary for the building will still be included in the estimate for the building. If, however, no separate estimate is required for paths, there is no reason why these items of digging for paths should not be measured with the corresponding items for the building, if found more convenient and if it can be done at the same time.

Levels.—Before foundations are measured, three sets of levels must be known:

(1) Bottom of concrete foundation.

(2) Natural ground level.

(3) Floor level.

(1) and (2) are necessary to measure trench digging, and (1) and (3) are necessary to calculate correct heights of brickwork or other walling. The natural ground level, as has been pointed out, will probably vary and have to be averaged either for the whole building or for sections of it, and, if floor level and bottom of concrete are each uniform, the measurement of trench digging is fairly simple. However, both bottom of concrete and floor level may vary in different parts of the building, there being steps at each break in level, and sometimes the measurement of foundations becomes very complicated on this account. It will be found useful to mark on the plan the levels of natural ground at corners of the building, and if these cannot be approximately calculated from given levels they must be scaled on sections or elevations from a datum specially selected. In the same way the levels of bottom of the concrete could be marked on the foundation plan (if any), and it will be found in difficult cases that the different levels of concrete foundation will stand out if the foundation plan is hatched with chalks of distinctive colours to represent the varying depths of bottom of concrete. If no foundation plan is supplied, the outlines of foundations can be superimposed on the plan of the lowest floor.

Trench Excavation.—The measurement of trench excavation and other foundation work will normally divide itself into two sections:

(a) external walls,

(b) internal walls,

the former being dealt with first. In the simplest type of building a collection will be made of the length of external walls as described in Chapter 3, and this same length will serve for measurements of excavation, concrete foundation and brickwork. This length, being the mean length of the walls, will also be the mean length of the concrete foundations, on which presumably the walls are central. The width of trench will be the width of the concrete foundation as shown on the sections or foundation plan. The depth of trench will, if the bottom of concrete foundation is at one level, be the difference between that level and the average level of ground, after making allowance for the stripping of surface soil or excavation to reduce levels already measured. Where the bottom of concrete is at different levels, theoretically the digging for each section of foundation between steps should be measured separately, the lengths when measured being collected and checked with the ascertained total length. It may be found, however, in practice that, the steppings to bottom of trench being small, and the ground normally falling in the same direction, an average depth can be decided on for larger sections of the building, if not for the whole. In Example 1 (page 42) the 900 mm figured on the drawing is the assumed difference between average ground level and bottom of concrete foundation. The main measurement of digging for external walls having been set down, digging for any projections on this foundation can be measured.

It has been assumed above that the external walls have trenches of a uniform width all round. If there are several different widths, as would be the case where the thickness of wall varied, each width would be dealt with separately, different lengths of the same width being collected together on waste, and the whole being carefully checked with the ascertained total length. Trenches not exceeding 300 mm wide will be measured lineal, stating the average depth (S.M.M. D 13.6a), and those over 300 mm wide will be measured cube (S.M.M. D 13.6b).

Internal walls must be collected up in groups according to the width of their foundation and the average depths decided on. Allowance should be made in the length for overlap where an internal wall abuts against an external wall by deducting from the length of the internal wall the projection of concrete of the external wall at this point. A similar allowance should be made where internal walls intersect. The necessity for this is best shown diagrammatically:

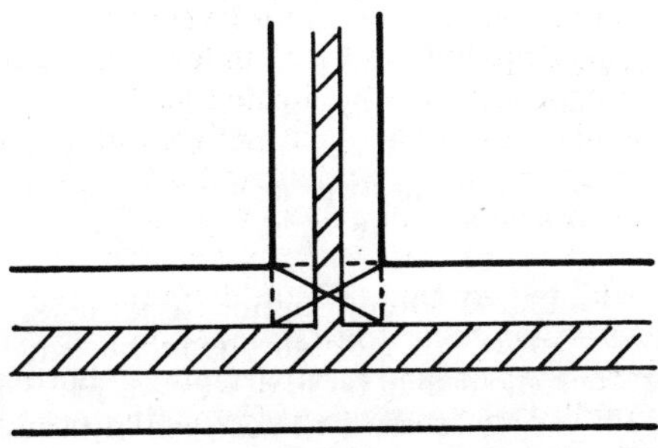

Fig. 16

It will be seen that if the foundation for the internal wall were measured the same length as the wall (i.e. as dotted) the area marked with a cross would be measured twice over for excavation and concrete. The amount involved being comparatively small, some surveyors may ignore the deduction, but to do so, if there are many intersections, is to take an unnecessary and definite full measurement without any really justifiable reason. On the other hand, it will sometimes be found that when walls enclose a small room it is not practicable to leave the earth within the surrounding trench, as the amount of this earth is so small. It may in such cases be necessary to take for digging out this earth, though there may not actually be much difference in cost when the saving of earthwork support is taken into consideration.

Students seem to find it difficult to decide whether the maximum depths for trench excavation, etc., should be calculated from natural ground level or from the level of the ground after surface soil has been stripped, where this is separately measured. It is usual to measure from the latter level as being the 'starting level' within the meaning of S.M.M. D 13. If the terms 'surface trench' or 'ground level' are used, the meaning of 'surface' or 'ground' can be defined in a preamble.

Basement Digging.—Basement digging will be measured from the underside of the stripping of surface soil or from the reduced level down to the underside of the basement floor, the trenches below being measured separately as trenches from such a level. Where only part of the area of a building has a basement, it will be found most convenient to measure first all the basement complete up to a certain level, say Ground Floor or general damp-proof course and afterwards to measure the remaining foundations up to the same level.

Earthwork Support.—Earthwork support must be measured to excavation, whether it will actually be necessary or not, to cover the builder's responsibility to uphold the sides. It is for the builder to decide, from his information as to the nature of the soil, the extent and strength of support that he will require. Even if he decides that he will not use any, there is still a risk to be priced: if excavation falls in, he will have to re-excavate at his own expense. The surveyor gives the whole area to be supported (S.M.M. D 15) and the distance between opposing faces (S.M.M. D 17): the builder may price the item at a nominal rate to cover a small risk, or at the full value of close-boarded timbering, if he considers this necessary throughout, or at some intermediate rate proportionate to the amount of timbering he considers necessary.

In Example 1, the earthwork support has been measured to the face of the surface strip, although that face does not exceed 150 mm, because the edge of the strip is in the same plane as the trench under and the total face to be supported exceeds 150 mm. Had the strip for any reason extended beyond the face of the trench excavation then support would not be measured.

It will be seen from S.M.M. D 18 that support to trenches immediately below the sides of an excavation, or within a distance from the side of an excavation equal to the depth of the trench, shall be so described. In Example 2, where the working space of 0.60 m is only measured to the top of the concrete foundation, the 350 mm high support to the trench falls within this category.

Disposal of Excavated Material.—It must be ascertained how the excavated material is to be disposed of. It is naturally cheaper if the material can be disposed of on the site, but there is often no room for it, and it must then be carted away. The special circumstances of each case must therefore be considered and the disposal fully described accordingly. Care must be taken to see that every item of excavation in the dimensions has an appropriate item of diposal measured. Where part is to be returned and rammed and part removed from site or otherwise disposed of, it will be found simplest to measure the whole excavation in the first instance as return fill in and ram as marked by a cross on fig. 17. When concrete and brickwork are later measured an adjustment can be made of the volume occupied by these as:

Ddt. r.f. & r.
&
Add. rem. exc. mtl.

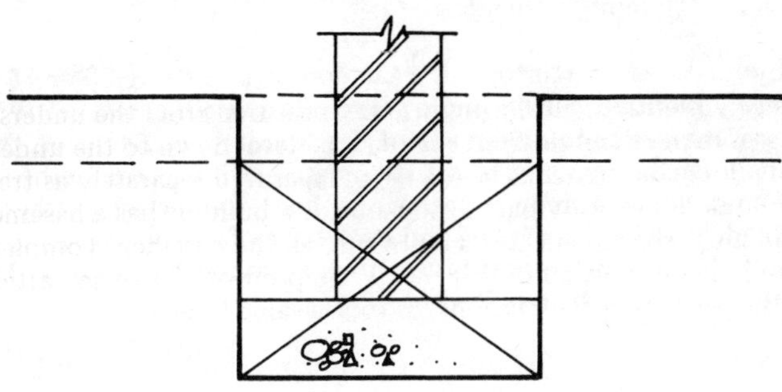

Fig. 17

If r.f & r. is thus deducted for the volume occupied by concrete and brickwork (shown hatched), that remaining of the original measurement will be the volume of space to be filled in. It is simpler to calculate the volume of the brickwork than to arrive at the volume of the spaces on each side. This is too an example of the advantage of the over-all system of measurement. Since all is measured in the first instance as r.f & r., if adjustment for removal is forgotten, the error is less serious. Care is necessary in making the adjustment for the volume occupied by the wall to see that the height is not taken above the level from which r.f. & r. was measured in the first instance. In the case of basement excavation it would probably be found more convenient to measure all for removal, and adjust subsequently for r.f. & r. round the outside.

Working Space.—The illustrations in the *Practice Manual* explain clearly the allowances to be made under the various circumstances required by S.M.M. D 12. From this clause it will be seen that working space, like earthwork support, is a contractor's risk item which does not fall to be adjusted if not done. It will be seen from S.M.M. D 12.2 that the working space item includes digging, backfilling and additional earthwork support as one composite item. In Example 2 a 600 mm width has been allowed from the face of the brick wall but because under S.M.M. D 13.4 the basement excavation has been measured to the outside of the foundations, only 200 mm falls within the working space item under S.M.M. D 12.2.

Concrete Foundations.—The length measured for excavation of trenches will usually be found to serve for the measurement of the concrete. The width will be the full width of trench and the thickness as shown on the drawings. Where the concrete foundation is not at a uniform level throughout it will be found easiest to measure it as if it were, additional excavation and concrete being afterwards added for the laps with formwork to the face of steps, the extra earthwork support being negligible. Again the advantage of over-all measurement shows itself. If each section is measured piecemeal, there is more danger of error through a section being missed, unless a careful check is made of the sum of the lengths, with the total length.

Concrete foundations are sometimes reinforced by either steel fabric or bars. In such cases it is important to remember that a finer aggregate is necessary than in ordinary mass concrete, and the concrete will therefore be of a different composition but would otherwise be measured in the same way, a separate item being taken for the reinforcement.

When foundations are reinforced, weak concrete blinding 50 or 75 mm thick is usually required. Such blinding is sometimes not shown on the drawings, in which case enquiry should be made of the Architect or Engineer whether it is wanted. The Engineer may not be satisfied with earth support to the sides of concrete foundations but require formwork: here, too the requirements should be ascertained, as the extra digging and back filling for working space will be substantial. Even if earth support is accepted, a flexible barrier or stabilisation of the excavated sides may be required.

S.M.M. F 11.3 requires that the weight of bars shall include for bends and hooks: for hooks one can usually allow nine times the diameter of the bar for each hook for extra length, after deducting the concrete cover to ends from the length of the concrete, i.e. in the case of a 12 mm bar 108 mm must be added at each end plus the amount of concrete cover.

EXAMPLE 1

WALL FOUNDATIONS

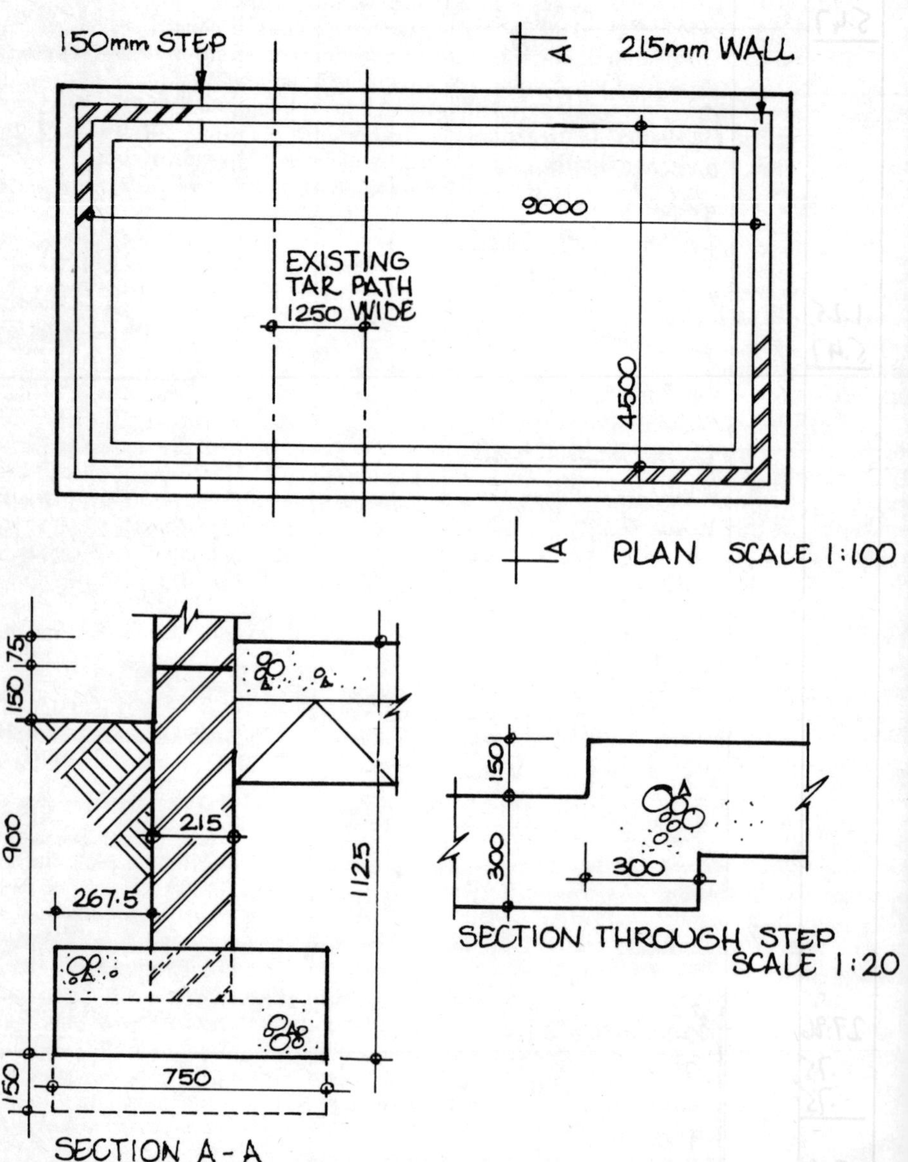

Fig. 18

Wall 2/215 Spread 2/½/535		9000 4500 430 430 535 535 9965 5465		27.86 .75		Level & compact bottoms of excavations
9.97 5.47		Excavate top soil average 150mm deep & Remove top soil average 100mm & deposit in heaps for re-use, x ·15 =	2/	27.86 .75		Earthwork support to excavation not exceeding 1.00 m deep & not exceeding 2.00 m between opposite faces
			2/	8.53 .15		
				30.88 .15		9.97 5.47 2/ 15.44 30.88 {Surf Excn
1.25 5.47		Extra on top soil excavation & depositing for breaking up & removing from site tarmacadam path & hardcore bed 150 mm deep		27.86 .75 .30		Concrete (1:6) in foundations 150-300 mm thick in trenches, poured against faces of excavation & Ddt Earth filling to trenches & Add Remove excavated material from site
			2/	.30 .75 .15		
		9000 4500 2/ 13500 27000 4/215 860 27.860				
		4500 2/1500 3000 7500 2/215 430 2/300 600 8530	2/	.75		Formwork to foundation not exceeding 250 mm high
						27.860 Wall 4/215 .860 Spread 4/268 1.072 29.792
27.86 .75 .75		Excavate trench starting at ground level & not exceeding 1.00 m deep & Earth filling to trenches		29.79 .27		Excavate in spoil heaps & wheel & deposit vegetable soil 150 mm deep /to replace vegetable soil
8.53 .75 .15						

(continued in Example 3)

EXAMPLE 2

BASEMENT FOUNDATIONS

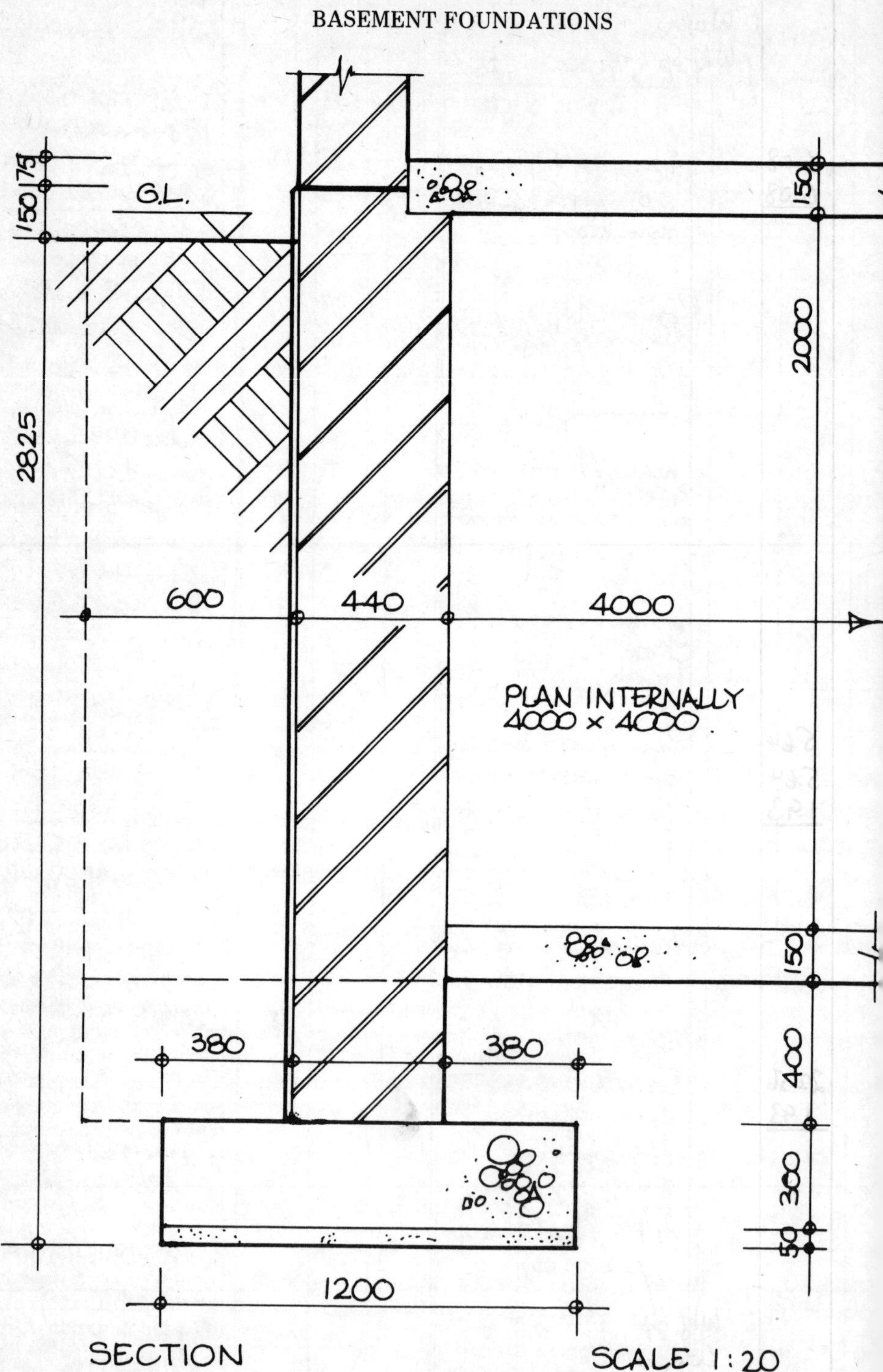

Fig. 19

4.000
Walls 2/ 440 880
Wkg Sp 2/ 600 1.200
6.080

6.08
6.08
Excavate surface soil average 150 mm deep

&

Remove vegetable soil ab.
× .150

4.000
Walls 2/ .440 .880
Conc 2/ .380 .760
5.640

2.825
Surf soil .150
Trench .750 .900
1.925

5.64
5.64
1.93
Excavate basement starting at ground level & not exceeding 2.00 m. deep

&

Remove excavated material from site

4/5.64 22.56

22.56
1.93
Earth support to excavation not exceeding 2.00 m deep & over 4.00 m from opposite face.

4/ 6.080 24.320
Wkg sp .600
Conc .380
4/ .220 .880
23.440

600
380
220

23.44
.22
1.93
Excavate working space around basement starting at ground level & not exceeding 2.00 m deep & fill with material from excavations

4/ 6.080 24.320
4/ 600 2.400
21.920

21.92
.60
Excavate in spoil heaps & deposit vegetable soil in making up levels 150 mm deep

4.000
4.000
2/ 8.000 16.000
4/ .440 1.760
17.760

17.76
1.20
.75
Excavate trench starting 2.23 m below ground level, exceeding 0.50 m wide & not exceeding 1.00 m deep

&

Remove excavated material from site

17.76
1.20
Level & compact bottom of excavation

Times	Dimensions	Squaring	Description
	23.44 .22 .40		Excavate working space around trench starting 2.23 m below ground & not exceeding 0.50 m deep & fill with material from excavations.
2/	17.76 .75		Earth support to excavation not exceeding 1.00 m deep & not exceeding 2.00 m from opposite face
			1.200 4/5.640 22.560 .440 4/.380 1.520 .760 21.040
	17.76 .76 .40		Ddt Remove exc mat from site & Add Earth filling to trenches
	21.04 .38 1.93		Ddt Remove exc mat from site & Add Earth filling to basement excavation
	17.76 1.20 .05		Fine concrete (1:12) blinding not exceeding 100 mm thick on earth
	17.76 1.20 .30		Reinforced concrete (1:2:4) foundations in trench 150–300 mm thick, poured against faces of excavation

Times	Dimensions	Squaring	Description
	17.76 1.20		Steel fabric reinforcement to BS 4483 Ref A 142 weighing 2… kg/m² with 200 mm laps, in foundations

Alternative to fabric reinforcement

Times	Dimensions	Squaring	Description
			4.000 Wall 2/.440 880 Spread 2/.380 760 5.640 Cover 2/.040 80 5.560 Hooks 2/9/.012 216 5.776
4/4/	5.77		12 mm Diameter mild steel bars in foundations
			4.000 2/.380 760 Spacing .300) 3.240 (300 240 300 1.200 Cover 2/.040 80 1.120
4/10/	1.12		6 mm Diameter …

CHAPTER 6

WALLING, BLOCKWORK AND PARTITIONS

References to S.M.M.

G	1–5, 7–13, 26–33, 37
J	1–8, 10–11
L	1, 3–4
N	1–3, 29, 31

Brickwork or Walling in Foundations.—The excavation and concrete of foundations having been measured, the next section to deal with will be the general brickwork or walling. S.M.M. G 3.1a requires foundation brickwork and blockwork to be kept separate and it is therefore necessary to measure first up to a general level such as ground floor or damp-proof course.

The measurement of external walls below damp-proof course will be followed by similar items for internal walls. Where the concrete foundation is stepped, each length from step to step will have to be measured separately up to the level decided on, and, as this piecemeal measurement is necessary in such a case, the lengths measured should be added together on waste and checked with the ascertained total. Alternatively, the total length can be taken by the minimum height, the extra heights added for each section built from a lower level. It should be noted here that the lengths of internal walls will not coincide with those of their concrete foundations, if the adjustment of the latter has been made at intersections as described in the last chapter.

The measurement of foundations will be completed by the damp-proof course (slate, asphalt, lead, bituminous felt, etc.), first horizontal and then vertical (if any).

Metrication.—On the introduction of metric sizes the clay and calcium silicate brick industry decided to adopt a single metric standard size of 215 x 102.5 x 65 mm, which with a 10 mm joint will become 225 x 112.5 x 75 mm, a size very close to the imperial measurement brick with a $\frac{3}{8}''$ joint. This means that wall thicknesses will be as follows:

Half brick	102.5 mm
One brick	215 mm
1½ brick	327.5 mm
2 brick	440 mm

These are the sizes assumed in the examples that follow. The exact width of a cavity is not critical, so a two-skin brick wall has been assumed at 250 mm (102.5 + 45 + 102.5 mm).

Measurement of Brickwork Generally.—Brickwork generally is measured the thickness of the wall and the old device of reduced brickwork has disappeared. This means that in the unlikely event of measurement of footings being required, rather than describe each course as a wall so many mm wide, it would be sufficient to measure extra over in the same way as oversailing courses in manholes, etc. Varying thicknesses of walls will also be encountered in the measurement of chimney stacks.

It should be noted that deep brickwork in narrow trenches has to be separately identified under S.M.M. G 5.3.

Walls.—The measurement of superstructure walls will follow on the same principle in the following subdivisions:

(a) External walls.

(b) Internal walls.

(c) Chimney breasts and projections.

(d) Stacks.

All openings, recesses, etc. will be disregarded. In dealing with external walls the heights will often be found to vary, in which case it will usually be possible to measure up to some general line, e.g. main eaves, and to make adjustments for gables, lower eaves, etc. Internal walls will be measured in convenient stages, generally floor by floor. The area of brick chimney breasts and piers will be measured and the extra thickness they contain written in the description column and described as in projections (S.M.M. G 5).

It must be remembered that if the thickness of a wall is reduced on one side (as at a floor level or parapet) the centre line of the wall is moved, and, therefore, the collection calculating the perimeter of a building is altered. In Example 1 the centre line of the one brick wall is 27.86 m, but a one and a half brick wall of the same internal dimensions would have a centre line of 28.35 m.

Extras on Brickwork.—While measuring walls it must be remembered that certain special extras have to be measured:

(a) Work in Cement Mortar.—When the general brickwork is in a gauged or cement-lime mortar certain parts of the building will probably be required to be built in cement mortar, and the extra cost of this will be measured in the same way as the brickwork, thus:-

	0.69 1.83		one brick wall & one brick wall E.O. in ct.

or it may be put down simply as:

	0.69 1.83		one brick wall in ct.

it being left to the worker up to take the item first as brickwork and then as extra for cement. If all brickwork is in cement, it will be sufficient to write a general instruction 'All bkk. is in ct.', and in such a case there will, of course, be no separate item of 'extra for cement', and cement need not be mentioned every time in the brickwork description.

(b) Rough Cutting.—The extent to which rough cutting is to be measured is defined by S.M.M. G 10 and will be seen to be limited to forming chamfered and rounded angles.

In all other cases rough cutting is deemed to be included.

(c) Bonding to Old Walls (S.M.M. G 13).—Where the walls of a new building abut against an old building the new work is measured up to the old face only and a separate item is taken for bonding:

2/	5.50	L. & m.c.t. & b. 1B wall to old

The bond of the brickwork will normally be the same throughout and given in a preamble. If there is doubt the description should say that the bond of the wall is English bond or otherwise.

(d) Eaves Filling.—This is sometimes measured in the 'Roofs' section and sometimes in the 'Brickwork', and where the taking off is divided it is necessary to see that this item is not overlooked. The labour in eaves filling is deemed to be included. All that is necessary, therefore, is to measure the additional brickwork.

(e) Key for Finish (S.M.M. G 8, 40).—In the case of such a smooth surfaced brick as the Fletton, bricks are made with grooves on the face to serve as a key for applied rendering, etc. With other bricks in the best work the raking out of joints would be sufficient. The extra in either case would be measured as a separate item when the plastering or other surface finish is measured.

(f) Arches.—These are dealt with in the chapters on windows, doors, etc.

(g) Damp-Proof Courses (S.M.M. G 37—38).— The general damp-proof course will be measured after the foundation brickwork and a further damp-proof course is usually required to chimney stacks above roof level, and sometimes to parapet walls. Wherever hollow walls are built off solid walls or off beams, it must not be forgotten that some form of damp-proof course is necessary to divert moisture from the bottom of the cavity.

Hollow Walls.—Each casing of a hollow wall is measured separately and described as such and a separate item is measured for forming the cavity, including the supply and fixing of ties (S.M.M. G 9). The relative items of measurement would be, say:

2/	15.25 3.00	H. b. casing to h.w. in ct.-lime mortar
	15.25 3.00	L. forming 50 mm cavity in h.w. inc. ties a.d.

The specification and spacing of ties would probably be in a preamble, but could be embodied in full in the description of the item. Where the outer casing is in facing bricks, it would be measured as such, not as common brickwork with facings as 'extra over'.

Blockwork.—The measurement of blockwork has been given a separate subsection of the S.M.M., but the rules will be found generally to follow those for brickwork. Special note is made concerning blockwork designed to be built without cutting.

Partitions.—Following the measurement of walls will come the main measurements of partitions, whether brick, concrete or patent slab, again ignoring openings. If extensive, they may form an entirely separate section. Although in the case of half-brick partitions no bonding to brick walls will be measured, an item for this must be taken in the case of block partitions, the units being of a different size from bricks, on the same lines as in the case of bonding brickwork to old walls. Any cuttings and items of bonding at angles, etc., in slab partitions will then be measured. Stud partitions will also be measured in this section, but in this case openings are best taken into consideration at the same time, the various door-posts, heads, etc., being measured the extra thickness specified and deductions made from studs for openings. Any bridging pieces or sole plates to carry wood or slab partitions must be taken with the partitions.

EXAMPLE 3

BRICKWORK IN FOUNDATIONS

(Continuation of Example 1, see fig. 18, page 41)

		.150 .900 1.050 Found. 300 .750			**Alternatives to Last**
27.86 .75 7.93 .15		One brick wall in common bricks in cement mortar (1:3) in foundations Lower fdn as waste, Example 1	27.86		20 mm Asphalte horizontal damp proof course in two coats 150-300 mm wide on brick walls, including fair edge.
27.86 .22 .45 7.93 .22 .15		Ddt Earth filling to trenches & Add Remove exc. mat. from site a.b.			or
		.900 .150 300 .450 .450	27.86		Horizontal damp proof course 215 mm wide of two courses of slates laid breaking joint bedded in cement mortar
27.86		Fibre base & lead damp proof course to BS 743 Ref E 215 mm wide, on walls, with 150 mm laps. (no allowance made for laps)			

EXAMPLE 4

BASEMENT WALLS

(Continuation of Example 2, see fig. 19, page 43)

			2.000 150 400 2550
	17.76 2.55		Two brick wall in common bricks in cement mortar (1:3), loadbearing
			4/4000 16.000 4/2/.1125 900 16 900 4/.3275 1.310 18.210
	18.21 .08		One & a half brick wall in common bricks in cement mortar (1:3) loadbearing
	18.21 .33		Fibre base & lead damp proof course on walls a.b.
	19.52 2.63		20mm Portland cement & sand (1:3) vertical damp proof course on walls, the cement mixed with 5% by weight of "X" waterproofing compound in accordance with the manufacturers' instructions & Rake out joints of brickwork as key for rendering

4/	2.63		Internal angle on vertical cement damp proof cours
	19.52		Fair splayed top e to vertical cement damp proof cou
			Alternative to last
	18.21 .33		20mm Asphalte horizontal damp proof course in tw coats on brick wal including extern angles
	19.52 2.63		20mm Asphalte vertical damp pro course in three coa on brick walls & Rake out joints o brickwork as key for vertical aspha

EXAMPLE 5

WALLS AND PARTITIONS
(Above damp-proof course)

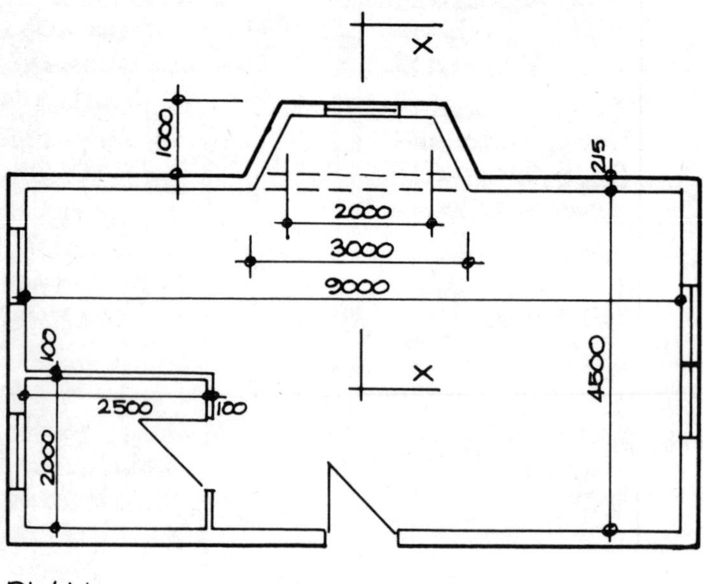

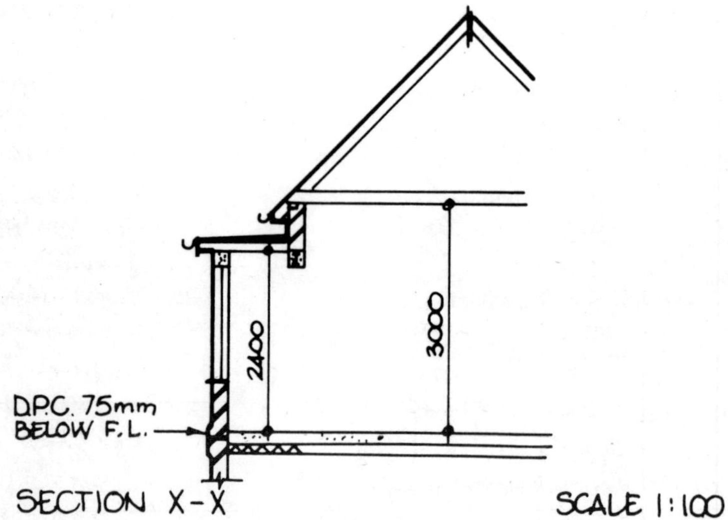

Fig. 20

Assumed that bricks & blocks can be cut without saws.			9.000 4.500 13.500 2/= 27.000 4/215 .860 27.860 3.000 .075 .150 3.225
	27.86 3.23		One brick wall in common bricks in cement lime mortar (1:1:6), load bearing
			3.000 2/.075 .150 3.150
	3.15 2.48		Ddt Dr 2.400 .075 2.475 (girth of bars 1.120 2.150 1.120 4.390
	4.39 2.48		Add
			Ro cutting } Beam filling } not measurable
	3.43		178 × 102 × 21.54 Kg/m steel joist to BS 4 Part 1 Table E, & hoisting & fixing approximately 2.25m above ground, (in Nr 1 beam 3.43 m long) 3.000 2/.215 .430 3.430 {b.i. ends {not measurable

	2	150 mm Precast concrete (1:2:4) splayed padstone 200 × 230 mm & building in
	2.92 .22 .30	Concrete (1:2:4) casing to isolated steel beam 0.03–0.10 m² sectional area
	2.92	Formwork to isolated beam casing 215 × 300 mm (in Nr. 1)
2/	.24	Raking cutting on formwork.
		2.500 2.000 4.500 .100 4.600 Door .700 3.900
	3.90	Fibre base & lead damp proof course 100 mm wide
	4.60 3.00	100 mm Concrete blockwork to BS 2028 Type C, bedded & jointed in cement lime mortar (1:1:6), in non load-bearing partition. {Ro cutting to soffit {not measurable

2/	3.00	Bonding 100 mm blockwork to brickwork, including forming pockets for alternate courses and extra material

Alternative if building gabled

		4.500
	.215	
	.150	
2/	65	130
		2) 4.630
		2.315

2/½/	4.62 2.32	One brick wall in common bricks a.b.
		{Ro. raking cutting {not masble

Alternative for 100 mm internal stud partition

2.500	
.100	2.600
2.000	
.100	2.100
	4.700
Door	.700
	4.000

	4.70 4.00	75×100 mm Impregnated softwood partition {Head {Sill
	3.00	100×100 mm Do. {Angle post
2/	3.00 .90	75×100 mm Do {Dr post {Dr head

.360) 2.500 (7
2.520

2.7/	3.00 .90 4.00	50×100 mm Do {Studs {Do over door. {Noggings

(Plinth measured with facings)

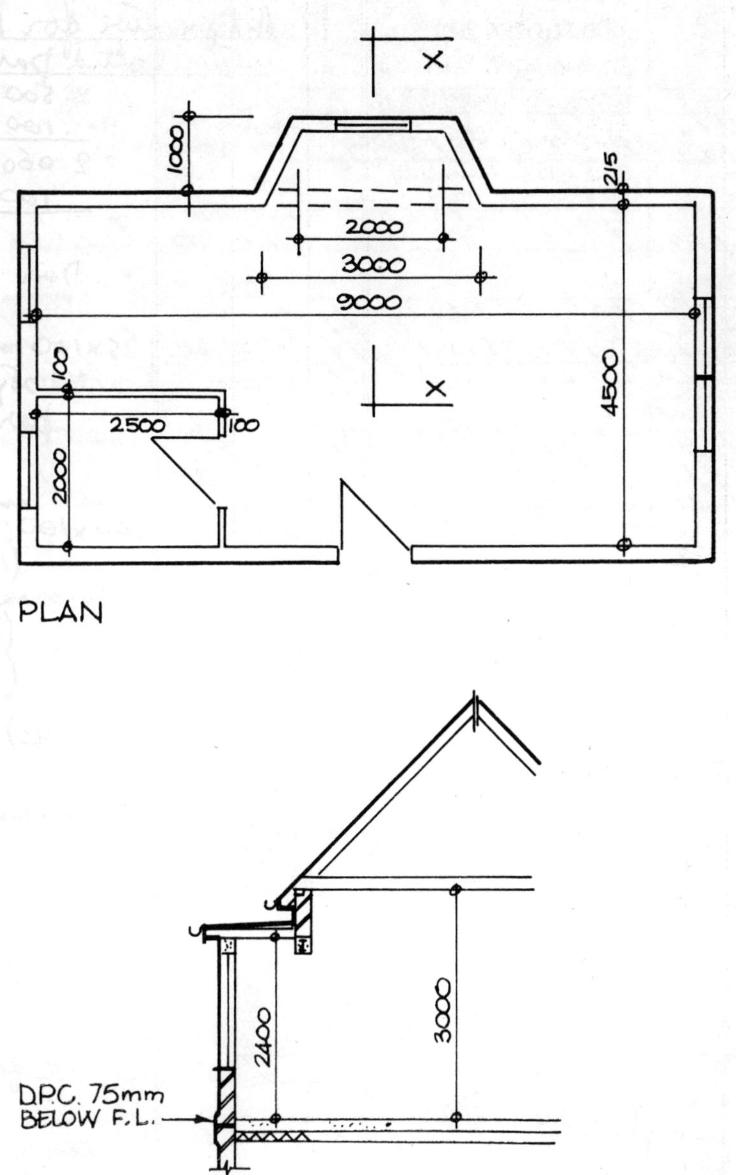
X
1000
215
2000
3000
9000
4500
X
100
2500
100
2000
PLAN
3000
2400
D.P.C. 75mm
BELOW F.L.
SECTION X-X
SCALE 1:100

Fig. 20

EXAMPLE 6

PROJECTIONS, ETC., IN BRICKWORK

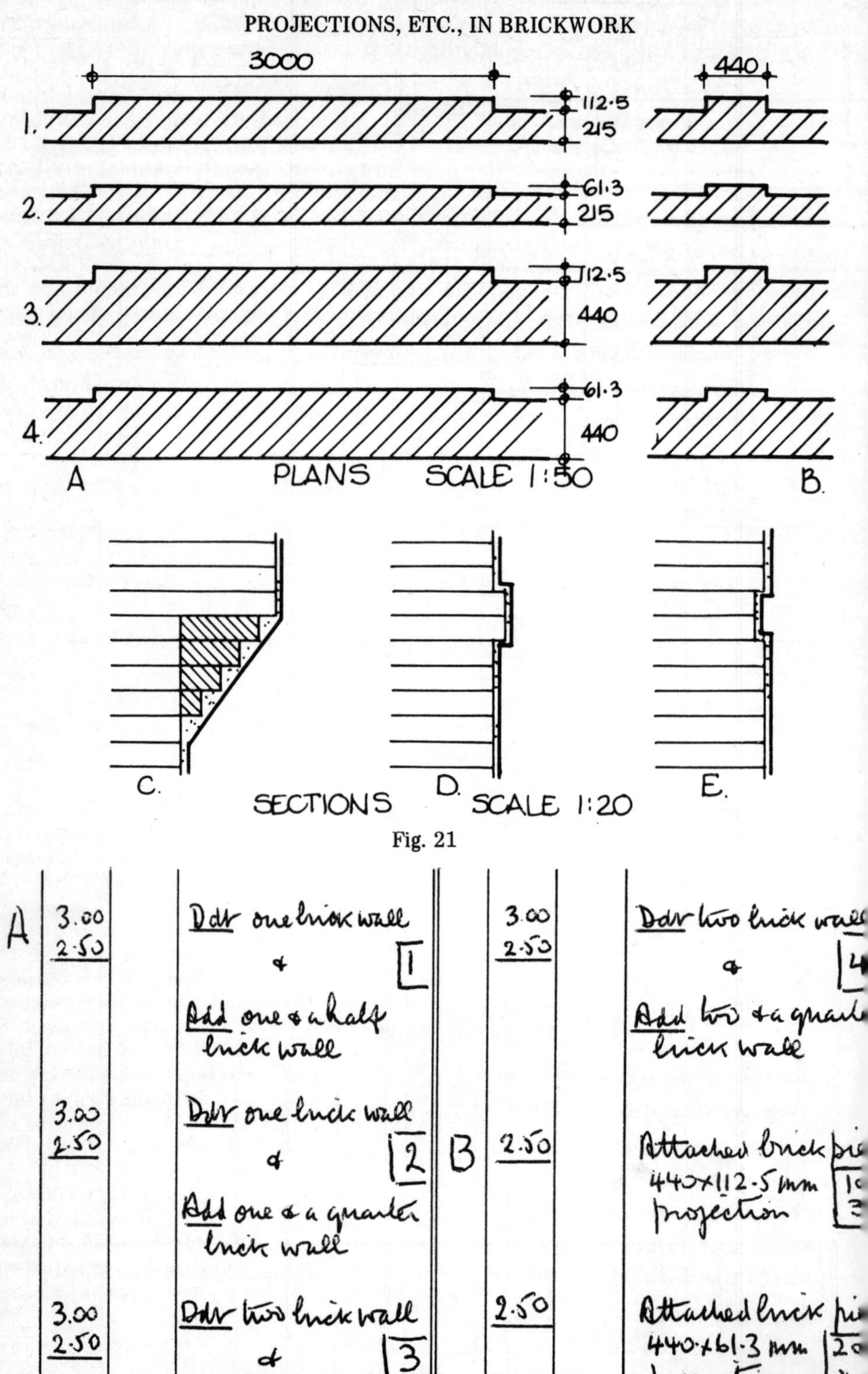

3000
440
1.
112·5
215
2.
61·3
215
3.
112·5
440
4.
61·3
440
A
PLANS
SCALE 1:50
B.
C.
D.
E.
SECTIONS
SCALE 1:20
A
3.00
2.50
Ddt one brick wall
&
Add one & a half
brick wall
1
3.00
2.50
Ddt one brick wall
&
Add one & a quarter
brick wall
2
3.00
2.50
Ddt two brick wall
&
Add two & a half
brick wall
3
3.00
2.50
Ddt two brick wall
&
Add two & a quarter
brick wall
4
B
2.50
Attached brick pie
440×112·5 mm
projection
2.50
Attached brick pi
440×61·3 mm
projection

Fig. 21

C			(Brickwork assumed already measured except as hatched)
			.225 .056 2 | .281 .141
	3.00		Brickwork in oversailing courses average 141 mm projection & 300 mm high
D	3.00		Brickwork in projecting band 28 mm x 150 mm high
E	3.00		Set back face of brickwork 30 mm x 150 mm high
			Note: This might be described as a rough chase.

CHAPTER 7

FACEWORK

References to S.M.M.

G	14–22, 34–36
J	9, 12–14
K	1–5, 9–32
N	1, 4–8, 11–12
T	1–6
V	1–4

The external facework may be in brick, some form of roughcast or rendering, stone or other special finishing. The scope of this book so far as general facework is concerned is intended to cover the first two only, which are the most common form. The term facework includes a fair face in the structural material.

Facing Bricks and Pointing.—It will probably be possible from the collection of the walls to calculate the perimeter of the building on the external wall face, and the main item of facings will be measured up to a general level, adjustments being made for gables, etc., as was done with the brickwork, and the facing of stacks added. The description of the mortar and p.c. of the bricks should be given, but may eventually be extracted and made a short preamble to the 'Facings' section of the bill. Where the facing bricks are subject to a p.c. sum some indication of the type of brick envisaged should be given. The height of facings should be measured from the point where the facing bricks begin, but in measuring from drawings it is usual to take from 75 mm below the ground line shown to allow for possible part courses or irregularities of the ground. Immediately following the main item of facings will come any curved cutting and squints or birdsmouths. Squints should be described as 'rubbed', as part of the cut portion of the brick is exposed. Alternatively, special bricks will be used. When a particular facing brick is specified (for which the builders tendering are getting their own quotations), then 'specials' can be similarly specified. If, however, the facing bricks have a p.c. price, prices must be given for all specials, as the builder obviously cannot price a special brick under these circumstances. If a more expensive common brick is used in foundations than above damp-proof course, the facings in each case must be kept separate, as the extra value will differ. If the foundation brickwork is in cement mortar and the superstructure in cement-lime mortar the facings to the former must be described as including raking out joints and pointing in cement-lime mortar if the same appearance is to be presented.

Quoins.—Where the main quoins of a building are in different bricks or in stone, they will be measured here. Like all facings, brick quoins will usually be measured as extra over common brickwork, facings already measured over being deducted.

Plinths, Bands, String Courses, etc.—Following the above main items of facings will be measured any plinth, band courses, etc., usually starting at the bottom of the elevation and working upwards, also any ornaments on the elevation not part of a window or door feature. Where dressings form part of such a feature they will usually be measured with the opening. Example 8 illustrates some common forms of bands, etc. in faced brickwork.

Copings and Parapets.—Copings to parapet walls, also chimney caps and similar items, will be measured with the 'Facings' section. An item apt to be overlooked is the facing inside parapet walls, which if the wall is 1B thick requires an adjustment of the brickwork, thus:

	27.00 0.46	Ddt. 1B wall in ct-lime mortar.
	27.86 0.46	Ddt. fcgs. (outside as msd.).
	27.00 0.46	Add 1B wall in fcgs. in ct. faced and ptd. b.s.

It will be noted from the S.M.M. (G 14.9) that one-brick walls where fair or faced on both sides are to be kept separate. This is done as there is some extra cost in picking headers to the exact thickness of wall and more careful labour is needed in setting them. On the other hand, compared with the facing of thicker brickwork, there is some saving on the number of facing bricks used owing to headers serving both faces. Half-brick walls faced both sides are also to be kept separate.

Roughcast, etc.—Where the external walls are roughcast or similarly treated a corresponding order will be followed. The main measurements will be taken first, ignoring all windows and other openings, and they will be followed by the arrises to main angles. If the plinth is of brick this would be measured first as described above, and any special labour on the roughcast, such as a 'bell-cast' or projecting lip, measured to suit. Any band courses or other features in the roughcast would be taken after the main measurements. All reveals to openings, etc., will be taken with the openings and not in this section.

EXAMPLE 7

EXTERNAL FACINGS

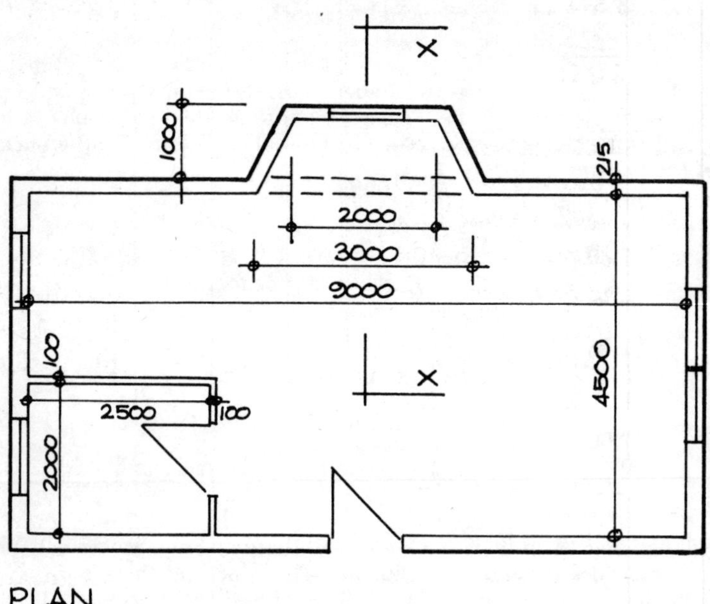

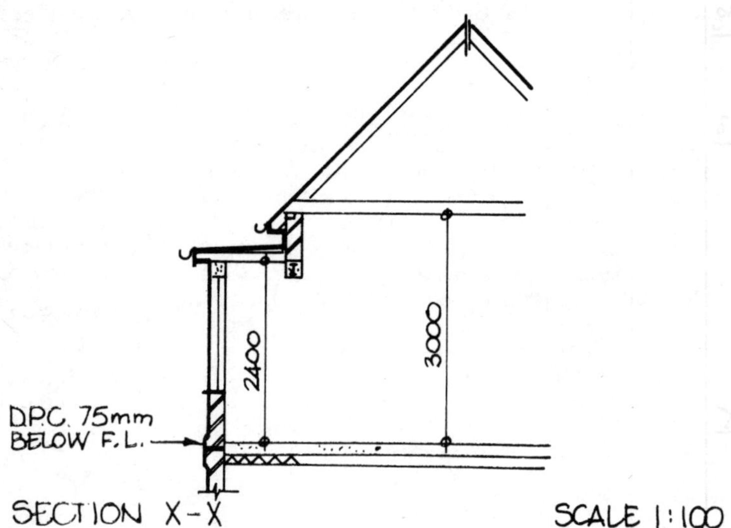

Fig. 20

Timesing	Dimensions	Squaring	Description
			Flr to clf 3.000 · To d.p.c. .075 · 4/.215 · Below d.p.c. .300 · 3.375 · 225 · 3.150 · 27.360 · 860 · 28.720
	28.72 / 3.15		Extra on common brickwork for facing with facing bricks as described & pointing with flush joints (referred to as facings A)
			3.000 · 2/1/75 300 · 3.300 · 2.400 · 75 · {bay 300 · 2.775
	3.30 / 2.78		Ddt
			2.300 · 2/450 2.300 · 4.600
	4.60 / 2.78		Add
2/	2.78		Fair cut birdsmouth in facings A & Extra for squint quyle bricks in facings A
4/	3.15		Extra on common brickwork for facing with facing bricks (facings B) to flush quoin average 400 mm girth, including all cutting & bonding with facings A and pointing to match
4/	.40 / 3.15		Ddt facings A
			9.000 · 2/215 430 · 9.430 · Quoins 2/400 800 · 8.630 · 2/500 1.000 · 7.630 · 2/1.120 2.240 · 9.870
	9.87 / .38		Extra on common brickwork for facing A to plinth 30 mm projection & Ddt facings A
2/	9.87 / .38		Extra for facings A & pointing to margin
	9.87		Ddt fibre base & lead d.p.c. 215 mm wide on walls
			215 · 30 · 245
	9.87 / .25		Fibre base & lead damp proof course on walls

Timesing	Dimensions	Squaring	Description
			<u>Alternative to above</u> White cement rendered with facing brick plinth all round.
			28.720 3.300
			2.300 25.420
2/	1.120		2.240 4.540
			29.960
4/2/			30 240
			30.200
	30.20 .38		Extra on common brickwork for facings A to plinth 30 mm projection
	30.20		Extra for facings A & pointing to margin
1/	.38		Fair cut b.m. in fcgs A ab. & Ex for sq. angle bks in fcgs A a.b.
	29.96		<u>Ddt</u> fibre base & lead d.p.c. 215 mm wide on walls
	29.96 .25		Fibre base & lead d.p.c. on walls ab.

Timesing	Dimensions	Squaring	Description
			Fcgs 3.150 Plinth .375 2.775
	28.72 2.78		15 mm Rendering on brick walls externally the backing coat of cement & sand (1:3), the finishing coat of white cement & sand (1:2½) finished with a wood float & Rake out joints of brickwork as key for rendering
	3.30 2.40		<u>Ddt</u> <u>both</u>
	4.60 2.40		<u>Add</u> <u>both</u>
4/ 2/	2.78 2.40		Arris
	30.02		Extra on white cement & sand rendering for small bellcast, including dubbing
	4		External mitres
	2		Irregular external mitres
	2		Irregular internal mitres
			(Plinth to adjust for doorway)

		Alternative if building gabled and faced	
2/½/	4.93 2.50	Fcgs A ab.	
		4.500 $2/.215$ .430 4.930 (Height scaled	
2/½/	3.50	Fair raking cutting on facings A	
		(assumed saw cutting reqd	
		Alternative if building gabled & rendered	
2/½/	4.93 2.50	15 mm White cement rendering ab. & Rake out joints of brickwork for rendering ab.	

EXAMPLE 8

PROJECTIONS, ETC., IN FACINGS

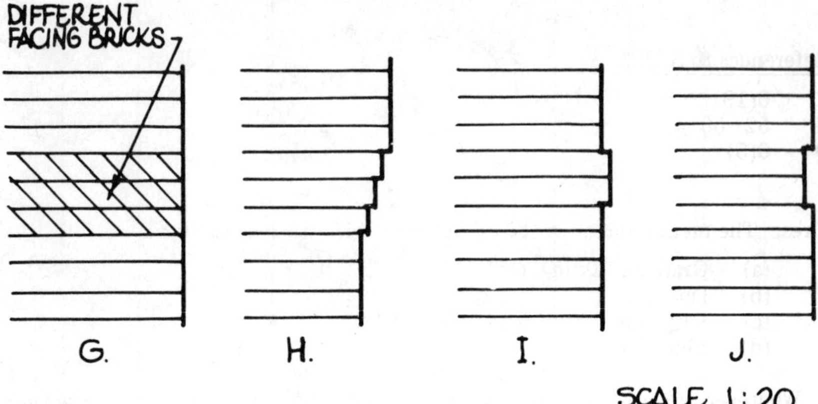

Fig. 22

Ref	Timesing	Dimensions	Squaring	Description
G		3.00		Extra on common brickwork for facings B in flush plain band 225 mm wide & pointing
				&
				Ddt Fcgs A × .23
H	4/	3.00		Extra on common brickwork for facings A to oversailing course & pointing face & margin
		3.00 .30		Ddt Fcgs A
I		3.00		Extra on common brickwork for facings B & pointing to projecting plain band 150 mm high & pointing face & margin
		3.00 .15		Ddt Fcgs A
J		3.00		Extra on common brickwork for facings A to sunk plain band 150 mm high set back 30 mm & pointing to face & margins
				&
				Ddt FcgA × .15

CHAPTER 8

FIRES AND VENTS

References to S.M.M.

F 6(19)
G 52–56
Q 6(5)

Fires.—The measurement of 'Fires' divides itself into four sections:

(a) Grate and fixing, etc.
(b) Opening.
(c) Surround, hearth and chimneypiece.
(d) Flue.

Whatever type of fireplace is being dealt with it will be found that these four subsections must be considered. Everything in connection with the fireplace is measured in this section. The stove or grate is usually a p.c. sum, but the general type of stove must be decided on to enable the fixing to be properly described. Any boilers for central heating or hot water systems will usually be left to be dealt with in a separate section unless combined with the fireplace.

The items commonly met with are best illustrated by the example, which should explain itself.

The S.M.M. makes no requirement to keep tiling to fireplaces separate, but it would seem best to separate such screed and tiling from any similar general work, following the suggestion in the general rules to the S.M.M. This case shows that the surveyor has no discretion to alter the rule of the S.M.M., even though he may think that there can be no value in the item. At the same time, if he thinks that fuller detail will help the estimator he is at liberty (but not bound) to give it.

Brickwork and facings to stack with chimney cap, etc., will usually be measured in the 'Brickwork' or 'Facings' section as already described and not here.

A common type of fireplace at the present day is the slabbed tile surround, hearth and kerb with a firebrick interior and grate, perhaps of the slow-burning type. These will fairly certainly be the subject of a p.c. sum, unless the exact requirements are selected, when a merchant's catalogue references can be quoted. The fixing will be enumerated, the hearth and kerb being usually given as a separate item from the surround and grate, or each of the four can be separately enumerated, since they involve four separate operations.

The S.M.M. makes no special provision for brick fireplaces, but the surround may be formed in facing bricks with, perhaps, an open hearth. Measurement would probably resolve itself into two or three enumerated items, the important thing being to convey the requirements clearly in the descriptions. If any air duct is required to provide draught, this will be measured at the same time as the fireplace.

Gas or Electric Fires.—These would usually appear in the section where gas or electric services are dealt with, where all work in connection with them would also be taken. If, however, they have similar chimneypieces, etc., to the coal fires, it may be found more convenient to measure the work in connection at the same time, leaving probably only the fire and its fixing to be taken with the gas or electric services.

Ventilation.—Vent gratings and air bricks generally are dealt with in the same section as the fires. Those which are purely for the ventilation of hollow wall cavities may be measured in the 'Brickwork' section and those ventilating hollow floors may be taken in the 'Floors' section. There may be air brick ventilation to w.c.'s, larders, cupboards, etc. The opening should be measured as a separate enumerated item and the internal finish, whether air brick, metal or fibrous plaster grating, etc., must be remembered.

If vents are into a separate brick flue instead of directly through an external wall, the measurement of the grating will be followed by the flue items as in the case of fireplaces, the upper outlet being either a chimney pot or a grating in the side of the stack.

Where a special ventilation scheme is designed for the whole or part of the building this will usually be dealt with in a separate section, and is generally the subject of a p.c. sum as being carried out by specialists. Vents behind radiators, being in connection with heating work, would be taken in that section.

EXAMPLE 9

FIREPLACE

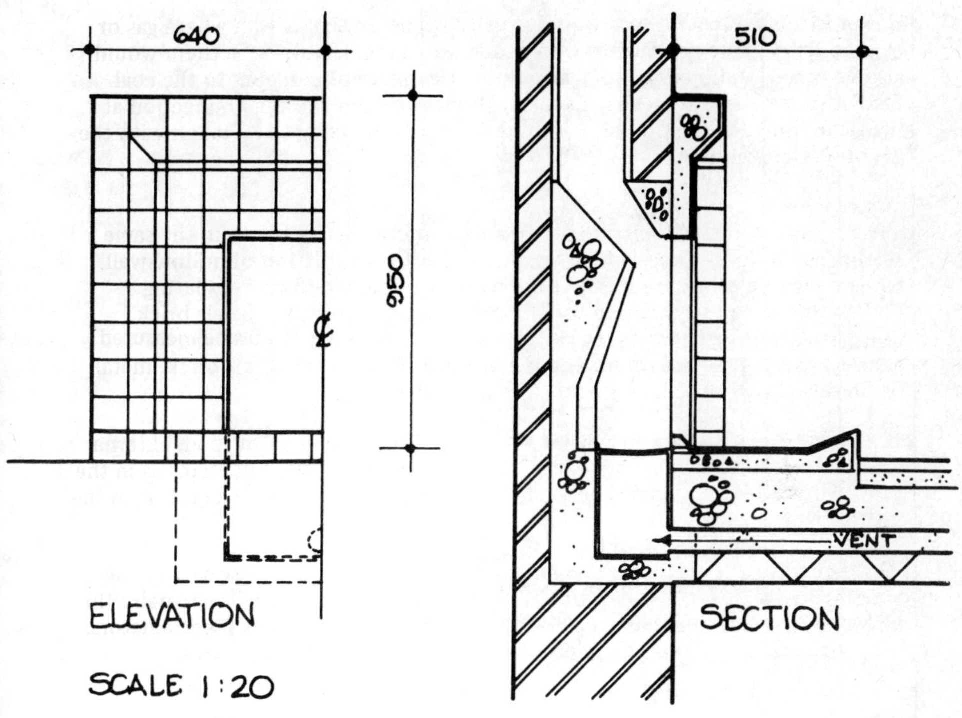

Fig. 23

			Allow the p.c. sum of £ for fireplace surround, hearth, kerb, firebrick back, grate & ashpan
			Add profit
	1		Fix slabbed tile fireplace surround 1280 × 950 & 150 mm thick with precast tile hearth & kerb, including assembling & jointing & bedding surround, hearth & kerb in cement mortar & cutting & pinning legs to brickwork
	1		Fix fireset of flow, ashpan, firebrick back, gas ignition point & operating tool, & setting in opening & bedding back in fire cement
	.55 .70		Ddt two brick wall in common bricks a.b. & Add half brick wall in common bricks a.b.

Timesing	Dimensions	Squaring	Description
			660 1/100 200 860
	1		103×150 mm Precast concrete (1:2:4) splayed & rounded lintol 860 mm long with one 12 mm mild steel bar
	1		Concrete (1:2:4) in thickening to floor 1280×510 & 40 mm high including formwork to front & two edges & Do in surround for ash pan 810×390×340 mm deep with formwork to sinking 500×280×200 mm deep
	.80 .35		Ddt 2B wall in cement mortar
	6.00		75 mm Diameter asbestos cement air duct internally, including laying in hardcore bed & hand-packing around
	2		Extra for bend
	1		Joint 75 mm diameter asbestos cement duct to cast iron fire set with asbestos wool & cement /Vent to external wall measured with air bricks

Timesing	Dimensions	Squaring	Description
	4.50		229×229 mm Square rebated chimney flue lining to BS 1181 type A1 in 295 mm lengths, jointed in fire cement, bedded in cement mortar as the work proceeds & cutting brickwork around. {Length assumed
	2		Extra for 22½° curved unit, including cutting
	1		216×216 mm Square based clay chimney pot to BS 1181 type D 305 mm long, bedded solidly & flaunched up in cement mortar

EXAMPLE 10

VENTS

3		300 x 230 mm Square hole pattern terra cotta air brick & building in
		&
		Forming cranked opening 300 x 230 mm in 1½B wall rendered in cement
		&
		300 x 230 mm Fibrous plaster louvred vent grating & setting in plaster & making good around.
1		300 x 230 mm TC air brick a.b.
		&
		Forming opening 300 x 230 mm in 250 mm hollow wall & sealing cavity all round with slates in cement
		&
		300 x 230 mm Fibrous plaster vent grating a.b.

CHAPTER 9

FLOORS

References to S.M.M.

D 33–39
F 1–4, 6–15, 18, 26–32
G 38–39
L 1–5
N 1–8, 29, 31
P 1–5
Q 6(2)
T 1–3, 8–12, 14

Sizing of Timber.—This chapter introduces for the first time the measurement of timber and it is important to understand the various forms in which timber sizes can appear on drawings. S.M.M. N 1.3 assumes that all sizes will be basic (formerly nominal) unless otherwise stated. The *Practice Manual* indicates that the intention of the S.M.M. is that the sizes shown on the drawings should be the sizes measured. Difficulties arise when there is a mixture of basic and finished sizes as sometimes happens and a decision must be made as to which is going to be measured. Traditionally, dimensions were nominal on all drawings, except those drawn to full size when the rule was finished sizes; today architects vary, some do one some the other. At first glance it would seem sensible to measure the finished size because this is the only determinable size; however due to tolerance and sometimes planing margins the size which eventually gets built in will differ slightly from the finished size and where this is not critical is of little importance but may have resulted in a more economical scantling being used. For this reason basic sizes are preferable; the architect then knows that what he will get is the nominal scantling reduced by a planing margin and tolerance. If he states finished sizes that is what he will get, subject only to tolerance, and it may be very expensive.

S.M.M. N 1.3 also requires the limits on the planing margins to be given and this will be done by way of a preamble. The actual margins used will be stated or reference will be made to the relevant B.S.* which sets out in great detail what these margins are, not only for the various sizes of timber but having regard to the end use as well; i.e. the margin on a piece of timber used as door frame will be different from that on the same piece of timber used for an architrave. In the examples that follow basic sizes have been used in all cases.

Subdivision.—The measurement of floors subdivides itself naturally into construction and finishings, each part being further subdivided according to the storeys. The taking off should be done accordingly in a systematic order, such

*B.S. 4471 Dimensions for softwood.

as:

Finishings

(a) 1st Floor
(b) Ground Floor
(c) Basement

Construction

(a) 1st Floor
(b) Ground Floor
(c) Basement

or it may be more convenient to adopt the following order:

1st Floor

(a) Finishings
(b) Construction

Ground Floor

(a) Finishings
(b) Construction

Basement

(a) Finishings
(b) Construction

It may appear to be putting the cart before the horse to measure finishings before construction, but this is often done, since a knowledge of the finishings measured may govern the form of construction, e.g. if an upper floor of wood construction has tile or similar paving, the portion so paved may be constructed differently. There is, however, no reason why, if preferred, construction should not be taken first, always with an eye on the type of finishing. Some surveyors measure floor finishes with general Internal Finishings, as the areas can often be taken as the same as ceiling plaster with slight adjustments.

Floor Finishings.—The measurement of these is generally a question of areas and measurable cuttings. In the case of work in a material of a plastic nature, such as cement paving, terrazzo, etc., the question of cutting naturally does not arise. Such finishes as vinyl and rubber flooring are preferably dealt with by provisional sums, as, owing to the width in which rolls are made, the waste varies very considerably according to the size of the rooms, and cannot be properly valued if included in a superficial measurement, nor even if a lineal measurement is made for straight cutting.

In measuring floor finishings generally it is important to bear in mind the actual thickness of each material, where all are to finish at the same level. Where, for instance, a concrete floor is to be covered in different rooms with 229 x 229 mm and 152 x 152 mm quarry tiles and vinyl sheet, the screeds under these finishes will have to vary in thickness to suit. The thickest finish being the 229 x 229 mm tiles (usually 1¼″ or 32 mm thick), these will have the minimum screed of, say, 28 mm, making a total thickness of 60 mm. The vinyl sheet therefore (assumed at 6 mm thick) will need a 54 mm screed and the 152 x 152 mm tiles ($\frac{7}{8}$″ or 23 mm thick) will need a 37 mm screed. It is possible sometimes to alter the thickness of concrete or to keep the same thickness and raise or drop the whole concrete to suit the thickness of floor finish, but even if possible this may not be done unless particularly specified. Cement screeds are required for all tiling laid by a plasterer or tile fixer, but where quarry tiles are laid by a bricklayer the screed is often omitted, the tiles being bedded direct on the concrete with a somewhat thicker cement bed.

Floor finish in doorways may either be measured here or left to be done with the door openings, and it should be remembered that the bearers for wood flooring on brick walls must be included with the item. Where several takers-off are working it would be best for the one measuring floors to deal with floorings in the openings, as he will be conversant with the various finishes. Where, however, the same taker-off is dealing with the whole, it is a matter of taste whether such floor finish is done in the 'Floors' or the 'Doors' section. In either case it is important to bear in mind that a door is usually on the side of a wall on which it opens, so that if a door opens into a room the outside floor finish will go through the opening and not that of the room, the joint being on the line of the door and so not visible when the door is shut.

With floor finishings should be remembered any bars inserted at joints of different floor finishes, also mat frames and their sinkings, and margin to hearths.

Skirtings.—Some surveyors measure skirtings with this section of the taking off, but it is perhaps more convenient to measure them with the 'Internal Finishings', as when doing that section the taker-off has at hand the girth of the walls for plaster, and the same girth with adjustments can be used for skirtings.

Wood Floor Construction.—The measurement of construction of wood floors divides itself into:

(a) Plates and/or beams.

(b) Joists.

(c) Herringbone or other strutting.

In the case of hollow Ground Floors, sleeper walls and air bricks would also be taken in this section. Where plates are built in and brickwork is measured over them it is not necessary to measure the bedding of the plate separately, but if a plate or other timber is bedded, say, on a concrete floor, or if brickwork is measured to the underside only, an item of bedding must be taken (S.M.M. G 43.1). However, although this form of construction is provided for by the S.M.M., it is not generally adopted today. Instead joist hangers are used to support the ends of the joists and these are measured in the example. No item need be measured for building in joists to brick walls as the work proceeds (which would be the normal procedure with new walls), but if they are to be cut and pinned to old walls or for some reason must be built in after the wall is there, then an item is measurable. Joists, like all structural timbers, will be measured to their net lengths, as the estimator allows in his price for all waste such as is incurred by the need to order, say, a 4 m length for a joist only required 3.90 m long.

To ascertain the number of floor joists in a room, take the length of the room less, say, 100 mm (assuming that the centre line of the joists nearest each end will be 50 mm from the wall face) and divide this by the spacing of timbers. The result will be the number of spaces between joists, and one more must therefore be added to give the total number of joists, including those at both ends.

Hollow ground floors are now rarely met with in new buildings as room floors, but Example 12 shows this form of construction applied to a small stage such as might be found in a Primary School Assembly Hall.

If there is no specification, herringbone or solid strutting to joists may be overlooked, as it quite possibly will not be shown on the drawings. One row should usually be taken to all spans over 2.50 m and two rows to spans over 4.50 m.

The trimming of wood floor construction for staircase, hearths, trap doors, etc., is usually taken with the floor construction, the necessary deductions being also made to the floor finish (if measured in the 'Floors' section). Some may prefer to take this adjustment with the item itself, e.g. when measuring the trap door in the 'Doors' section, but is perhaps more convenient to take it while the floor construction is in mind.

Concrete Floors.—Concrete floors are of two kinds:

(a) Concrete beds laid on the ground or on hardcore.

(b) Suspended floors.

In the former case all that is necessary is the area of the concrete measured cube and classified according to thickness, and the measurement of hardcore filling under from the level to which surface excavation has previously been measured up to the underside of the concrete. These will be measured the full areas inside and between walls whose foundations pass through the surface concrete. Where concrete beds are carried through openings in walls, as in external doorways, the concrete may be added to the general area and brickwork deducted to correspond. Although some surveyors do not make such adjustments, the difference in value being very slight, as a matter of principle the adjustment is perhaps best made. It must be remembered that the surface of hardcore needs blinding to receive concrete and a layer of building paper or plastic sheeting may be interposed.

Suspended *in situ* floors may usually be measured in four parts:

(a) Concrete.

(b) Formwork.

(c) Reinforcement or filler joists.

(d) Beams.

It must be remembered in measuring the concrete to add the additional area for bearings on walls, etc., whence it follows that the area of concrete is not the same as the area of formwork which is inside bearing walls only. Chases in walls for bearing are not measurable (S.M.M. G 11). In this connection it should be noted that the bearing of the concrete in a steel filler joist floor is on to the wall parallel with the filler joists. Concrete floors will be measured over all supporting beams, adjustment for these being made later. It is not here proposed to deal with reinforced concrete floors, but an example is given at the end of the chapter of a filler joist floor and beam. This is a simple form of suspended concrete floor not often found in use now, but it provides a good preliminary exercise in taking off before attempting the more complicated taking off of suspended reinforced concrete. It will be noted that the concrete measured as in beam casing is only taken the extra depth below the underside of the floor slab which has been measured across, and that adjustment of formwork is made with the beam and no attempt made to measure the formwork in separate bays, which would in a large floor obviously be less simple. It will be realised how, when dealing with a large floor, an overall measurement such as this, with adjustment for the various beams, saves the possibility of a whole bay being missed.

Suspended floors are often constructed of a series of precast (often prestressed) concrete beams laid alongside each other. These beams would be enumerated (S.M.M. F 18, 33—39) and the number in each floor space must therefore be worked out from the known width of the beams.

Hollow Block and Reinforced Concrete Floors.—The measurement of these in detail is outside the scope of this book. They are, however, often used and their measurement is fully explained in the S.M.M. (F 26—32).

EXAMPLE 11

SOLID GROUND FLOOR

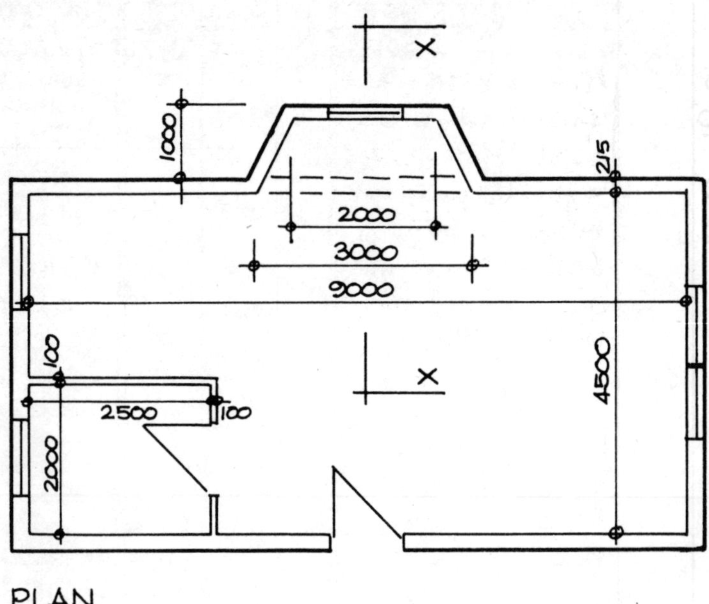

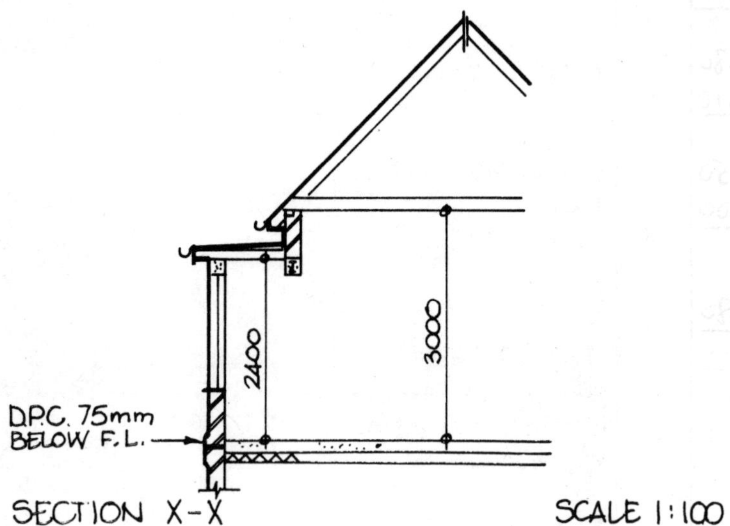

Fig. 20

Finishings

Timesing	Dimensions	Squaring	Description
			3000
			2000
			2) 5000
			2500
	9.00 4.50 2.50 1.00		152×152×19 mm Red quarry tiles to B.S. 1286 Type A bedded & jointed in cement mortar as paving, with 10 mm joints, on screeded bed, internally.
			&
			19 mm Portland cement & sand (1:3) screeded bed on concrete, internally
	2.60 2.10		Ddt both (want
	.80 .10		Add both (Intl Door
	2.50 2.00		38 mm Granolithic paving on concrete, internally
	.80		3×32 mm Black plastic dividing strip & bedding at joint of floor finishes
			Note Floor finish may alternatively be measured with Internal Finishings

Construction

Timesing	Dimensions	Squaring	Description
	9.00 4.50 .15 2.50 1.00 .15		Concrete (1:6) bed 100-150 mm thick spread & levelled on hardcore
	9.00 4.50 2.50 1.00		150 mm Hardcore bed spread & levelled & blinded with ashes for concrete (Bwk in Doorway
			(Surface digging & levelling assumed made to u/s of hardcore)

EXAMPLE 12

HOLLOW GROUND FLOOR (STAGE)

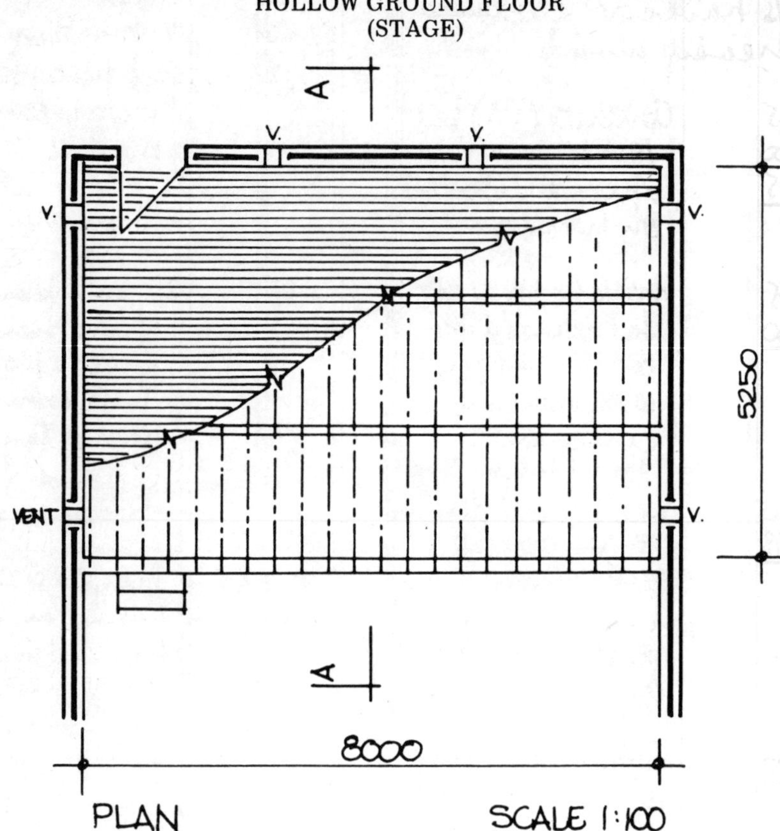

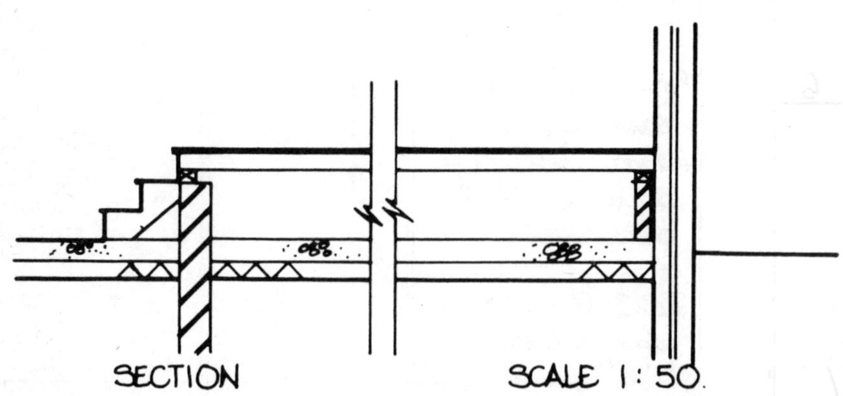

Fig. 24

Timesing	Dimensions	Squaring	Description
			(Excavation over site & levelling & compaction to u/s hardcore assumed already msd).
	5.25 8.00 .15		Concrete (1:6) bed 100-150 mm thick spread & levelled on hardcore
	5.25 8.00		100 mm Hardcore bed spread & levelled & blinded with ashes for concrete
3/	8.00 .38		Half brick dwarf support walls in common brickwork in cement mortar (1:3) built honeycomb
1+3/	8.00		Fibre base & lead damp proof course to half brick walls (Support walls 3 Apron wall 1
	6		Form 230 × 150 mm opening in 280 mm wall, including slate lintol & sealing to cavity, & fibrebase & lead damp proof apron over.
6/	2		230 × 150 mm Square hole pattern terra cotta airbrick & building in.
1+3/	8.00		75 × 100 mm Sawn softwood floors & Bed plate 100 mm wide in cement mortar 5.25 Apron wall .215 5.465
	5.47 8.00		25 mm Sawn softwood square jointed flooring in 175 mm widths with splayed heading joints, well cramped up, each board nailed to each joist with two 57 mm flooring brads well punched in, & cleaning off on completion
			(Steps, fascia, finishings to apron wall, escape door & threshold msd elsewhere

EXAMPLE 13

WOOD UPPER FLOOR

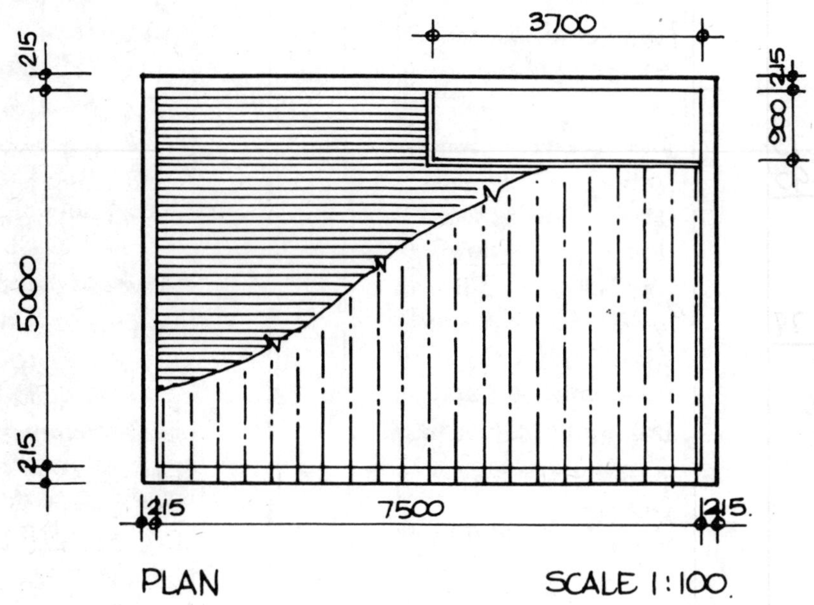

Fig. 25

	7.50 5.00		25 mm Oak tongued & grooved flooring in 75 mm face widths, with tongued & grooved heading joints, well cramped up, each board secret nailed to each joist, & cleaning off for sealing on completion. & Two coats of sealer on strip flooring
	3.70 .90		Ddt both { Stair well 3.700 .075 3.775
	3.78		Extra on 25 mm oak flooring for 25×75 mm rounded nosing tongued to edge of flooring, including groove. 900 .075 .975
	.98		Do for 25×75 mm do., including groove crossgrain
			7.500 2/= .100 375) 7.400 (20+1 7.500
21/	5.00		50×225 mm Sawn s.w. in floors 375) 3700 (10 3750
10/	.90 5.00		Ddt

	5.00 3.70		75×225 mm Sawn sw. in floors
21/	2		3 mm Welded galvanised mild steel hanger for 50×225 mm joist & notching & fitting end of joist including building top flange into joint of brickwork
10/	1 2		Ddt do.
10/	1		Add do including nailing top flange to softwood.
1.	2		3 mm Welded galvanised mild steel hanger for 75×225 mm joist & notching & fitting end of joist including building top flange into joint of brickwork
	1		Do including nailing top flange to softwood
	1		Trim 50×225 mm joists around stair opening 3.70 × .90 m
2/	7.50		38×50 mm Herring bone strutting to 225 mm joists

EXAMPLE 14

CONCRETE UPPER FLOOR

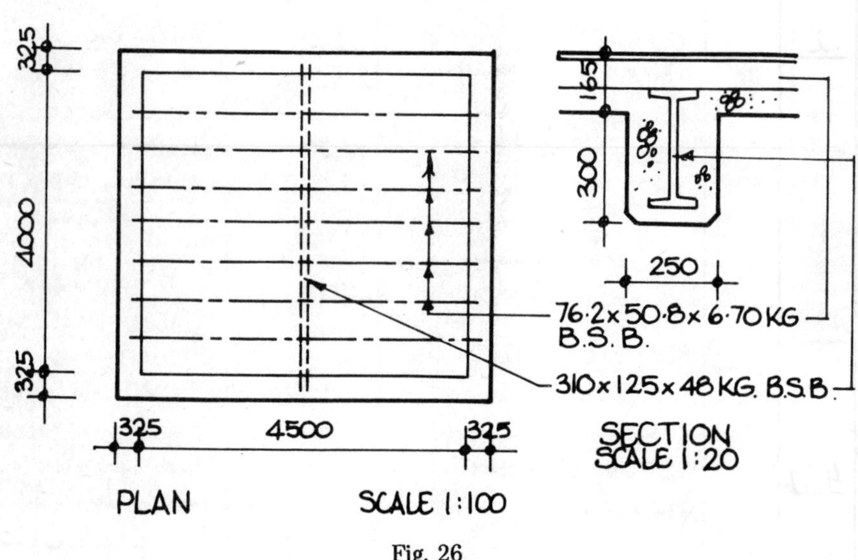

Fig. 26

Timesing	Dimensions	Description
		Y/.225 4.000 .450 4.450
	4.45	305×127 mm × 48 Kg/m steel universal beam to B.S.4 Part 1 Table 5, & hoisting & fixing approximately m above ground (in No 1, 4.45 m long)
	2	150 mm Precast concrete (1:2:4) padstone 345 × 225 mm & building in
		(Bldg in ends of beam assumed not measurable
		Y/.112 4.500 224 4.724
7/	4.72	76×51 mm ×6.67 Kg/m steel filler joist to B.S. 4 Part 1 Table 8, & hoisting & fixing approximately m above ground (in No 7, 4.72 m long)
	7	Connection of 76×51 mm filler joist to top of 305×127 mm beam with 12 mm bolt & tapered washers
		Y/= 4,000 .225 4.225

Timesing	Dimensions	Description
	4.50 4.23 .17 4.00 .25 .30	Conc (1:2:4) suspended filler joist floor 150-300 mm thick
		4.500 .250 4.250
	4.25 4.00	Formwork to soffite of suspended floor (in No 2)
	4.00	Formwork to attached beam casing with chamfered external angles 250× 300 mm (in No 1)
	4.50 4.00	25 mm Oak tongued & grooved block flooring laid herring bone pattern with two block plain border, bedded in mastic & cleaned off for sealing & 20 mm Portland Cement & Sand floated bed (1:3) on concrete & Two coats sealer internally on hardwood block flooring.

CHAPTER 10

ROOFS

Reference to S.M.M.

F 1—13, 15
L 1—11
M 1—56
N 1—12, 17—18, 29—31
P 1—8
R 1—16
T 11—12
U 1—2, 16—18

The measurement of roofs, as of floors, subdivides itself into coverings and construction and may be further subdivided according to the position of the roof, e.g. main roof, roofs of wings, etc. Where a building has two or three different kinds of roof, e.g. tiled roofs, asphalt flats, etc., each should be dealt with entirely separately, but where there are several roofs of a similar kind it may be convenient to take these together. The rainwater goods, unless designed and detailed with the plumbing, are usually measured in the 'Roofs' section, and may be either taken separately with each roof or all taken together at the end.

If no roof plan is provided one must be drawn out and may often be superimposed on the top floor plan. Special care must be taken to see that all hips, valleys, etc. are correctly drawn on, either a hip or a valley being necessary at each change of direction in a sloping roof. In the case of flat roofs it will be necessary to mark on all rolls, gutters, drips, etc., which may not be shown.

Slate or Tile Roof Coverings.—The first measurement in this type of roof should be the roof area for slating or tiling with battens, the same measurement usually serving for boarding and felt. This should be followed systematically by eaves, verges and any measurable cuttings, ignoring for the moment adjustment for chimney stacks, dormers, etc. Ridges, hips and valleys follow with their cuttings, the coverings concluding with any adjustment for stacks, skylights, dormers, etc. The calculation of lengths of roof slopes and of hips and valleys has been dealt with in Chapter 3.

Unless otherwise specified, customary widths for leadwork are as follows:

Cover flashings	150 mm
Stepped flashings (over soakers)	200 mm, or (without soakers) 300—350 mm
Aprons	300 mm
Soakers	200 mm (length = gauge + lap + 25 mm) (number = length of slope ÷ gauge)

Sloping Roof Construction.—Measurement of the construction may begin with plates, common rafters and collars, continuing with ridges, hips and valleys, followed by purlins (if any) with struts or trusses, and finishing with the ceiling joists. The general principles of measuring constructional timbers given in the last chapter in regard to floors are also applicable to roof construction. When the main construction has been measured, adjustment must then be made for stacks, dormers, etc. In the latter case the joinery and the adjustment of plaster internally will probably be taken with the windows, but otherwise the dormer must be complete with cheeks and top.

The number of rafters should be calculated by taking the total length of the roof between end rafters, dividing it by the centre to centre spacing of rafters, and adding one to the result to allow for a rafter at each end. In the case of a hipped end the rafters may be measured in the same way as if the ridge ran through to a gable with one added for the extra rafter in the centre of the hip as shown by the following sketch:

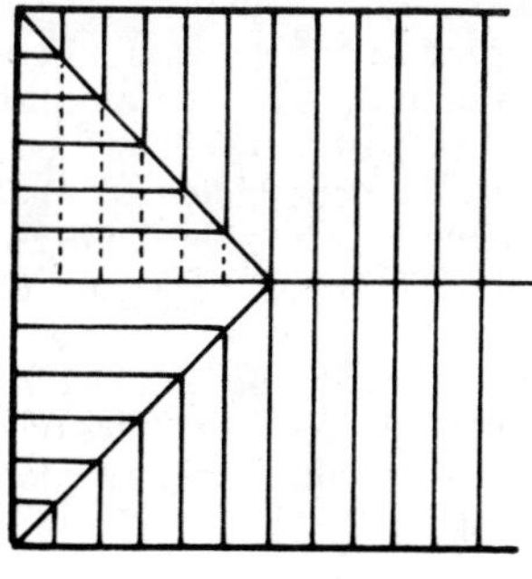

Fig. 27

It will be seen here that the jack rafters on the hipped end are equal to the lengths (shown dotted) which would have been there if the roof were gabled, but the central rafter is entirely extra. The spacing may not always make the central rafter necessary, but it should be taken; there is actually slightly more than the theoretical length in jack-rafters due to the splay cutting up to hips and valleys. The number of ceiling joists will be calculated in the same way, bearing in mind that the length to be divided by the spacing of joists is the length inside walls less 100 mm, as explained in the case of floor joists.

With the roof construction should be taken any walking boards in the roof space, a provisional quantity often being measured to be adjusted when the work is carried out. Trap doors for access with any ladders may also be taken in this section, though sometimes measured with 'Doors'. The measurement of trap doors will follow the rules for other doors dealt with in Chapter 13.

Gutters and Down Pipes.—Eaves or other gutters must then be taken with rainwater pipes up to the point where the drains begin. It saves a lot of abstracting on a large job if instead of measuring paint on rainwater goods an instruction is written to the worker-up such as, 'Take ③ on all eaves gutters, r.w.ps. and heads'. Where items such as these are constantly repeated the risk of forgetting to take the paint on one occasion is lessened by dealing with it in this way. Paint on gutters and heads should be described as 'inside and out' if this is required.

Care must be taken to make clear the method of fixing of gutters, e.g. whether on brackets screwed to fascia or to rafters, or as in the case of a box gutter bedded on an eaves cornice, or with some special fixing. Rainwater pipes, too, may be fixed with ears or holderbats, the method to be used being made clear and any distance pieces, blocks, etc. included in the description.

A careful note should be made to see that all rainwater outlets and pipes are shown on the drawing and a check made with the drainage plan. If sizes of rain-water goods are not specified, these must be decided, but it should be noted that a variety of sizes of the same gutter or pipe does not tend to economy, though it may be theoretically correct.

Finish to eaves such as fascia, soffite, wrot ends of rafters etc., may be conveniently taken at the same time as eaves gutters, or they may be taken when eaves course is dealt with under 'Coverings'.

Flat Roofs.—The same natural subdivision of these can be made into coverings and construction, the construction being measured on the same principles as a similar floor. The formation of gutters in the flat must be dealt with and rain-water goods measured as before. Asphalt flats will be found fairly simple, but lead flats will need more care. Two complete examples of these types of roof are given at the end of this chapter. The measurement of the roofs will be followed by that of any lantern lights or trap doors, etc.

A simple example is given of a small flat in reinforced concrete. Construction might alternatively be with steel joists on the lines of the concrete floor in Example 14. It is not contemplated that a hollow block and concrete floor or flat comes within the scope of this book.

Flashings.—It will be seen from S.M.M. M 48.2 and 3 that the description of flashings must include clips or tacks and state the extent of laps. These particulars would usually be incorporated in a preamble (see page 238) to save repetition in the measured bill.

A point which is a little doubtful is the meaning of 'lap' in such a case as the flashings to the chimney stack in Example 19. The writers interpret the word to mean intermediate laps, not the extra lengths round the corners of the stack which are part of the length of the flashing. With flashings in such short lengths as this, the interpretation makes a substantial difference.

Sundry Roofs.—The 'Roofs' section will conclude by the measurement of any sundry roofs such as glass or corrugated sheeting roofs. There will possibly be some items of a borderline nature, such as canopies over an entrance or small balconies, which though in the nature of roofs are also part of an external door feature, and as such would be measured in the 'Doors' section. If the taking off is divided it must be settled which taker-off will deal with such items, or they may be missed.

EXAMPLE 15

PITCHED ROOF

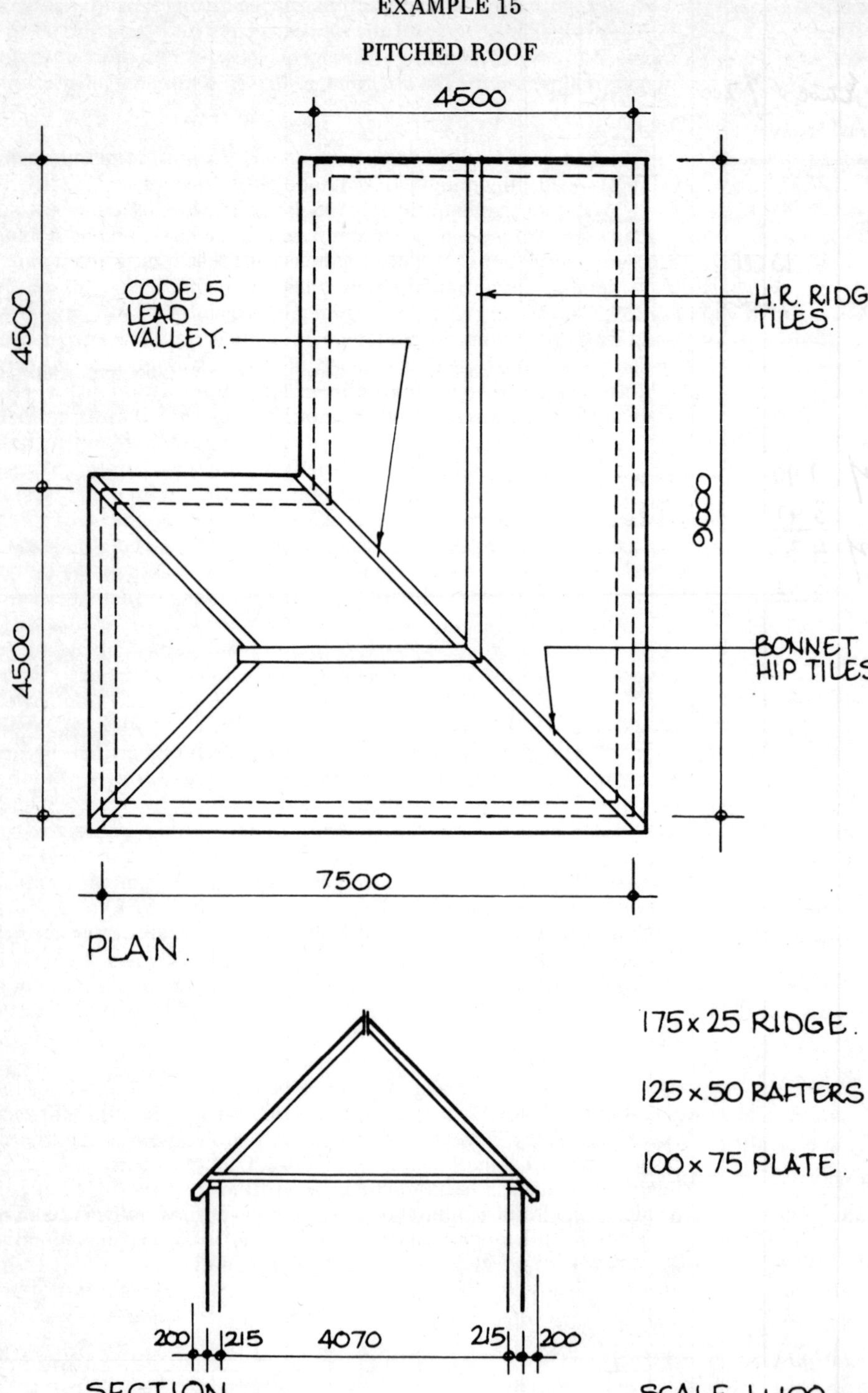

Fig. 28

			Coverings
			7.500 4.500
Eaves 2/.200			.400 Verge .075
			7.900 4.575
			Less Eaves .200
			4.375
			4.000
Wall 2/.215			.430
Eaves 2/.200			.400
			2) 4.830
			2.415 × Sec 45°
			= 3.415
2/	7.90		Hand made sand faced tiling with 65 mm lap to sloping roofs at 45° pitch, every fourth course nailed with two galvanised nails, including 25 × 38 mm sawn softwood battens
	3.42		
2/	4.38		
	3.42		
			&
			25 × 50 mm Sawn Softwood counter-battens at 350 mm centres fixed with galvanised nails
			&
			Reinforced bitumen felt to BS. 747 type 1F laid with a slight sag over rafters & lapped 450 mm at joints & closely nailed with galvanised clout nails (measured net without allowance for laps)
			&
			19 mm Softwood close jointed boarding to sloping roofs

			9.000
			.075
			.200
			9.275
			7.900
			17.175
			2/ = 34.350
			Gable 4.500
			2/.200 .400 4.900
			29.450
	29.45		Extra for double course at eaves & bedding in cement mortar
			&
			75 × 75 mm Sawn softwood eaves fillet
2/	3.42		Extra for verge with undercloak & bedding & pointing in cement mortar
			7.000
			3.500
			10.500
	10.50		250 mm Diameter approved half round ridge tiles to match general tiling & bedding & pointing in cement mortar
	1		Mitre
	2		Fair end filled solid with pieces of tile in cement mortar

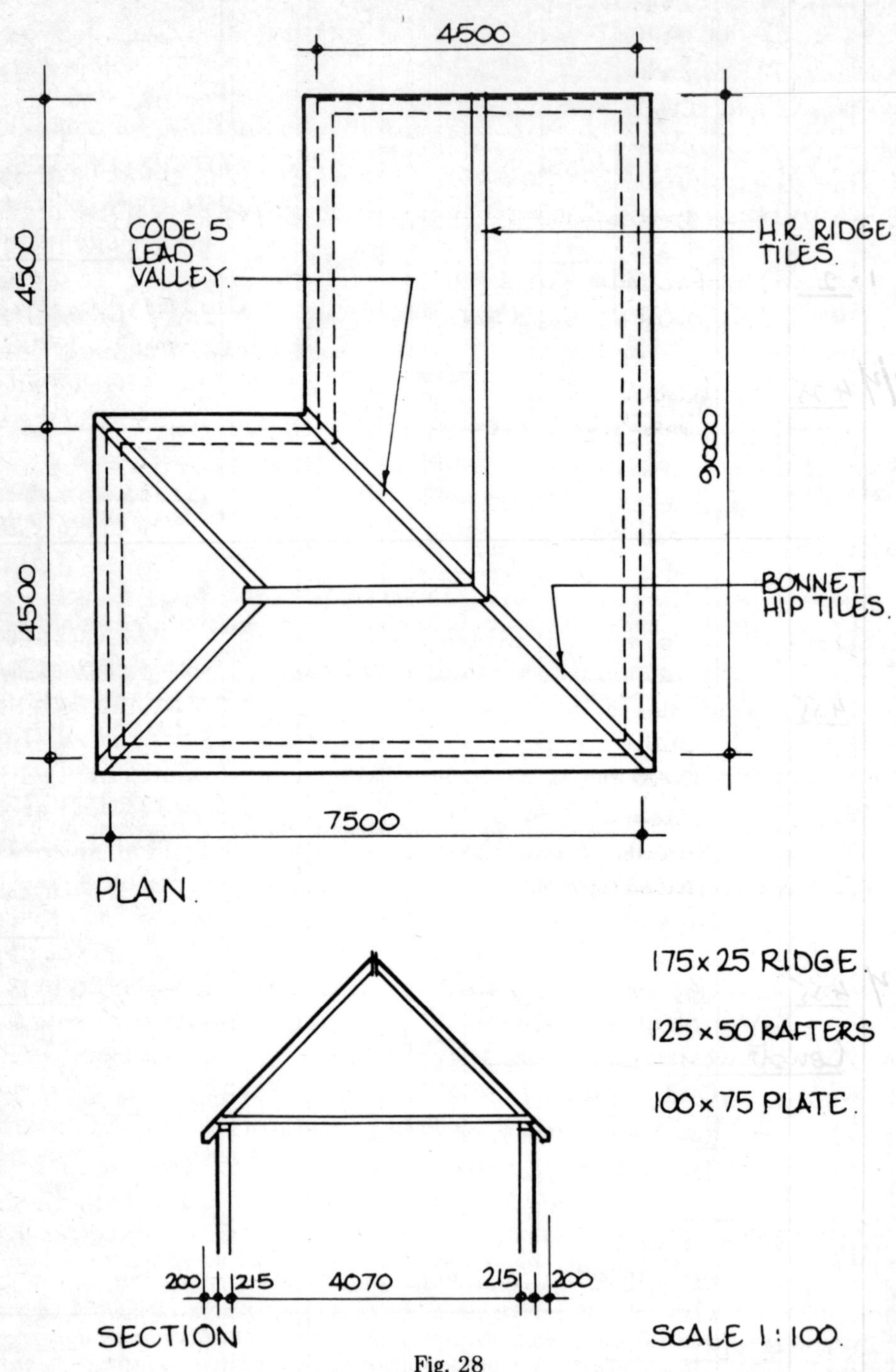
4500
4500
4500
9000
7500
CODE 5
LEAD
VALLEY.
H.R. RIDGE
TILES.
BONNET
HIP TILES.
PLAN.
175 x 25 RIDGE.
125 x 50 RAFTERS
100 x 75 PLATE.
200
215
4070
215
200
SECTION
SCALE 1 : 100.

Fig. 28

1·2/	4.25		Extra on tiling for bonnet hip tiles to match, course & bond with general tiling, nailed at every course, & bedding & pointing in cement mortar
	1·2		Fair end filled in solid in cement mortar
·3/2/	4.25		Raking cutting on 19 mm roof boarding & Do on felt
			4.250 Ends 2/.150 .300 4.550
	4.55		Code 5 lead valley gutter 600 mm girth lapped 150 mm at joints & dressed over tilting fillets, (measured net without allowance for laps)
2/	4.55		19x38 Sawn softwood tilting fillet

Construction

4500
− 200
4300
+ 75
350) 4375 (13
350
875
1050
13 spaces
=14 rafters

Rafters:-
7.500
2/200 400
350) 7.400 (23
700
400
1050
23 spaces
= 22 rafters

1·22/14/	3.48 3.48		50x125 mm Sawn softwood in pitched roofs (Hipped end
			9.000 7.500 2/ 16.500 33.000 2/4/ .215 1.720 Gable 4.070 5.790 27.210 3/2/ .100 .600 Halved joints 2/2/.075 .300 28.110
	28.11		75x100 mm Sawn softwood in pitched roofs (plate 10.500 Scarf 2/.175 .350 10.850
	10.85		25x175 mm Sawn softwood in pitched roofs (ridge
1·3/	4.35		50x225 mm Do (hips & valley 4.500 2/.215 430 4.070 ends 2/.150 300 4.370

7.500
2/.214 430
7.070
2/.050 .100
350) 6.970 (20 spaces
7.000 = 21 joists

350) 4.500 (13 spaces
350 = 14 joists
1000
1050

21/14	4.37	50×125 mm Sawn softwood in pitched roofs {clg jsts
	4.37	Ddt 50×125 mm do & Add 75×125 mm do {trimmer
		350) 4.070 (12 spaces 350 = 13 joists 570 200
	13	3 mm Welded galvanised mild steel hanger for 50×125 mm joist & notching & fitting end of joist, including nailing top flange to softwood

Eaves & R.W. Goods

	29.45	25×150 mm Wrot softwood moulded & grooved fascia
	4	Mitre
	2	Returned mitred end
		29.450 Int. angles 2/.225 450 29.900
	29.90	19×225 mm Wrot softwood tongued & rebated eaves soffite
	4	Angles
	2	Fitted ends

	2	19 mm Wrot softwood spandril boxed end to eaves 225×400
		9.000 7.500 4.500 3.000 4.500 28.500 3/2/.038 .225 28.725
	28.73	38×50 mm Sawn softwood bearer plugged & 25×38 mm Wrot softwood bedmould
		150 25 175
	29.45 .18	KPS & (3) woodwork extly - General surface
	29.00 .26	29.45 2/225 45 29.00
2/	.23 .30	soff. .225 bed m. 35 .263
		29.450 2/.115 230 29.680
	29.68	114 mm Cast iron half round eaves gutter with socketed joints bolted together including galv steel brackets screwed

Timesing	Dimension	Description
		$2/1\frac{4}{7}/114$ = .360
	29.68 .36	(3) Emulsion on cast iron gutter
	4	Extra for angle to gutter
	2	Do for stopped end to do & Do for outlet to do with nozzle for 76 mm pipe & Galvanised wire balloon grating & fixing in 76 mm outlet of eaves gutter
2/	3.65	76 mm cast iron rainwater pipe with socketed joints & ears cast on & fixing externally with galvanised pipe nails & galvanised barrel distance pieces to hardwood plugs in brickwork
		$3\frac{1}{7}/.076$ = .239
2/	3.65	(3) Emulsion on cast iron pipe 150-300 mm girth
2/	1	Extra for offset to pipe 229 mm projection & Cement joint to drain

EXAMPLE 16

LEAD FLAT

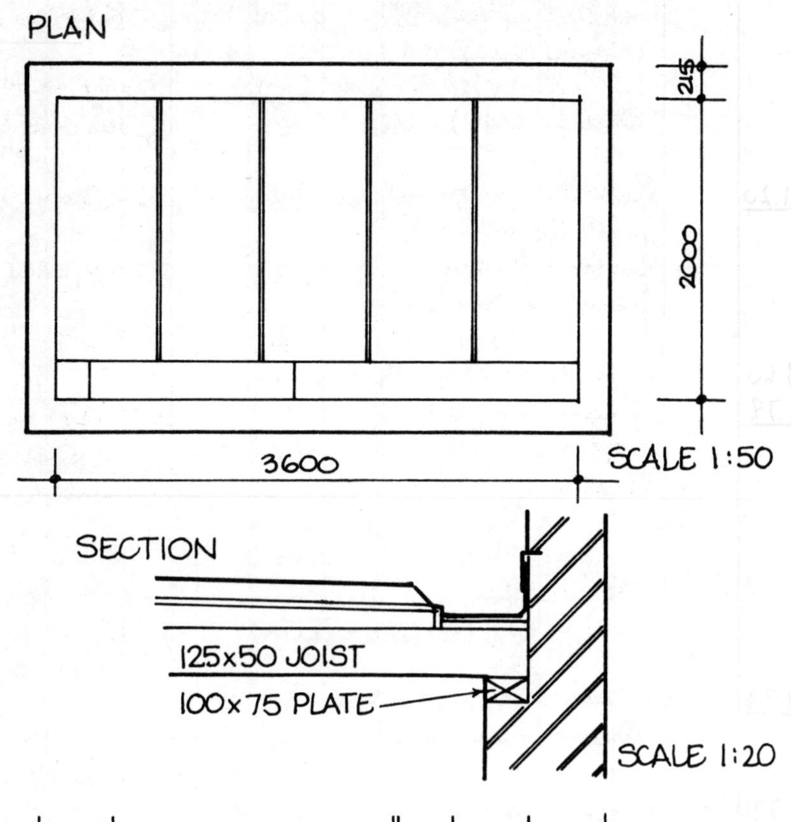

Timesing	Dimensions	Squaring	Description
			3.600 rolls 4/.250 1.000 turn up 2/.150 .300 4.900 2.000 gutter .220 1.780 turn up .150 turn down .050 1.980
	4.90 1.98		Code 5 lead covering to flat roof
			sole .230 3.600 turn up .150 ends 2/.150 .300 .150 lap .180 .530 4.080
	4.08 .53		Code 5 lead gutter
	1		Extra over Code 5 le gutter for lining t cesspool 220×220× 75 mm deep, soldere at angles, with 7 mm diameter outle
4/	2		Bossed end to roll
			3.600 2.000 2/5.600 11.20 4/.150 .60 11.80

Timesing	Dimensions	Description
	11.80	Code 4 lead flashing 150 mm girth lapped 150 mm at joints, including lead wedging (measured net without allowance for laps)
	11.20	Rake out horizontal joint of brickwork for lead flashing & point in cement mortar
	3.60 1.78	25 mm Wrot softwood tongued & grooved boarding to flat roof traversed for lead
		3.600 1/.050 .100 350) 3.500 (10+1 3.500
11/	1.78	50 mm Sawn softwood firrings average 75 mm deep
4/	1.78	50 mm Softwood rounded roll for lead & Copper nail lead at 38 mm centres
		3.600 .220 3.380
	3.38	25 x 225 mm Wrot soft-wood gutter board traversed for lead, including bearers
	1	220 mm length 40 x 63 mm wrot softwood crossrebated drip for lead

Timesing	Dimensions	Description
	1	25 mm Wrot softwood dovetailed cesspool 220 x 220 x 75 mm deep with hole for outlet
	2.00	25 x 100 mm Wrot softwood gutter side for lead
	1.60	25 x 63 mm Do
	.90	75 mm Lead outlet
	2	Extra for bend to do
	1	End of 75 mm lead pipe tafted & soldered to cesspool & Hole for large pipe through one brick wall & making good facings & Cast lead rainwater head with ears nailed to & including hardwood plugs in brickwork, Extg
	3.00	75 x 100 mm Cast lead rectangular rainwater pipe fixed with sockets (measured separately), Extg
	2	Double beaded socket for cast with ears nailed to & including hardwood plugs in brickwork, Extg
	1	Shoe with ears nailed as last

2/	3.60		75×100 mm Sawn softwood in flat roofs			
11/	2.00		50×100 mm Do			

EXAMPLE 17

ASPHALT FLAT

(Flat roof shown in fig. 29, page 96, but constructed of 125 mm reinforced concrete slab, the falls being formed with a lightweight cement screed and asphalt (no drips).)

Timesing	Dimensions	Squaring	Description
			Coverup
	3.60 2.00		20 mm Asphalte flat in two coats laid to falls on screeded bed, on & including black sheathing felt underlay finished with white spar chippings
			.125 + .075 2) .200 .100
			100 mm (Av.) Lightweight aggregate & cement a.d. screeded bed to falls, finished with 19 mm cement & sand
	3.60		One course of common bricks 102 mm wide in cement mortar laid flat
			.220 {gutter side side .050 .270
	3.60		20 mm Asp lining to gutter sole 270 mm girth including angle filler & rounded arris
			{Skty mod on wall
	3.60 .22		Ddt 20 mm asp flat
	3.60 .22		40 mm (Av) Lightweight agg a.b. screeded bed to gutter sole to falls finished a.b.
			.220 .102 .322
	3.60 .32		Ddt 100 mm (Av) screeded bed for asp.
			3.600 2.000 2/ 5.600 11.200
	11.20		12 mm Asp skirting av 200 mm high including angle fillet & turning in top edge
			&
			Rake out & enlarge joint of brickwork for asphalte skirting & point in cement to top edge
	4		Internal angle to skirting with angle filler

Timesing	Dimensions	Squaring	Description
	1		Form 220×150mm opening in one brick parapet wall in facings for rainwater outlet, including arch over
			&
			Line bottom & sides of 220×150 mm outlet in one brick wall, including arrises, angle fillets & fair edges to lead apron
			&
			Code 5 lead apron 500×500mm dressed between layers of asphalte & into rainwater head.
			(Rainwater head & pipe ab.)
			Construction
			2/= 3.600 + 215 = 3.815; 2.000 + 215 = 2.215
	3.82 2.22 .13		R. Conc (1:2:4) suspended slab 100-150 mm thick
	3.60 2.00		Formwork to soffite of horizontal suspended slab (in No 1)

Timesing	Dimensions	Squaring	Description
			2.215 Hooks 2/108 216 2.431
			150) 3.600 (24 3 00 600 600
24/	2.43		12 mm Dia mild steel bars in suspended slab
4/	3.82		6 mm Do {Dist bars
			(Offset all round)

EXAMPLE 18

DORMER

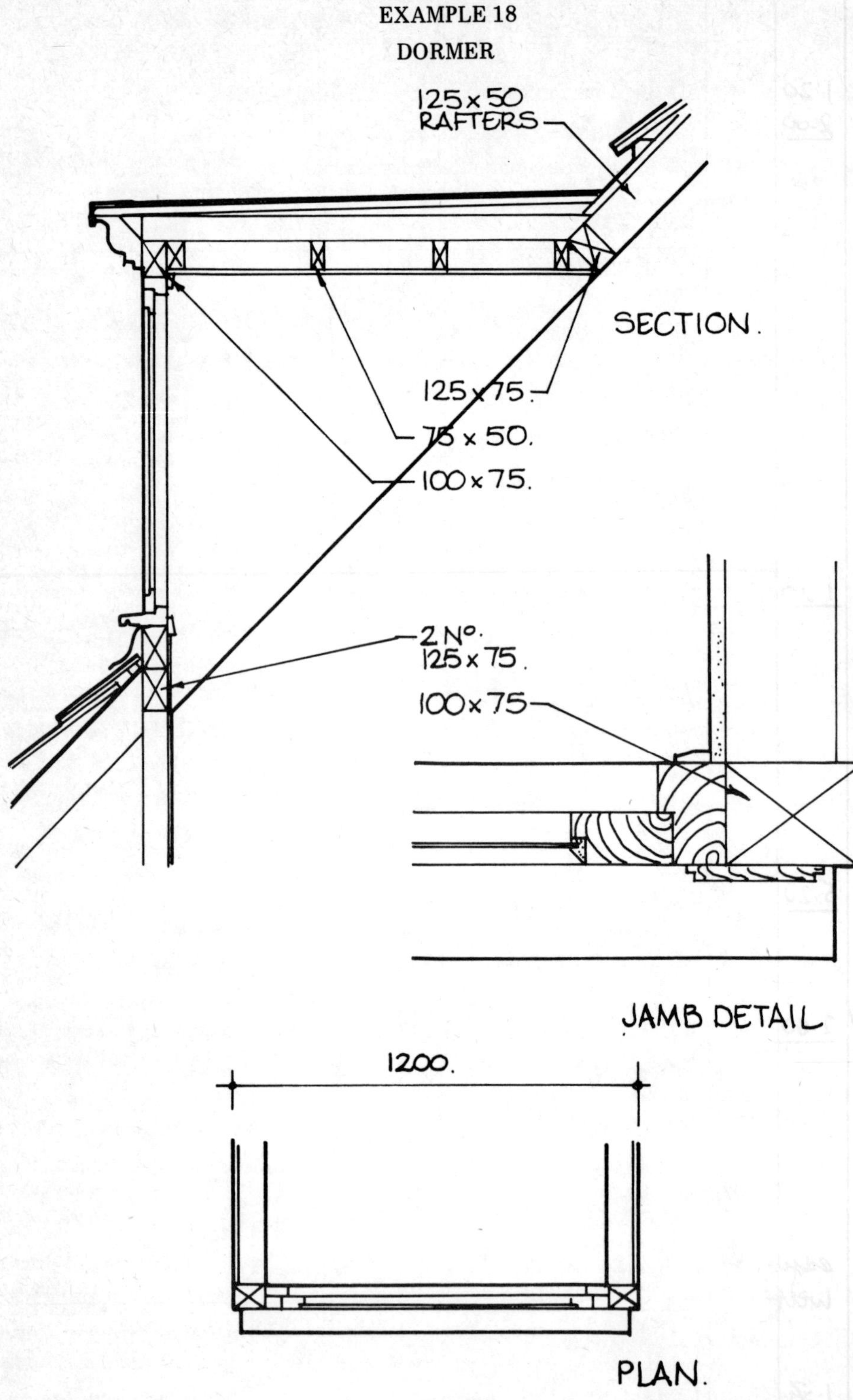

Fig. 30

Timesing	Dimensions	Squaring	Description
			Coverings
	1.20 2.00		Ddt roof tiling & battens & Ddt 25×50 mm sawn softwood counter battens & Ddt felt & Ddt 19 mm softwood roof boarding
	1.20		Extra for eaves ab. & 75×75 mm Sawn sw. eaves fillet ab.
			1.200 2/2.000 4.000 5.200
	5.20		Square cutting on tiling around opening
2/	2.00		38×50 mm Sawn softwood tilting fillet sides
			1200 2/150 300 1500 1470 edges welt 2/30 60 30 30 upslope 375 1590 1875
	1.59 1.88		Code 5 lead covering to dormer top

Timesing	Dimensions	Squaring	Description
	1.88		Welted seam to Code 5 lead & Sinking in softwood for welt
			1470 2/1500 3000 4470
	4.47		Copper nailing lead at 38 mm centres
2/½/	1.30 1.30		Code 5 lead covering to dormer cheeks
2/	2.00 .23		Extra area to form secret gutter
2/	1		Bossing & dressing code 5 lead over end of oak sill & copper nailing
2/	2		Soldered dot & brass screw & Sinking in softwood for soldered dot
2/	1.30		Copper nailing lead at 25 mm centres
			1200 2/150 300 1500
	1.50		Code 5 lead apron 250 mm girth, lapped 150 mm at joints, one edge bedded in mastic (measured net without allowance for lap) sill

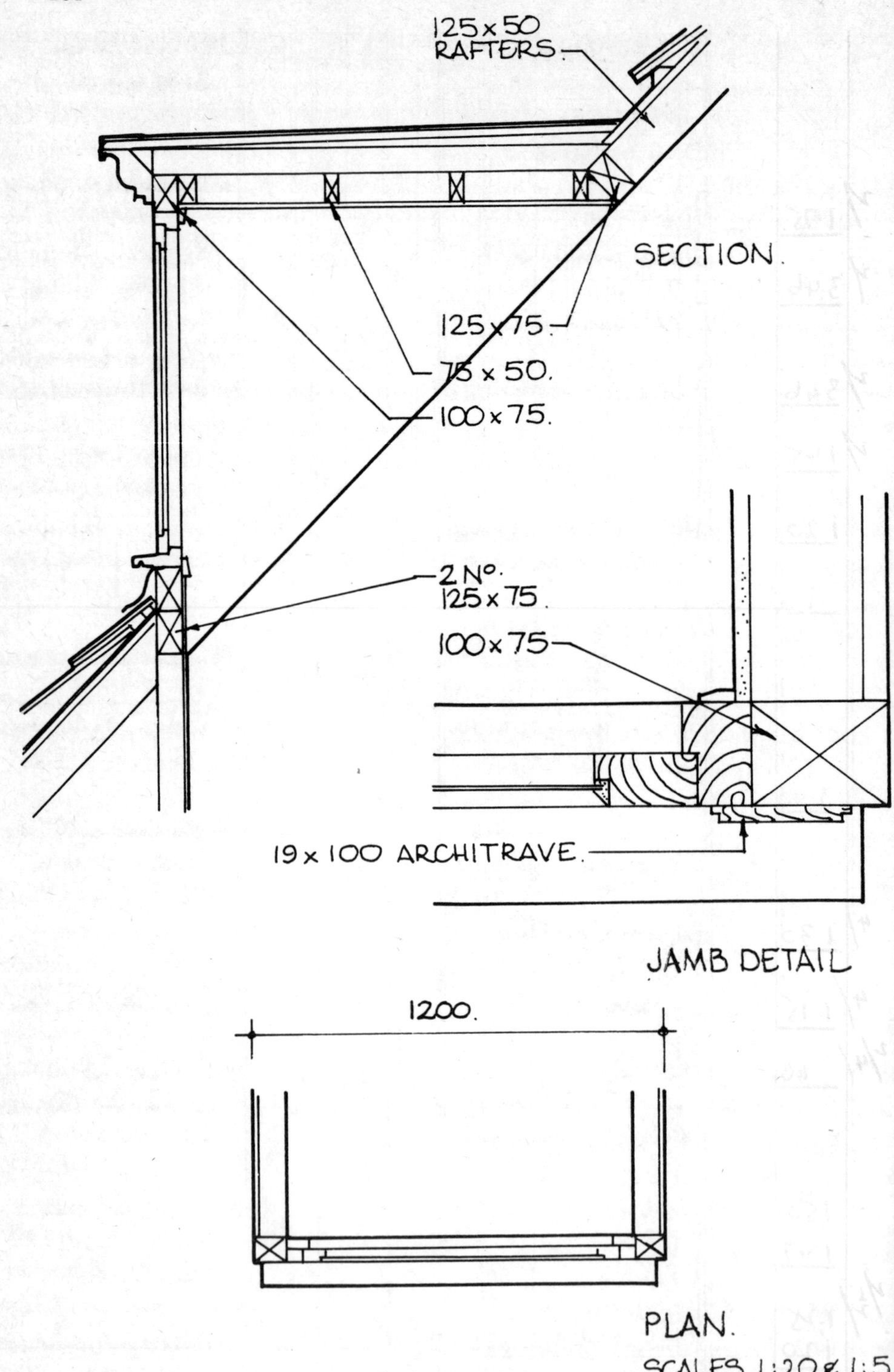
125 x 50
RAFTERS.
SECTION.
125 x 75.
75 x 50.
100 x 75.
2 N°.
125 x 75.
100 x 75
19 x 100 ARCHITRAVE.
JAMB DETAIL
1200.
PLAN.
SCALES 1:20 & 1:5.

Fig. 30

Timesing	Dimensions	Squaring	Description
			Construction
			350) 1050 (3-1
			1050
2/	1.75		Ddct 50×125 mm sawn s.w. in pitched roofs {trimmer rafters
2/	3.46		{trimming rafters
2/	3.46		Add 75×125 mm do
2/	1.45		{trimmers to head & sill
	1.20		{inst under wdw sill
	1		Trimming 50×125 mm rafters to opening 1.00×1.80 m 1200 2/1100 2200 3400
	3.40		75×100 mm Wrot softwood dormer frame {head & posts
4/	1.30		50×75 Sawn softwood in pitched roofs {flat brs 1000 2/75 150 1150
4/	1.15		{clg jsts
2/4/	.60		{cheek jsts 1200 2/150 300 1500
	1.50 1.47		25 mm Wrot softwood tongued & grooved boarding to tops & cheeks of dormers
2/½/	1.25 1.20		
2/	1.75		Raking cutting on 25 mm boarding

Timesing	Dimensions	Squaring	Description
4/	1.30		50 mm Sawn softwood firrings average 25 mm deep 1500 2/1470 2940 4440
	4.44		75×200 mm Wrot softwood twice splayed & moulded on face cornice, one edge tongued to fascia, including groove & angle blockings
	2		External mitre & Splay fitted end 1200 2/1300 2600 3800
	3.80		25×125 mm Wrot softwood fascia
	2		Mitre & Splay fitted end
2/	1.00		19×100 Wrot softwood twice moulded cover fillet
	3.80		K.P.S. & (3) xtty Surfaces 200-300 mm girth
2/	1.00		Do 100-200 mm girth

Window & internal cover fillet to measure with windows

	Dimensions	Description		Dimensions	
	1.00 1.75	Ddt plaster lath ceilings intly & Ddt float & set plas lath clgs intly & Ddt twice emulsion plas clgs intly	2/	1.75 1.00	Labour arris
	1.00 1.25	Plaster lath dormer ceilings intly & Float & set plaster lath dormer ceilings intly & Twice emulsion plas clgs intly			
2/½/	1.25 1.25	Plaster lath dormer cheeks intly & Float & set plaster lath dormer cheeks intly & Twice emulsion plaster walls intly			
	1.00 .25	Plaster lath walls intly & Float & set plaster lath walls intly & Twice emulsion plaster walls intly			

EXAMPLE 19

ADJUSTMENT ON SLATED ROOF FOR CHIMNEY STACK

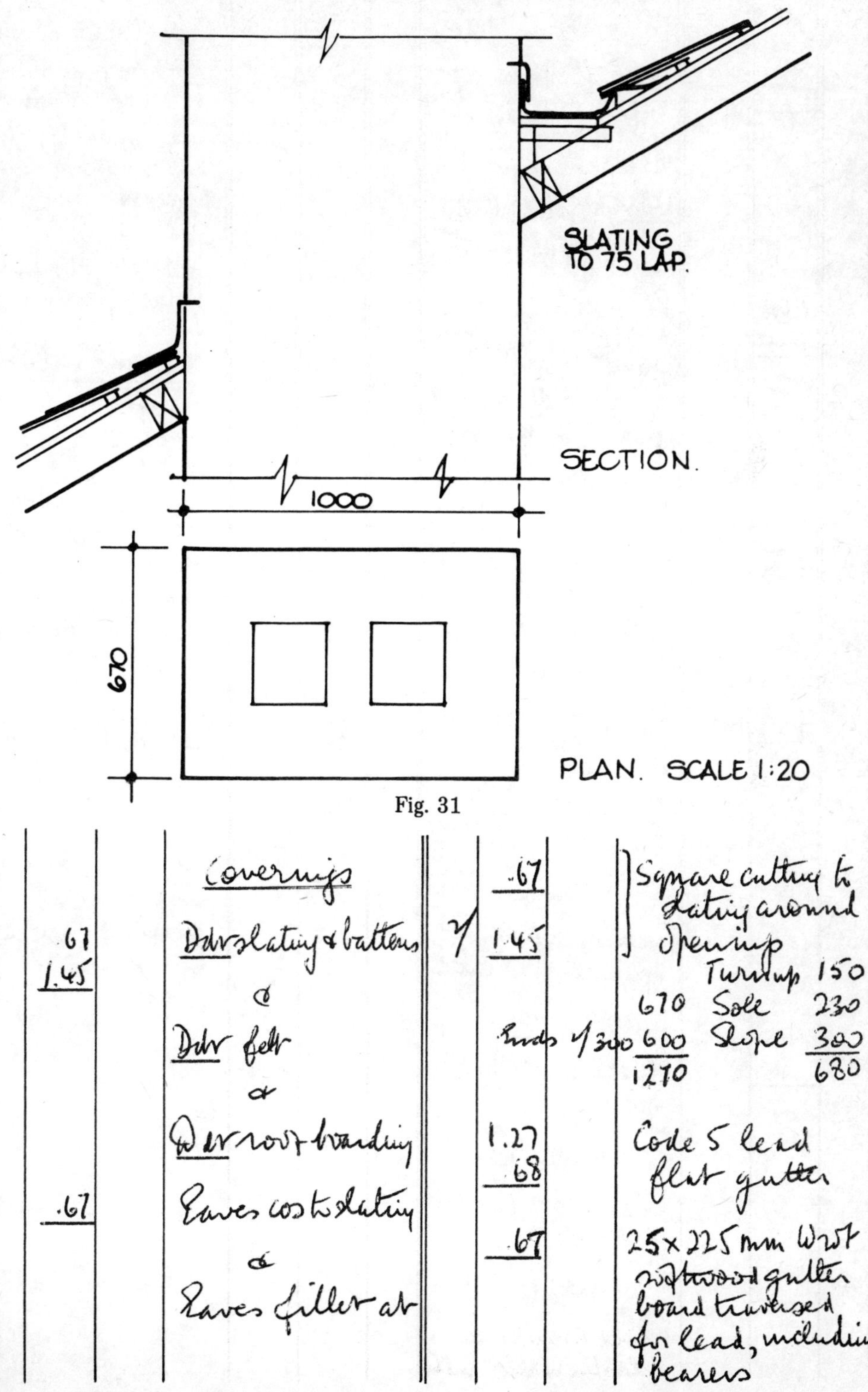

Fig. 31

		Coverings		.67	Square cutting to slating around openings
	.67 1.45	Ddt slating & battens	2/	1.45	
		&			Turn up 150
					670 Sole 230
		Ddt felt	Ends 2/300		600 Slope 300
		&			1270 680
		Ddt roof boarding		1.27 .68	Code 5 lead flat gutter
	.67	Eaves course to slating			
		&		.67	25×225 mm Wrot softwood gutter board traversed for lead, including bearers
		Eaves filler at			

Timesing	Dimension	Description
	2	Gusset ends to softwood gutter
		670
		2/100 200
		870
	.87	Code 5 lead flashing 150 mm girth lapped 150 mm at joints & lead wedging (measured net without allowance for laps)
	.67	Rake out horizontal joints of brickwork for lead flashing & point in cement
		1.170
		2/100 200
		1.370
2/	1.37	Code 5 lead stepped flashing 150 mm girth lapped etc as above
2/	1.17	Rakeout joints of brickwork for lead stepped flashing & point in cement
		gauge 220
		lap 75
		25
		320
		Length/gauge = 1450/220 = 7
2/	7	Code 4 lead soakers 200×320 mm
		&
		Fix lead soakers by slater

Timesing	Dimension	Description
		670
		2/100 200
		870
	.87	Code 5 lead apron 300 mm girth lapped 150 mm at joints & lead wedged (measured net without allowance for laps)
	.67	Rake out horizontal joints of brickwork [illegible]
		Construction
		670
		2/50 100
		350) 770 (2+1
		700 = 3 spaces
		= 2 rafters
2/	1.22	Ddt 50×125 mm sawn s.w in pitched roof
2/	3.80	{trimmed {trimming
2/	3.80	Add 75×125 mm do {trimming
2/	1.12	{trimmers
	1	Trimming 50×125 mm rafters around opening .67 × 1.20 m

CHAPTER 11

INTERNAL FINISHINGS

References to S.M.M.

F 8
G 15–24, 27–28
J 9, 12–14
N 4–12, 15–16
T 1–33
V 1–4, 11–13

Review of Work Measured.—The measurement of the previous section will have completed the work on the carcase of the building, leaving only the internal finishings to ceilings and walls and the windows, doors, etc., with their adjustments, staircase and joinery fittings. Besides these there will, of course, be plumbing and drains, electrical work, heating and hot water systems, and possibly other work of an engineering nature. The taker-off therefore may with advantage at this stage review his work on the carcase of the building, looking over the drawings with a view to finding anything overlooked. He must be satisfied that at any rate the building is structurally complete as he has measured it so far.

Subdivision.—It is advisable to keep distinct the internal finishings on each floor. As this will quite probably be the biggest section of the taking off, it will simplify tracing an item if the storeys are kept entirely separate. The principal subdivisions in the order recommended for measuring are:

(a) Ceiling finish.

(b) Wall finish.

(c) Cornices.

(d) Dadoes.

(e) Skirtings.

(f) Picture rails.

This assumes that floor finishes have been measured with the 'Floors' section, but if preferred these can be taken in this section.

Ceiling and Wall Finishes.—Ceiling areas will be measured from wall to wall according to the figured dimensions of the structure of each room. These will be measured right over all beams in the room, the adjustment for beams following the main ceiling measurements. It may even be an advantage to measure the ceiling itself over all internal walls and partitions in one or two dimensions, deducting the total lengths of internal walls and partitions squared by their respective thicknesses. In the case of wall finishes it is best to collect up on 'waste' the perimeters of all rooms having the same floor to ceiling height and the same finish. The areas of wall plaster will thus often have only two or three measurements to be squared instead of the large number there would be if each room were measured separately. As in the case of brickwork and facings, all openings will be ignored, the plaster or other finish being measured across. Any voids across which brickwork has been measured, whether filled in with joinery or not, must in the same way have the finish measured across to be deducted later. The measurement of wall surfaces will be followed by that of the arris or other labour to main salient angles as distinct from those which form part of an opening.

The necessary item of extra for grooved bricks, if to be used, may be taken with each item of plaster, although a general instruction could be given to take the total area of plaster and screeds on brick walls for this item.

In measuring plastering each background is kept separate (S.M.M. T 3.6) and it is important to watch for confined spaces, defined as compartments not exceeding 4.00 m^2 on plan. Compartments are further defined in the *Practice Manual* as cupboards, halls, lobbies and walk-in ducts as well as rooms.

Plastering on Concrete.—Plastering on concrete is automatically kept separate, and it will be necessary to measure some item for forming key. This may be hacking the surface or use of some bonding agent either on the formwork or applied before plastering. To avoid small adjustments, precast lintels can be described as with a surface (in whole or in part as the case may be) keyed for plaster.

Arrises.—With the present-day use of gypsum plaster, arrises are run in the same material, and are measured as external angles. When the arris is strengthened by the introduction of a metal casing bead it is usual to combine the two items and thus the casing bead is described in detail — the labour in fixing it including the formation of the arris.

Decoration.—The decoration to ceiling and walls should be measured with the plaster or other finish. If all are to be treated in the same way, e.g. emulsion paint, there will be no need to take a separate item of the decoration, but a general instruction can be written, such as 'Take 2ce. emul. on clg. and wall plaster'. If, however, there is a mixture of several types of decoration, such as emulsion, flat and gloss paint, it will probably be found best to measure the appropriate decoration as a separate description with each item of plaster. Where all is emulsion except perhaps gloss paint in one or two rooms, it would probably be found easier to ignore the gloss in the first instance and measure as if all were emulsion, making the necessary adjustment later of 'Ddt. emul.' and 'Add gloss'. Cutting in is not measured where there is any projection to guide the brush, but if there is a joint between two different paints without such a projection, e.g. at a ceiling cove or top of a dado, an item of cutting in must be measured to one. In the latter case, if there is a painted line cut in on both edges to be measured separately, no cutting in will be measured to the main surfaces.

Cornices.—The measurement of these will usually be straightforward, as they normally run all round the room without interruption. The measurement of them on beams must not be forgotten. The deductions from ceiling and wall finish will follow. Although logically cornices should be taken between the measurement of ceiling and wall finishes, they will usually be taken after the walls, as the collection used for wall surfaces will probably serve for these, and, the wall finish being measured, it will be known what adjustments to make.

Dadoes, Skirtings and Picture Rails.—The measurement of these may be an exception to the rule of measuring across openings, depending on the system followed. Some surveyors, to make their adjustment of openings complete, make the deduction and adjustment of such items with the openings, in which case they will here be measured as if the opening were not there. Others measure these items net, i.e. they make the adjustment when measuring the general finishings by deducting the length across openings and adding the reveals with the mitres or other special labour to angles. General plaster only will in this case be deducted with the measurement of openings, all skirtings, dadoes, etc., being ignored when these deductions are made. The disadvantage of the first method is that it somewhat increases the number of items in the dimensions, and though logically more correct, may not be considered by all as worth the additional abstracting necessary. Moreover, it means that where several takers-off are working together, the one taking windows and doors must ascertain the full detail of finishings to be adjusted. On the other hand the disadvantage of the latter method is that the taker-off doing finishings does not know the actual widths of openings and depths of reveals, the scaling of a 1:100 drawing for this not being at all reliable, but the margin of error should be small. Of course, in a thoroughly planned job there would be a schedule of windows and doors for each taker-off and the difficulty would not arise. The system to be followed is therefore a matter of individual choice, but once decided on, the same system should be followed always.

It may be noted that wall plastering is usually measured over wood skirtings (i.e. from the floor level) to cover rough rendering between the grounds and backings, though a separate item may be taken for this rough rendering, and should be if the skirting is unusually high, when plaster would be deducted accordingly. If there is no rendering between grounds plaster would be measured from, say, 25 mm below top of a wood skirting which would overlap it, or from the top of the screeded bed for tile, etc., skirtings. Wall decoration should be measured the actual surface decorated, i.e. from the top of the skirting. No deduction for plaster is made for the grounds of picture or dado rails. It is worth bearing in mind that a dado of eight courses of 150 x 150 mm tiles will probably measure 1.25 m high, not 1.20 m.

Temporary Rules.—Temporary rules are in some cases necessary to stop the edges of plaster, e.g. at the flush joint of two different plasters or at an edge against tiling, where the tiling cannot be done first. The S.M.M. makes it clear that such rules are not to be measured (S.M.M. T 3.11), but a lineal item is to be measured for flush joints (S.M.M. T 11.1). It must be remembered that a specialist laying, say, a terrazzo dado needs a straight edge to work to, and it would be advisable to draw the building contractor's attention to this need. 'Labour flush joint against specialist's finish' is not enough, as it might only imply that the specialist's finish was there to finish against.

EXAMPLE 20

INTERNAL FINISHINGS

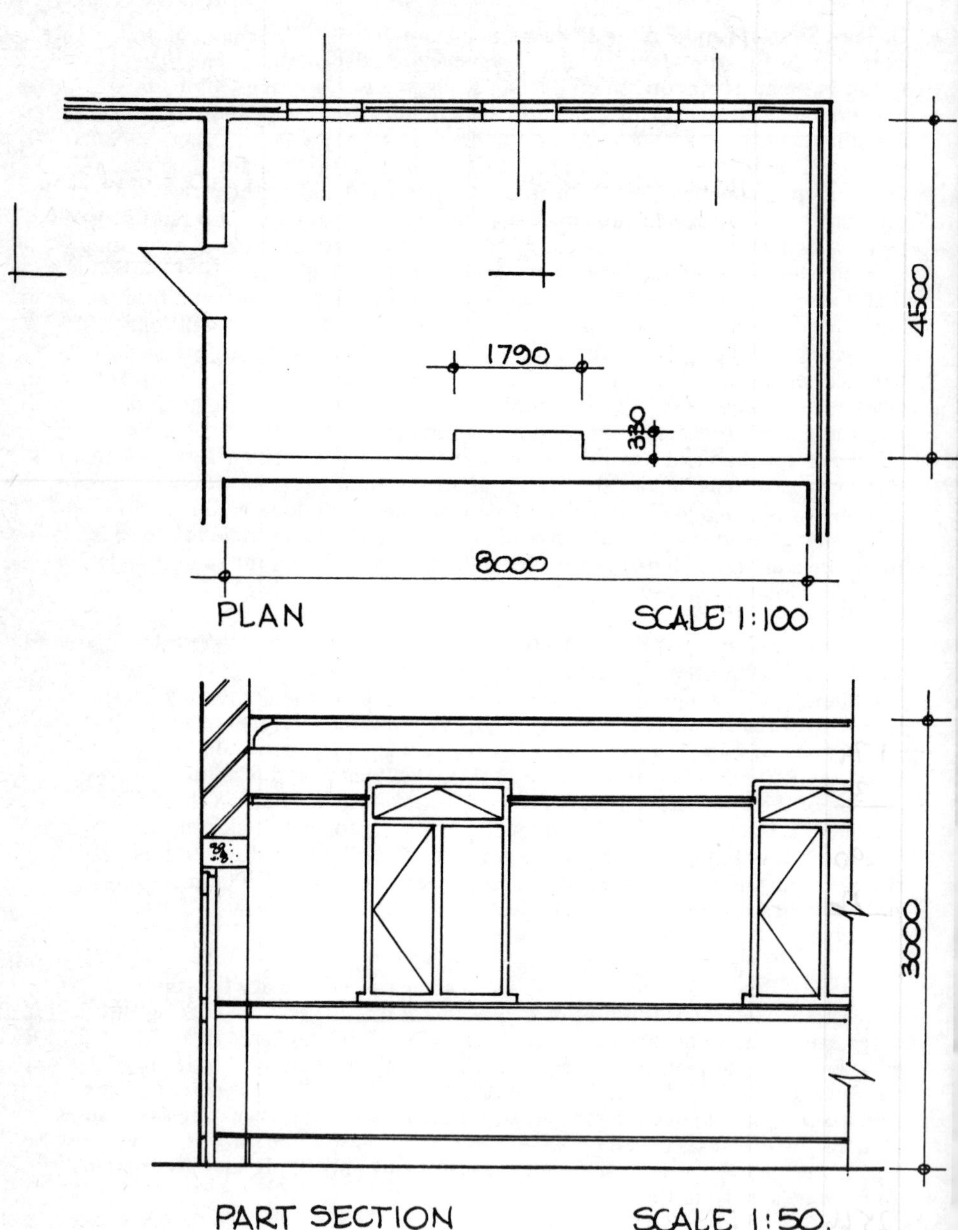

Fig. 32

Timesing / Dimensions	Description
3.00 4.50	Plaster lath ceilings intly & Float & set plaster lath ceilings intly & Twice emulsion plastered ceilings intly & 2mm Vinyl tiles 300x 300mm, colour group A, fixed to trowelled bed with an approved adhesive & 19 mm PCt & S (1:3) trowelled bed for vinyl flooring
1.79 .33	Ddt all
.90 .22	Add vinyl tile flooring & 19 mm trowelled bed 8.000 4.500 2/12.500 25.000 2/330 660 25.660
25.66 3.00	Float & set walls intly & Twice emulsion plas walls intly
2/ 3.00	Labour arris
25.66	Fine plaster coved & filleted cornice 400 mm girth, including dubbing & Twice emulsion plaster cornice sup x .40 =
6	Internal mitres to cornice
2	External do
25.66 .20	Ddt f & s walls & Ddt dist plas walls 25.660 4/.200 800 24.860
24.86 .15	Ddt f & s plas clgs & Ddt dist plas clgs 25.660 Wdws* 3/1.000 3.000 22.660 3/2/150 900 23.560
23.56	25x63 mm Wrot softwood moulded picture rail plugged & KPS & (3) intly. surfaces 00-300mm girth

Timesing	Dimensions	Description	Timesing	Dimensions	Description
		* 25.660 Door 900 Fire 900 1.800 23.860 2/250 500 24.360		24.36 .23	Ddt Twice emul non plastered wall (Skt
	24.36	38×100 Wrot soft-wood twice moulded dado rail plugged & KPS & ③ ctg surfaces 100–200 mm girth & 25×225 mm Wrot softwood moulded skirting & 13×63 mm Sawn softwood ground plugged ×2 = & KPS & ③ ctg surfaces 200–300 mm girth			
	6	Internal mitres to dado rail & Do to skirting			
2	2	External mitres to both			
2	2	Fitted ends to both			

*Alternatively, these deductions with adjustment for reveals can be made with the windows and door.

CHAPTER 12

WINDOWS

References to S.M.M.

G 1, 5, 10, 14–15, 19–22
J 1, 11–12, 16, 17, 19
K 1, 14, 20, 24–25, 29
N 1, 13–17, 21, 31–32
Q 1–3
T 1–6, 12, 14–18
U 1–14
V 1–5

Schedule.—Before taking any measurements of windows a schedule should be prepared such as given in Appendix 2. Elevations and plans must be compared carefully, special care being taken not to overlook windows on short return walls, which may not be drawn on any elevation. Any discrepancies between plan and elevation should be noted, and the intention of the architect ascertained. The windows will in this schedule be classified according to their type and floor, and possibly according to their type and floor, and possibly according to the elevation on which they appear. A total should be made of all windows on each floor of whatever type as shown on the schedule and these totals checked with a final count on the drawing to confirm the schedule as correct in the total number. It will be seen that this schedule can so set out the details of each window that it may hardly be necessary to refer to more than a typical detail drawing whilst measuring. Each type of window, e.g. sash, casement or metal, will be taken in turn and all work in connection measured, including adjustment for the openings. It should usually be possible with the schedule before one to measure together in one group all windows of one type irrespective of their size, thickness of wall, etc., a note being made at the head of the group showing how many windows are being dealt with, and care being taken throughout that this total is accounted for in each item. A common fault with beginners is the separate measurement of windows of the same type which are of different sizes or in different thicknesses of walls. Such a method perhaps gives less trouble but will take just as long, if not longer, in the end. Though the grouping of windows of different sizes may need more concentration and care, with proper use of the schedule it will be found considerably simplified.

Numbering of Windows.—In a building of any size it will be found a great convenience if all windows are given a serial number, the numbers being arranged in such an order as to facilitate the location of any window by its number, and the plans being marked accordingly. If these numbers are used on the schedule to indicate the location of the windows and in the dimensions for reference, it will be possible at a later stage to see at a glance from the schedule the size and particulars measured for any individual window, and also to trace the location of any window referenced where perhaps some special treatment has been measured.

Subdivision.—The measurement of each type of window divides itself into the following subsections:

(*a*) Window—

(1) Joinery or metal casement.

(2) Glass.

(3) Ironmongery.

(4) Paint.

(*b*) Opening—

(1) Deduction of brickwork and internal and external finish.

(2) Lintel and/or arch.

(3) External reveals.

(4) External sill.

(5) Internal reveals.

(6) Internal sill.

If these subdivisions are followed through systematically there will be little risk of items being missed. Whether the window or the opening is dealt with first is a matter for individual preference.

'Timesing'.—Window dimensions will probably contain a good deal of 'timesing', and great care is necessary to see that this is correctly done. As each of the above subsections is finished it is advisable to add up the timesing which represents number of windows as a check. If, for instance, twenty-four windows are being measured, timesing of deductions, lintels, sills, etc., should total twenty-four, unless in any item there is a particular reason for a lesser number.

Special Features.—With the windows will be taken any special feature which definitely belongs to a window, such as a small canopy over or apron or recessed brickwork under.

Dormer Windows.—In the case of dormer windows the window itself with ironmongery, glass and paint may be taken with other windows, while the adjustment of the roof would normally be taken with the roofs, This division will generally be found convenient, especially if the roofs and windows are not measured by the same person. Each taker-off will then deal with the items referring to his own section. The opening of a dormer window may sometimes be partly in the brick wall and partly in the roof, in which case the deduction and adjustment of wall would be done with the windows, as they would probably be taken on the same lines as in the lower part of other window openings.

Adjustments.—The advantage of making adjustments from a general measurement will often be evident in the measurement of windows. For instance, it may be that for the same type of window there are several different types of internal finish to be deducted, such as plaster and emulsion paint, plaster and gloss paint, fair face brickwork, etc. One of these finishes will probably predominate (say plaster and emulsion), and it may be found most convenient to deduct that finish for all, thus ensuring that deduction is made of some sort for the total number of windows dealt with. Adjustment can then be made for these windows in walls finished, say with fair face, by deducting that finish and adding back plaster and emulsion previously deducted. In the same way, if the windows are all glazed with clear glass except a small proportion which have obscure glass, the simplest way of measuring is often to take all as clear glass, and then, checking over carefully with the schedule, make adjustment for those which need obscure glass. If, as is not impossible, the measurement of obscure glass to one or more windows should be forgotten, the error will be much smaller than if the glass to those windows had not been measured at all.

Casements and Frames and Window Surrounds.—S.M.M. N 21 requires that casements, frames and window surrounds shall be described and enumerated and, unless they can be adequately described, supported by a bill diagram. This means that the overall size of the set must be given together with a full description of the component parts, i.e. jambs, heads, cills, transomes and mullions as well as the casements themselves. The bill diagram will immediately indicate the make up of the unit and the relative position of any fixed or opening lights as well as the layout of such things as glazing bars. A typical bill diagram for a four light window with two side opening and one top hung casements might be as follows:

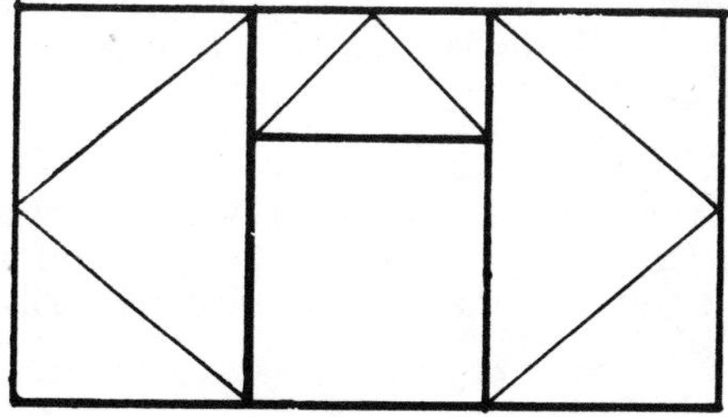

Fig. 33

and the accompanying description would give in addition to the size the scantlings and sections of the members. This enables an estimator to weigh up what he is being asked to price and the layout of the jointing is immediately apparent. The example which follows shows how this is put into practice for a double hung sash window and a casement window. Should the surveyor so decide he can fully describe the item without resorting to a bill diagram but it may produce an unnecessarily lengthy description and lose some clarity.

With the frame will usually be measured the necessary fixings (cramps, fixing bricks, water bar, etc.), also an item for bedding and pointing. It must not be forgotten that if a window is on the outside of a faced brick wall, fixing bricks cannot be used, as they would show; also if cramps are used for fixing a frame, fixing bricks or plugging may be necessary in addition for linings or architraves.

With frames will come architraves or cover fillets, and it must not be forgotten that where these have to fit against fair face brickwork or other irregular surfaces they should be described as 'scribed' unless they are bedded (e.g. externally in mastic). The extreme length must be measured at all mitres.

Glass.—The size of each pane of glass should be calculated from the overall size of casement or sash by making due allowance for stiles and rails as shown in the waste calculations in Example 21, page 121, below. For this purpose glazing bars can practically speaking be ignored, their thickness after deducting two rebates being negligible.

Ironmongery.—The separation of ironmongery fixed to hardwood from that fixed to softwood may generally be left to the worker-up, as if dimensions are properly taken it should be obvious into which group the item is to be abstracted. If, however, there is any doubt the taker-off must make it clear in his dimensions.

Paint.—The taker-off in setting down his dimension for paint should consider how the item is to appear in the bill, e.g. square, lineal, etc., not simply add '& ③' to the item without any such consideration. For instance, if a jamb lining with architraves is to be painted, there should be clear indication whether it is to be a lineal or square item. The decision as to the measurement of the girth and whether the item is to be square or lineal should not be left to the worker-up.

If any special treatment to the back of frames, such as treating with preservative, is required this should be measured as a separate item, in which backs of all frames could be grouped together irrespective of their width. It is quite usual for the priming coat of paint to be applied all round a frame in the shop irrespective of the fact that only part of the frame will have a painted finish, and such additional priming should be specified and measured accordingly. If joinery is delivered partly unprimed, it will naturally be more expensive to prime backs of frames, skirtings, etc., on the site.

Openings.—Where a frame is set behind, say, a 60 mm reveal the deduction of brickwork may be made in two parts, one for the outer half brick and facings and one for the rest of the wall (the same dimension probably serving for internal plaster).

It should be noted that throughout the examples in this book concrete lintels have been assumed as precast, and therefore are measured as enumerated items including reinforcement. They can be measured as cube concrete, if to be cast *in situ*, but in such cases formwork and reinforcement must be measured as separate items. It may sometimes be left to the builder to decide which method of construction to adopt, in which case they may be measured as for precast and described as 'precast or cast *in situ*' in the heading to the bill. Bearing in mind the weight of concrete, the student will realise that large lintels would not usually be precast, being too unwieldy to handle.

It is implied by S.M.M. G 48.2 and 3 that, where an item cannot be built in as the work proceeds, cutting and pinning must in all cases be measured. This labour may be forced on the contractor by late instructions or delivery of materials, so the method of doing the work cannot always be correctly anticipated.

Examples.—Examples 21 to 23 cover three basic types of window. Traditional double hung sash windows with boxed casings, sash cords and weights are rarely found now, except in alteration work, but double hung sashes with spring balances, as illustrated in Example 21, are used in new work to match the older type remaining in existing elevations. The wood casement example is of the simplest form of opening window and the metal window set direct to stone illustrates setting in an unusual surround. Stone jambs have been measured lineal, following S.M.M. K 20.

In practice windows to be measured are usually more complicated in detail, having a combination of fixed and opening lights in the same window, but application of the principles set down in these three examples should enable measurement of any kind of window to be understood.

EXAMPLE 21

DOUBLE HUNG SASH WINDOW

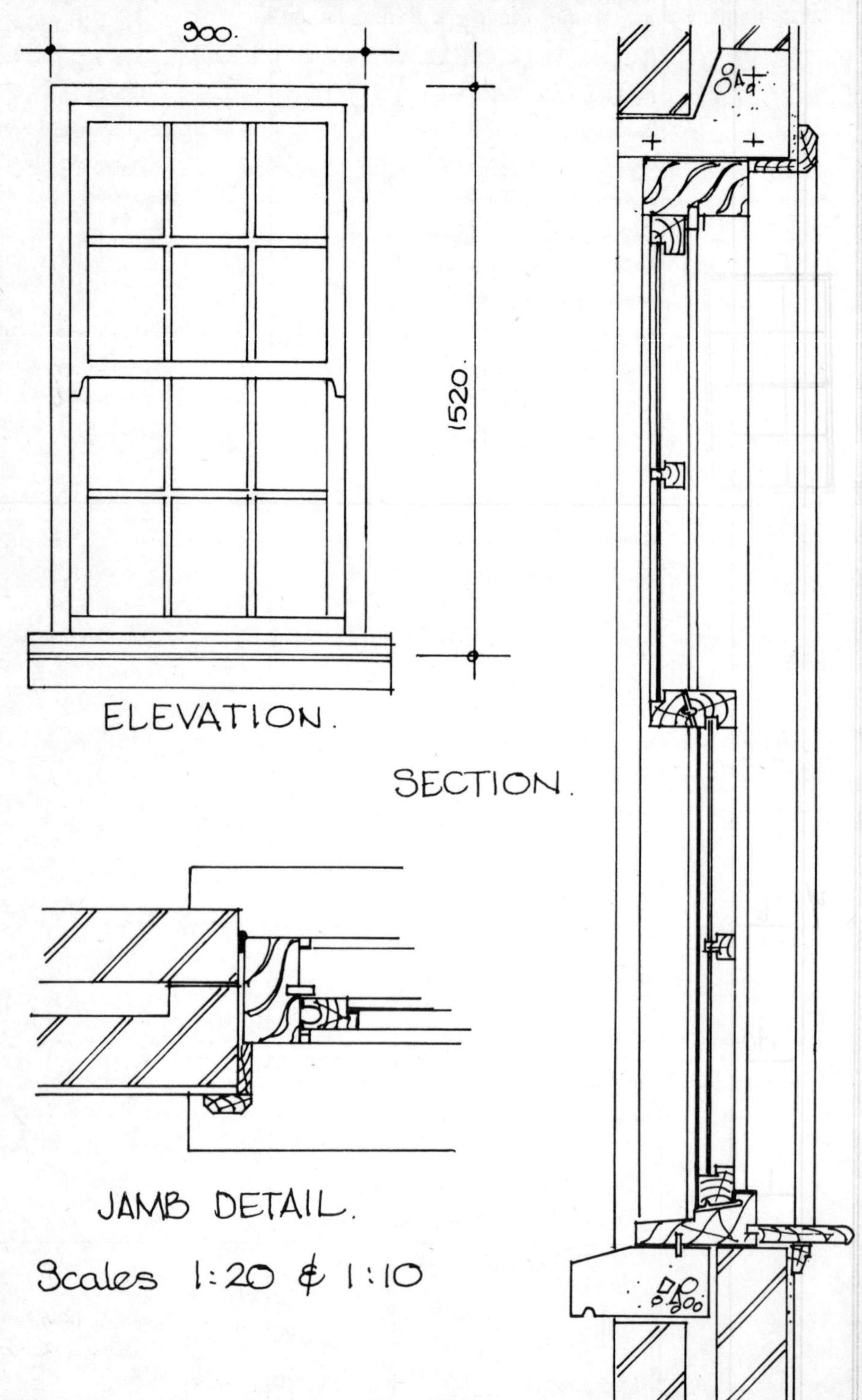

Fig. 34

Timesing	Dimensions	Description
	1	Softwood double hung sash window 900x1520 mm of 75x100 mm frame, 16x16 mm splayed inner & outer beads, 16x25 mm parting beads, 75x175 mm oak twice sunk weathered check throated & twice grooved sill, filled in with 50 mm rebated & moulded sashes, each in six panes, with splay rebated meeting & bottom rails, fitted & hung on & including X & Co spiral sash balances & including fixing BMA sash fastener & pair of BMA flush sash lifts (see P.C. for BMA items)
		900 / 1520 / 2/2420 4840
	4.84	Bed wood frame in cement mortar (1:3) & point one side in mastic
2/	6	Extra for breeze concrete fixing blocks & building in
	.90	3x25 mm Galvanised mild steel water bar bedded in mastic
	1	19x75 mm Wrot softwood rebated lining to head & jambs of opening 900x1520 mm
		900 / 2/1520 3040 / 4/75 300 / 4240
	4.24	25x75 mm Wrot softwood twice splayed architrave & 12x63 mm Sawn softwood grounds plugged.
		900 / 2/75 150 / 1050
	1.05	25x150 mm Wrot S.W. rebated & rounded window board plugged. & 19x38 mm Wrot SW bed mould
	2	Notched & returned rounded end to window board
		900 / 2/75 150 / 750 / 2/65 130 / 2/10 20 / 150 / 3)600 / 200
		75 / 50 / 2/40 80 / 15 / 2/10 20 / 1520 / 125 / 1395 / 115 / 4)1280 / 320
12/	.20 / .32	3 mm Clear sheet glass & glazing to wood with putty in panes not exceeding .10 m² (in No 12)
		900 / 2/1520 3040 / 3940
	3.94 / .10	Prime backs of frames etc
	.90 / .20	(sill

Timesing	Dimensions	Description
	.90 1.52	KPs & (3) on wood double hung sash window in small panes, extly & Do intly
	1.05 .28 4.24 .20	Add last only 75 / 2/25 50 / 75 = 200 150 / 25 / 50 / 38 / 19 = 282
		<u>Opening</u>
	.90 1.52	<u>Ddt</u> h.b. skin of h.w. in c.b. & <u>Ddt</u> do in fcp & ptg o.s. & <u>Ddt</u> forming 45 mm cavity & <u>Ddt</u> F. & S. walls & <u>Ddt</u> 2 ct emul plas walls
2/	1.52	Building 45 mm cavity of hollow wall solid with common brickwork half brick thick, including 100 mm width of fibre base damp proof course built in
		900 2/150 300 1200
	1	250×150 mm Precast concrete (1:2:4) rebated lintel 1200 mm long (150×150 mm splayed with 100×50 mm rebate 900 mm long) reinforced with three 12 mm mild steel bars & 16 gauge galvanised wire binders at 300 mm centres finished fair on front & soffite
	1.20 .15	<u>Ddt</u> h b skin of h w in c b & <u>Ddt</u> forming 45 mm cavity
	.90 .05	<u>Ddt</u> h.b. skin of h.w. in fcp & ptg 100 / 100 / 25 = 225 1200 / 2/75 150 = 1350
	1.35	Fibre base & lead damp proof course & cavity gutter 225 mm girth
2/	1.52	Extra for facings & pointing to margin
	1	200×100 mm Precast concrete (1:2:4) weathered throated & grooved sill 1.050 mm long with stool each end for square jambs.

1.05	Ddt h b skin of		
.10	h w in fcs		
	+		
	Ddt form 45 mm cavity		

Alternative description for traditional double hung sash window with cased frame

1	Softwood double hung sash window 900 x 1520 mm with cased frame of 25 mm inner & outer linings, 32 mm pulley stiles, 13 mm back linings, 6 mm parting slips, 13 mm parting beads & 19 x 25 mm inside beads all tongued & grooved together & framed to 75 x 175 mm oak twice sunk weathered, check throated & grooved sill, filled in with 50 mm rebated & moulded sashes each divided into six panes, with splay rebated meeting & bottom rails, including fitting & hanging sashes on X & Co's brass chains, pulleys & weights
	(Alternatively best flax lines, brass faced axle pulleys & lead weights)

EXAMPLE 22

WOOD CASEMENT WINDOW

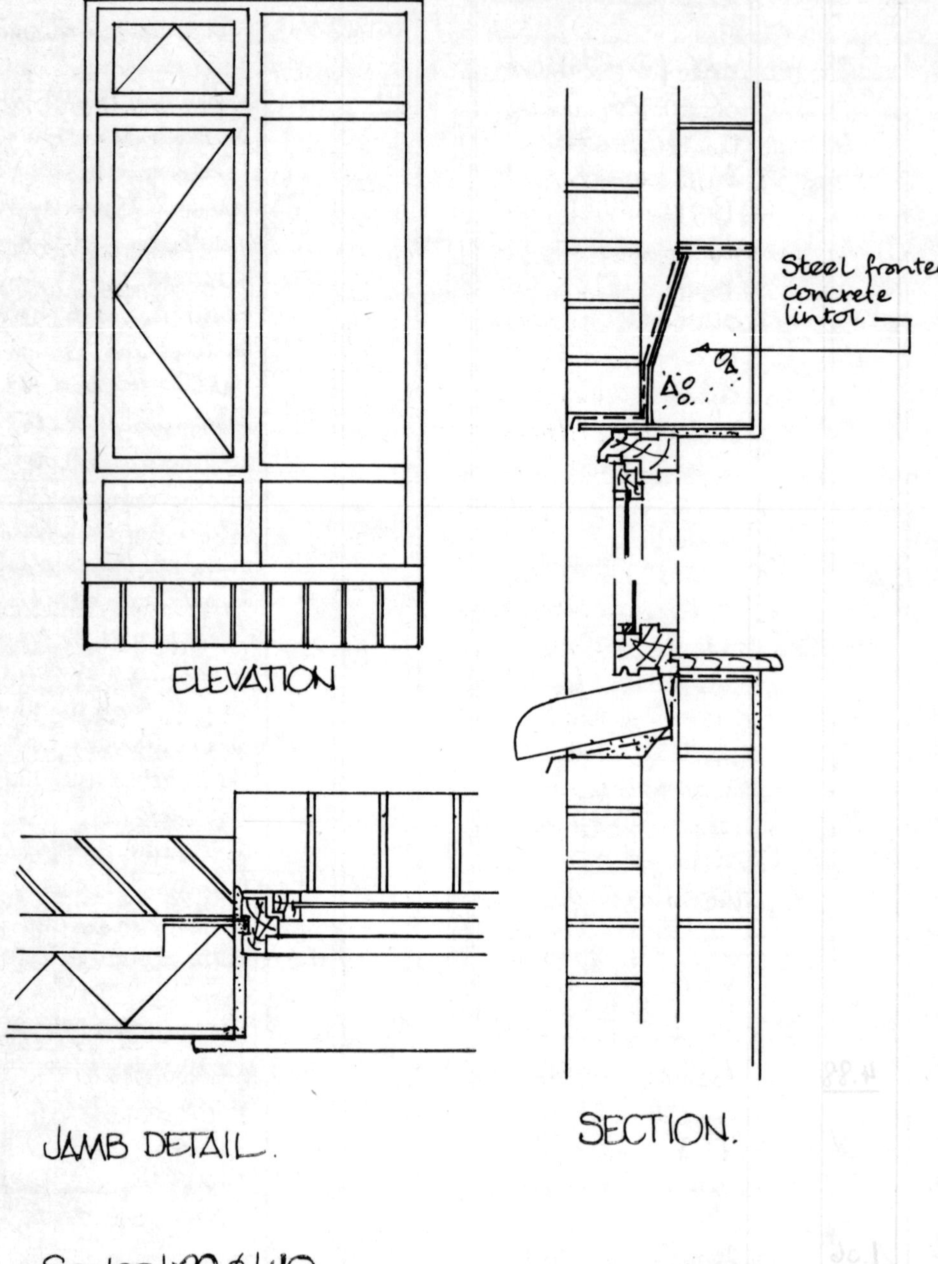

Fig. 35

Dim.	Squaring	Description
1		X & Co's standard sixlight softwood casement window 910 x 1530 mm (all sizes are finished sizes) with timber, timber members & butts conforming to B.S. 644 Part 1, of two fanlights, two mainlights & two sidelights, each light in one pane, one fanlight & one mainlight each with a 41 mm casement top hung & side hung respectively with:-
		70x57 mm head, jambs transomes & mullion
		70x70 mm sill
		32x32 mm drip to head
		38x19 mm drip to fanlights
		2 pairs cranked butts
		casement fastener & keep
		casement stay & 2 pins
		fanlight stay & 2 pins, including plugging frame
		910 1530 2/2440 4880
4.88		Bedding wood frame in cement mortar (1:3) & pointing one side in mastic
		910 2/75 150 1060
1.06		25x150 mm Wrot softwood rounded & tongued window board (groove in (standard sill
2		N. & R.R.E.

Dim.	Squaring	Description
1.06		19x50 Sawn softwood ground plugged
.33 .83	.27	3 mm Clear sheet glass & glazing to wood with putty in panes .10 - .50 m²
.39 .90	.35 .62	
.33 .17	.06	3 mm Do in panes not exceeding .10 m² (in No 4)
.39 .23	.27 .43	
		.62 .33 6) .95 av .16
.91 1.53		K.P.S. & (3) wood casement windows & frames, mullions & transomes, divided into average medium panes, intly
		&
		Do xtly
		407 252 910 407 2/1317 2634 2/659 1317
1.32		KPS & (3) x tly edges of opening casements
2.63		
1.06		Do intly surfaces 150-300 mm girth
1		X & Co's galvanised steel fronted concrete lintol 220x250 mm & 1200 mm long, with strip of metal lathing 100 mm wide welded to underside

Timesing	Dimensions	Squaring	Description
	1.22 .25		Hack face of concrete as key for plaster
	.91		215 x 65 mm Bullnose header on flat brick sill to BS 4729 Type 2.3.5.2 set raking & bedded & pointed in cement mortar
			head 100 225 100 425
	1.20		Fibre base & lead damp proof course 425 mm girth & building in.
			sill 100 75 200 375 910 2/75 150 1060
	1.06		Do 375 mm girth & do
			20 1530 100 1650
	.91 1.65		Ddt h.b. skin to h.w. in fcgs & ptg & Ddt form 50 mm cav to h.w. inc ties
			225 20 1530 1775
	.91 1.77		Ddt 100 mm conc bl csg to h.w.
	.91 1.53		Ddt F&S walls & Ddt twice emulsion plastered walls

Timesing	Dimensions	Squaring	Description
			910 2/1650 3300 4210
	4.21		Extra for facings & pointing to margins
2/	1.53		Building 50 mm cavity of hollow wall solid with 100 mm concrete blockwork bonded to inner skin, including 100 mm width of fibre base lead damp proof course built in
			910 2/1530 3060 3970
	3.97 .10		Float & set walls not exceeding 300 mm wide & Twice emulsion plastered walls
	3.97		Labour arris
	.90 .10		Extra for wall plaster on expanded metal lathing (measured separately)
	3.97		Make good plaster up to wood frame

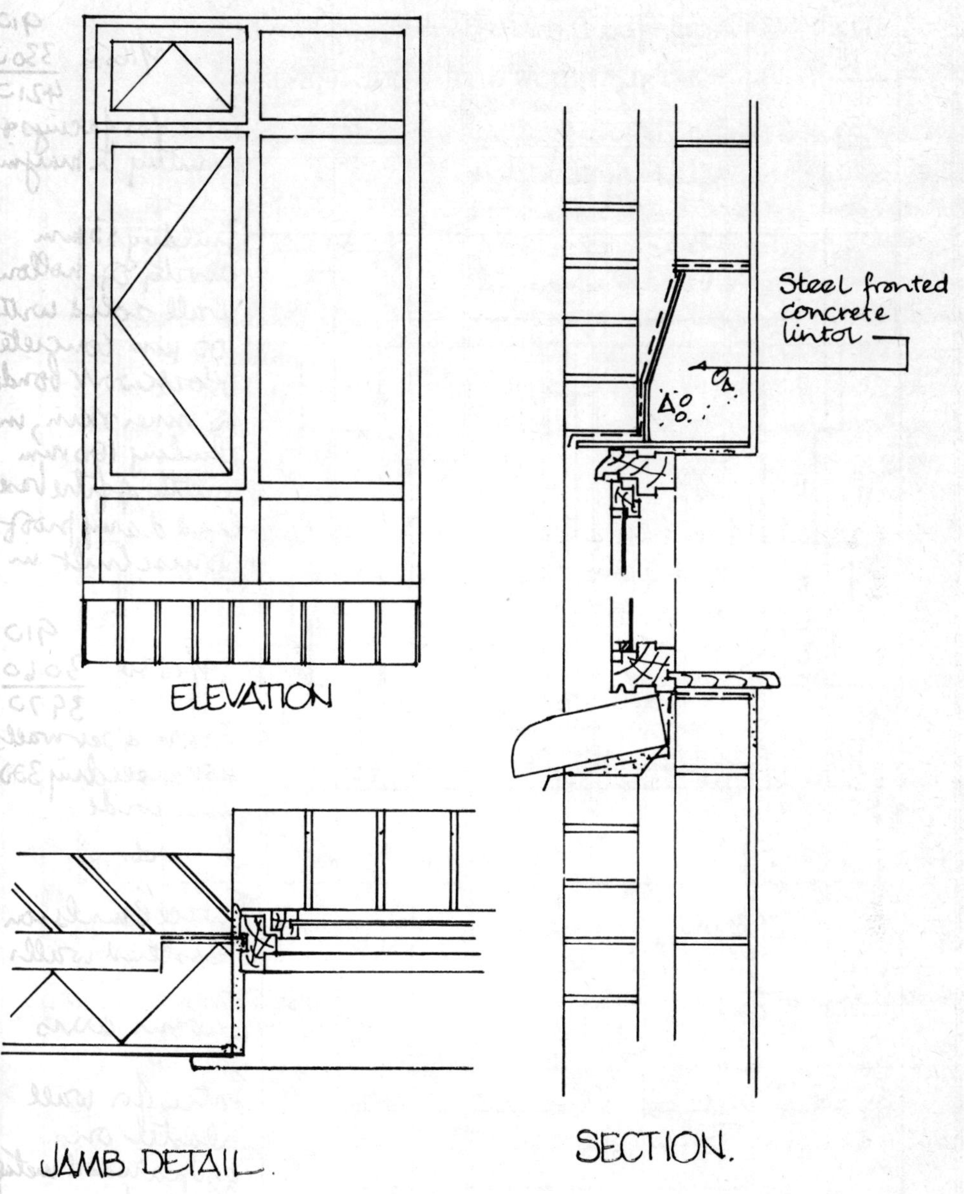

Scales 1:20 & 1:10

Fig. 35

EXAMPLE 23

METAL WINDOW WITH STONE DRESSINGS

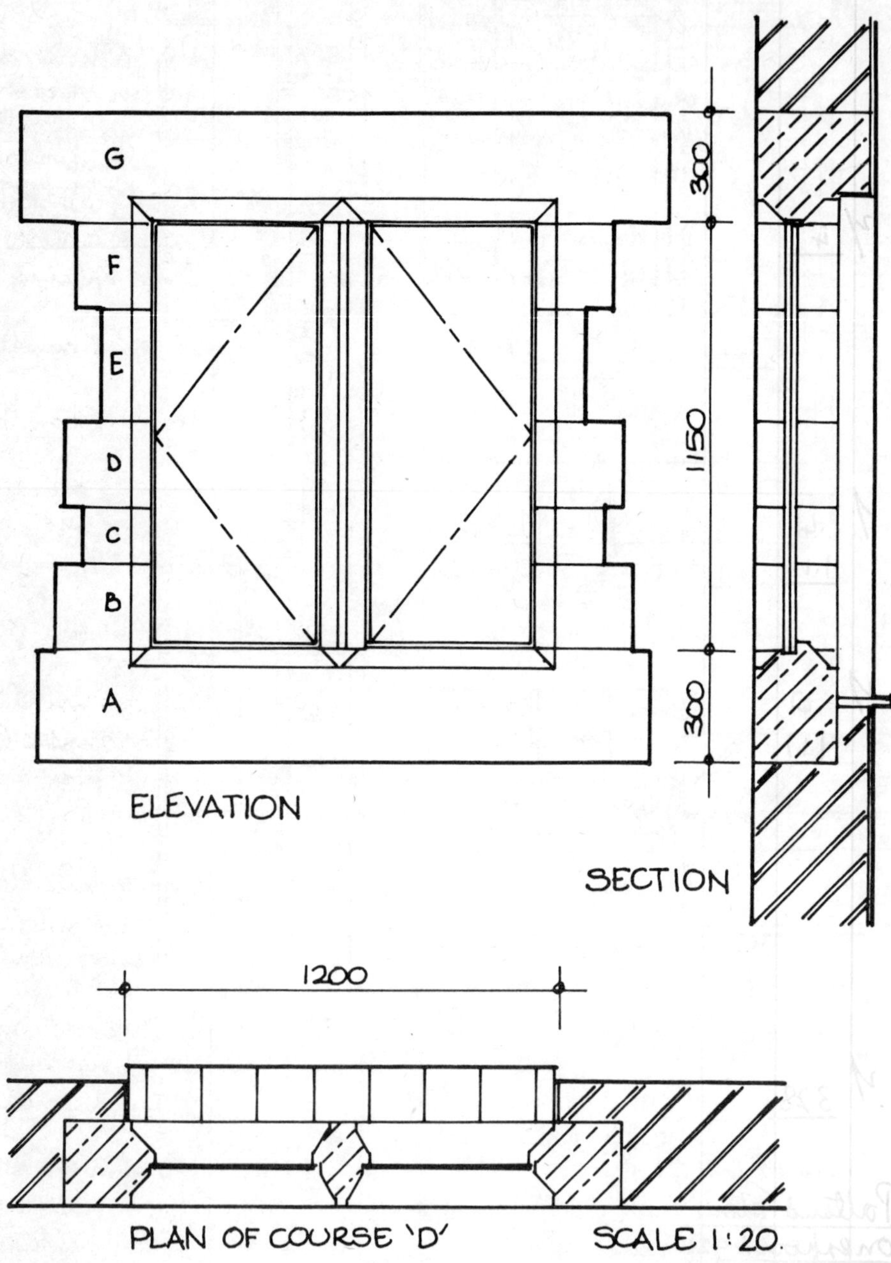

Fig. 36

Timesing	Dimension	Squaring	Description
	2		metal casement .47 x 1.17 m pc £10 each & screwing to lead plugs (measured separately) including bedding frame in cement mortar & pointing in mastic both sides
2/	4		Dovetailed mortice in stone & running with lead
			470 / 2/30 60 / 410 ; 1170 / 60 / 1110
2/	.41 1.11		4 mm Clear sheet glass & glazing to metal with putty in panes 0.10 - 0.50 m²
2/	.47 1.17		(2) metal casements in medium panes, extly & Do intly
			470 / 1170 / 2/1640 3280
2/	328		(2) metal casement edge extly

Portland Stone & all labours, rubbed on exposed faces, in window dressings in brick faced walls

Timesing	Dimension	Squaring	Description
	1.70		230x300 mm Sill sunk & twice sunk splayed, in 1.50 - 2.00 m length (A
	2		Extra on sill for stool for sunk & twice sunk splayed jamb
	1		Do for twice sunk & four times sunk splayed mullion
2/	.23		280 x 215 mm Jamb sunk & twice sunk splayed (B
2/	.23		250 x 215 mm Do (D
2/	.23		230 x 215 mm Do (F
2/	.15		200 x 327 mm Jamb twice sunk & twice sunk splayed (C
2/	.31		150 x 327 mm Do (E
	1.80		327 x 300 mm Lintol twice sunk & twice sunk splayed, in 1.50 - 2.00 m length (G
	2		Extra on lintol for stool for sunk & twice sunk splayed jamb
	1		Do for twice sunk & four times sunk splayed mullion
	1.15		150 x 230 mm Mullion twice sunk & four times sunk splayed

(End of Portland Stone)

Timesing	Dimensions	Squaring	Description
			1.040 ½/ar 265 530 1.570
	1.57 1.75		Ddt one and a half brick wall & Ddt extra for facing & pointing
			230 1.040 250 230 3) 760 2/ 253 506 1546 1200 2) 346 173
2/3/	1.70 .15 .17 .23		Half brick wall in backing to masonry including cutting & bonding (Sill / Jambs BDF)
	1.20 1.38		Ddt Float & set walls & Ddt Twice emulsion plastered walls
			1.200 2/1.380 2.760 3.960
	3.96 .11		Float & set walls not exceeding 300 mm wide & Twice emulsion plastered walls

Timesing	Dimensions	Squaring	Description
	3.96		L arris arris
	1.20		152×152×16 mm Red quarry tiles to BS 1286 type A to rounded sill 152 mm wide bedded & pointed in cement mortar
	2		Cut & fitted ends
	1.20 .11		13 mm Portland cement & sand screeded bed not exceeding 300 mm wide

CHAPTER 13

DOORS, INCLUDING OPENINGS WITHOUT JOINERY

References to S.M.M.

G, J, K } As for windows (see Chapter 12 above)
N 1, 13–17, 19–20, 31–32
Q, R, T, U, V } As for windows (see Chapter 12 above)

Subdivision.—Doors will be primarily divided into:

(a) external doors,

(b) internal doors,

and in the case of a building of any size each of these groups would form a separate section of the taking off. In any case the external doors are usually of a different type with different finishings and are best kept in a group by themselves. The measurement of each group can in turn be divided into the same sections as were given in the previous chapter for windows, with the exception that in place of sills in some cases flooring in the opening will have to be dealt with, if this has not already been measured in the 'Floors' section. Steps to external doors will be taken with them, also any hoods or special features in connection. Openings without windows or doors or other joinery will form a separate subsection, and will include all remaining places where walls and wall finishings have been measured through but have to be deducted. Adjustments will be made in the same way as in the case of window or door openings. Some surveyors make a separate section of all openings, dealing only with the windows or doors themselves in their appropriate section, but it is perhaps best to measure the openings whilst the details of joinery are in mind.

Schedule.—As in the case of windows a schedule should be made so that the whole of the doors can be surveyed at a glance, and doors may be numbered serially as described in the last chapter for windows. External doors may be numbered in the window series if preferred, and openings without joinery wherever brickwork has been measured across may be numbered in the internal door series.

Descriptions of Doors.—The description of doors needs some care. A general preamble may describe the material for panels if other than that of the framing of the door, e.g. plywood panels to softwood doors. The thickness of the panels if constant can also be stated in this preamble, otherwise it should be given with each type of door.

Frames and Linings.—In measuring door frames or linings the length is calculated from the size of the opening, allowance being made for the passings at the joints. S.M.M. N 20 requires the incidence of repetition of identical items to be recognised, and it may well be on a simple job that the frames would be enumerated because by enumeration the repetition factor is at once apparent and more information has been given. The lengths of 40 mm rebated linings and 100 x 75 mm rebated frame for a door 900 x 2000 mm would be:

	Linings		Frame
	2.00		2.00
	2.00		2.00
	0.90		0.90
4/25 mm	0.10	4/63 mm	0.25
	5.00		5.15

Fixings must again be taken as explained in the case of windows and dowels to feet of frames where required. Where a door is in a wall more than 1B thick with linings and architraves both sides it must be remembered that a double set of fixing bricks will be necessary, though in a 1B wall one set would serve as fixing for lining and both sets of architraves.

Fanlights and Sidelights.—With doors would be measured any fanlights or sidelights. If only some of the doors have these, they could be ignored in the first instance, all doors being taken in the same way. The fanlights could then be measured with their glass and ironmongery, and the transome and extra lengths of frame and architrave to jambs added. Sidelights can be similarly treated. The openings of fanlights and sidelights are best dealt with at the same time as those of the doors to which they belong.

Metal Casement Doors.—These are best taken in the 'Windows' section where metal windows are being measured, the principles of measurement being the same for both.

Paint.—Paint on general panelled or moulded surfaces of woodwork can be measured in two ways: either a calculation can be made of the girth of mouldings, etc., and the area put down accordingly, or the area can be measured flat and timesed by $1\frac{1}{8}$, thus adding one-eighth to the flat area, a generally recognised allowance to cover the extra girth of mouldings. This allowance will also cover edges, such as edges of doors, where the surfaces are measured in this way. The conventional allowance of one-eighth should, of course, be varied to meet the circumstances. It is too much in the case of flush doors, where it is better to measure the flat area and add the extra area of edges. Paint in this case would not be timesed by $1\frac{1}{8}$. In the case of heavily bolection-moulded doors with small panels the allowance of one-eighth would not be sufficient to cover extra girth of mouldings and edges. The dimension might be timesed by $1\frac{1}{2}$, or even by $1\frac{1}{6}$. In short, the object must be to give, as accurately as can reasonably be estimated, the area to be covered by one brush.

Fanlights and glazed doors are to be measured for paint like casement windows (S.M.M. V 5.1b) as an overall superficial measurement, with a lineal item for the edges of casements (V 5.1e). The half-glazed door in Example 24 has been measured as a glazed door. It is clear from the wording that edges are not measurable to glazed doors or sashes.

Examples.—The two examples, of a softwood panelled door and a standard flush door, illustrate the principles of measurement for any kind of door, whether hardwood or softwood.

The examples of arches are retained from previous editions as they are sometimes encountered and the dimensions illustrate the measurement of curved work of this nature.

EXAMPLE 24

EXTERNAL DOOR

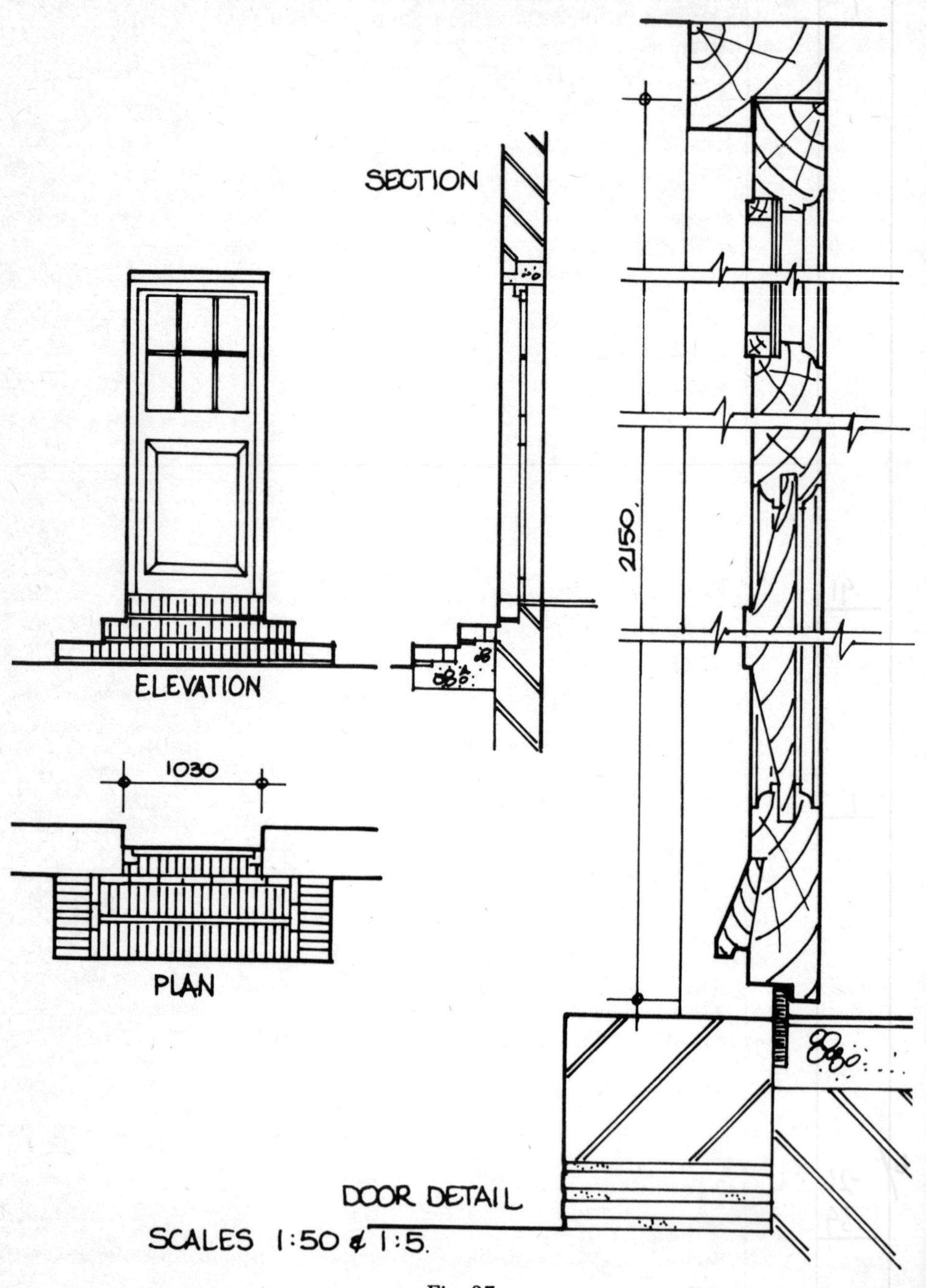

Fig. 37

Timesing	Dimensions	Description
		1030
		2/50 100
		930
	1	50 mm Wrot softwood two panel door 930 x 2150 mm, with rebated bottom rail, lower panel moulded on solid both sides, raised & fielded with splayed & sunk margins, the upper panel open, rebated & moulded & divided into six panes for glass
		930
		2/12 24
		906
	.91	25 x 75 mm Wrot s.w. splayed & throated weather fillet housed to bottom rail of door
	1	6 x 50 mm Galvanised mild steel water bar 930 mm long & setting in screed
		800 930
		12 2/65 130
		2/788 2/13 26 156
		394 3/774
		258
6/	.26 .39	3 mm Clear sheet glass & glazing to wood with beads & putty in panes 0.10 – 0.50 m²

Timesing	Dimensions	Description
6/	1.30	16 x 16 mm Hardwood rounded glazing bead fixed with brass cups + screws
		Ironmongery p.c. on col
	1	Fix to S.W. Pair 100 mm brass butts
	1	Do mortice lock & brass knob furniture
	2	Do brass barrel bolt 150 mm long & socket
		No 1 Door Frame Ser
		50
		2150
		10
		2210
2/	2.21	75 x 100 mm Wrot s.w. rebated & moulded jamb
		930
		2/50 100
		horns 2/75 150
		1180
	1.18	75 x 100 mm Do head
		930
		100
		1030
	1.03	Bed wood frame in cement mortar & point in mastic one side
2/	2.21	

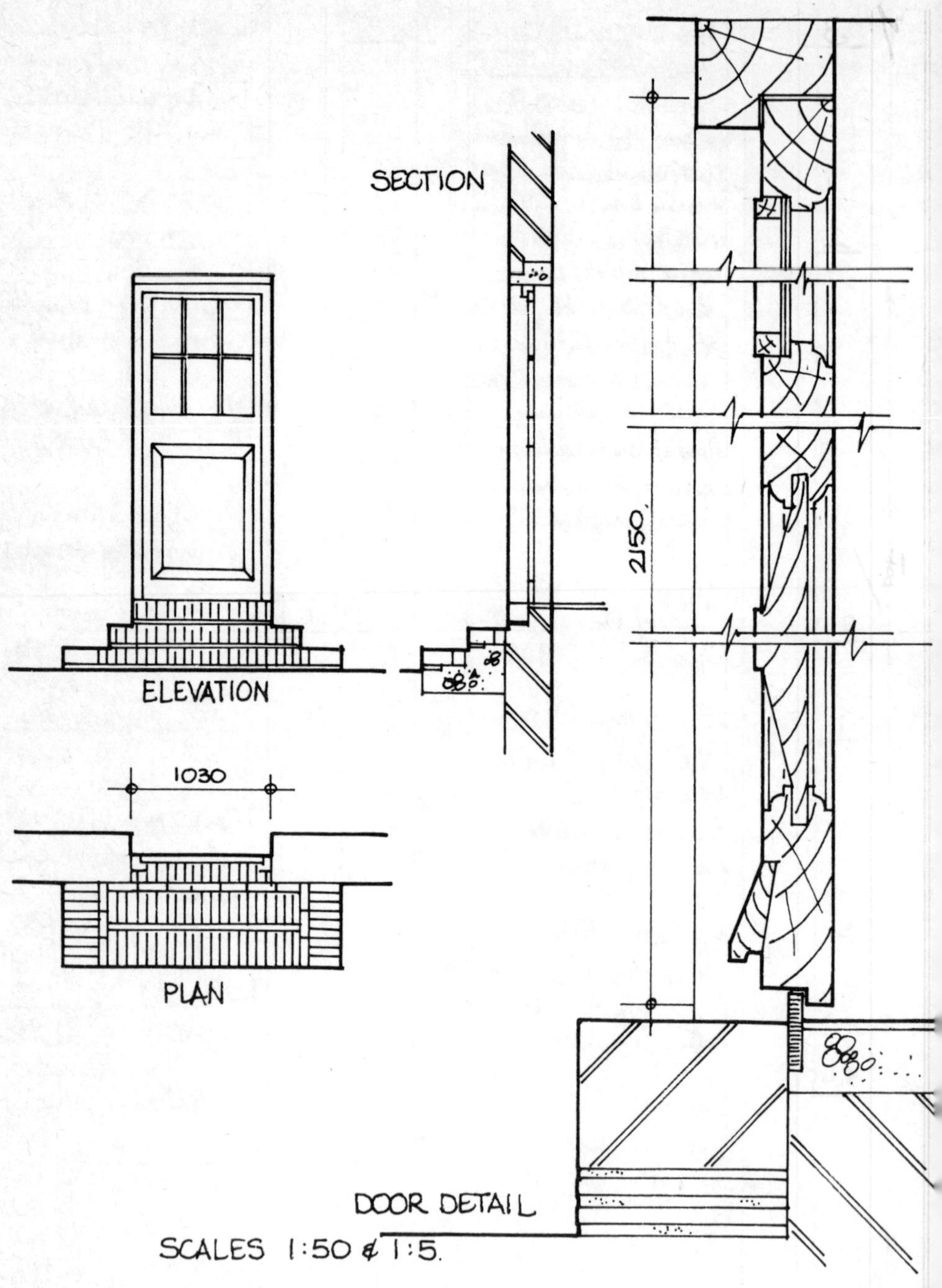
SECTION
ELEVATION
1030
PLAN
2150
DOOR DETAIL
SCALES 1:50 & 1:5.

Fig. 37

2/	3	4 × 25 mm Galvanised mild steel cramp 250 mm girth, screwed to softwood & built into brickwork		Opening
			1.03 2.21	Ddt 1½B wall & Ddt Ex for fcgs & Ddt F&S walls & Ddt twice emulsion plas walls
	2	10 mm Diameter mild steel dowel 75 mm long, including mortice in softwood & Mortice in brickwork for dowel & running with cement		
				2/150 1030 300 1330
1⅛/	.93 2.15	KPS & ③ wood half glazed door in medium panes, intly & Do., ex tly		
			1	327 × 150 mm Pre-cast concrete (1:2:4) rebated lintel 1.33 m long (215 × 150 mm with 112 × 75 mm nib 1.03 m long) reinforced with four 12 mm mild steel bars & 16 g. galvanised wire binders at 300 mm centres, finished fair on face & soffite of nib
		2/2210 1030 4420 5450		
	5.45	KPS & ③ woodframe not exceeding 150 mm girth, extly & Do intly		
			1.33 .15	Ddt 1½B wall & Ddt Ex for fcgs
			1.33 .08	Half brick wall in facings & pointing one side
			2/ .15 .07	

Timesing	Dimensions	Description
2/	2.21	Extra for facing to margins
	5.45 .15	Float & set walls not exceeding 300 mm wide & Twice emulsion plastered walls
	5.45	Labour arris & Make good plaster up to wood frame
	2.00 .60 .15 1.40 .30 .15	Concrete (1:6) in foundations to steps 100–150 mm thick 2000 2/300 600 1400
	2.00	Formwork to edge of foundation not exceeding 250 mm high (Excn for steps taken with strip surface)
2/	.60	
	1.40	
2/	.30	
	1.03	150×100 mm hard red paving horizontal brick on edge step with two courses of creasing tiles under, set & pointed on top & riser in cement mortar
	2	Cutting to end of last

Timesing	Dimensions	Description
		1400 2/600 1200 2600
	2.60 1.40	300×100 mm Brick on edge step with creasing tiles as last
	2	Cutting to end of last
	2	Fair pointed end to do., including pair of 25×3 galvanised coping cramps 225 mm girth built in
	2	Extra for angle to do., including do

EXAMPLE 25

INTERNAL DOOR

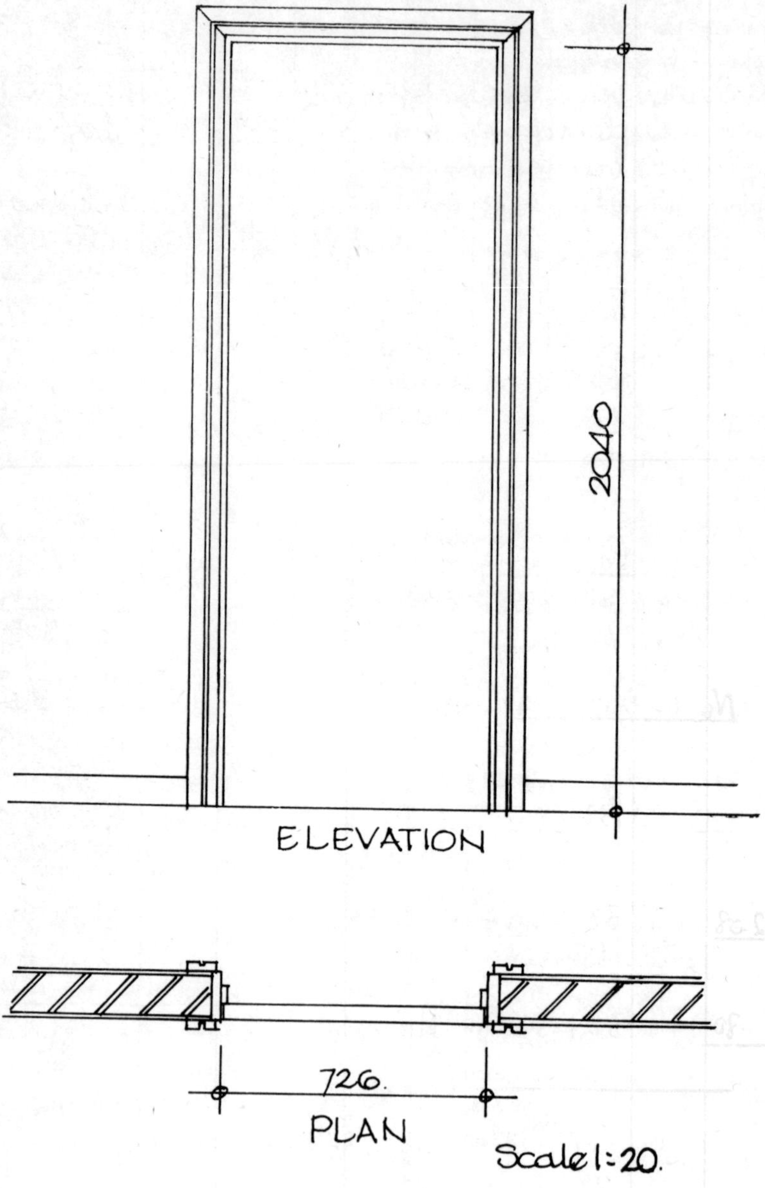

2040

ELEVATION

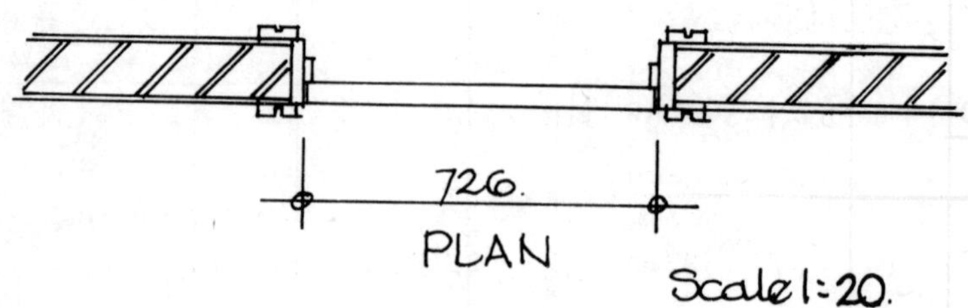

Fig. 38

Timesing	Dimensions	Description
	1	40 mm Standard pattern solid core flush door 726×2040 mm hardwood lipped on all edges, faced one side with mahogany veneer left clean for clear finish, with balancing veneer the other side for painting
		&
		Pair 100 mm pressed steel butts & fixing to softwood frame & hardwood lipped flush door
		&
		Fix morticelatch & SAA lever furniture to do
		No 1 Door lining set
		726 / 2040 2/38 76 / 38 802 / 2078
2/	2.08	38×150 mm Jamb tongued at angles
	.80	38×150 mm Head do
		726 2/2040 4080 4806
	4.81	19×38 mm Wrot softwood stop
		802 2/2078 4156 2/2/75 300 5258

Timesing	Dimensions	Description
2/	5.26	25×75 mm Wrot softwood moulded architrave
	6	Extra for fixing bricks
	.73 2.04	KPS & (3) uttly doors {Kitchen side
	4.95 .48	Do linings etc {Linings & archives
		150 2/19 38 2/19 38 75 2/25 50 2/125 250 476
		726 / 2040 2/40 80 / 40 806 / 2080
	.81 2.08	Two coats of polyurethene clear varnish on hardwood faced doors {Hall side

EXAMPLE 26

INTERNAL ARCHWAY

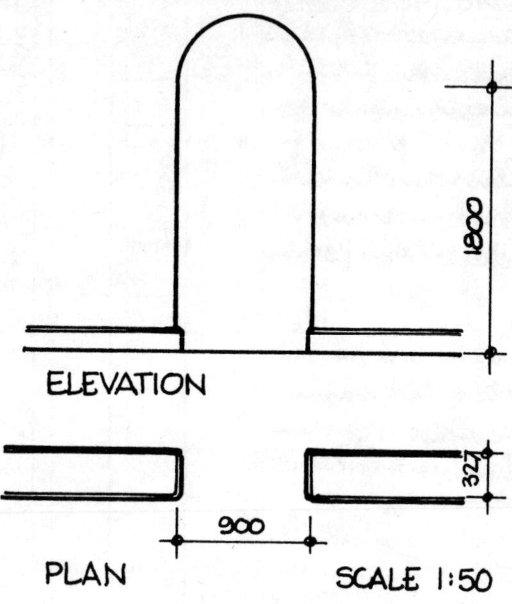

Fig. 39

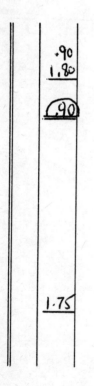

	.90 1.80	Ddt 1½ B wall & Ddt F&S walls x2 = & Ddt twice emul plas walls x2 =
	(.90)	
		900 2/½/215 = 215 ½/3 1/7/1115 = 1.752
	1.75	Extra over common brickwork for rough semicircular arch in two half brick rings in 327 mm wall

	1	Centre to semicircular brick arch with 327 m[m] soffite & 900 mm clear span
2/	.33 1.80	F&S walls & Twice emul plas w[alls]
½/3 1/7/	.33 .90	Float & set walls curved to 450 mm concave radius & Twice emul plas walls

2/2/	1.80	Labour external rounded angle 10-100 mm radius
2/1/2/3 1/7/	.90	Do curved to 450 mm radius
2/2/	1.80	Rough cut brickwork to form rounded angle 30 mm radius
2/1/2/3 1/7/	.90	

If flooring in opening is not measured with floors and skirtings to jambs with skirtings, then follow:-

	.90 .33	25 mm Softwood t & g flooring ab.
3/	.33	50×50 Sawn softwood bearers plugged.
		32 327 13 2/45 90 417
2/	.42	32×100 mm Wrot softwood moulded skirting & 13×100 Sawn softwood ground plugged & KPS & (3) Paint skirting 150-300 mm girth

		32 900 13 2/45 90 810
2/	.81	DDT Last three items 40 25 65
2/	2	Extra over skirting for external rounded corner piece 65 mm radius & Extra over ground for external rounded angle 40 mm radius

EXAMPLE 27

EXTERNAL ARCHWAY

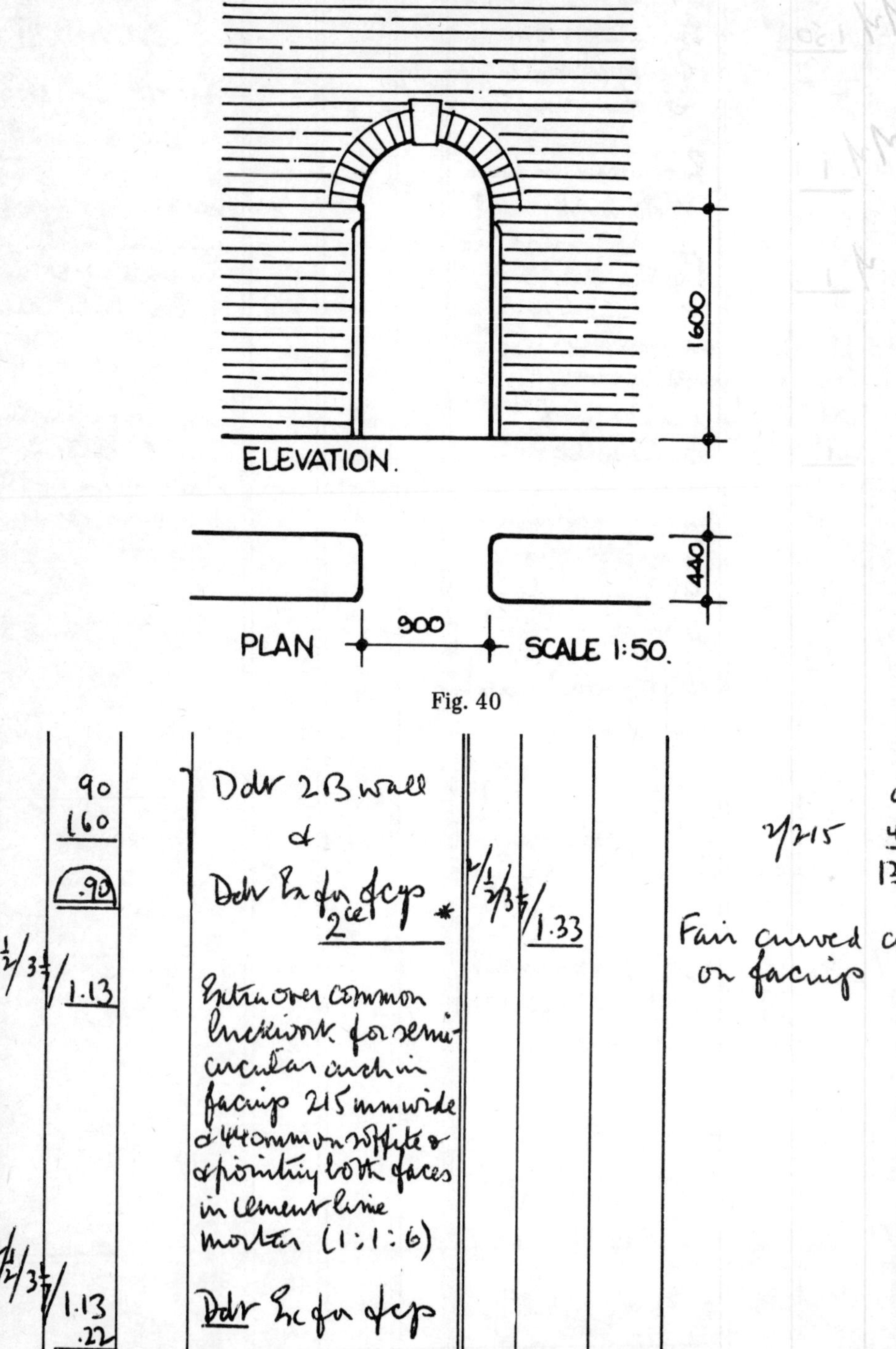

ELEVATION.
1600
440
900
PLAN
SCALE 1:50.
90
160
.90
½/3 1/7/1.13
Ddt 2B wall
&
Ddt Ex for fcgs
2ce *
Extra over common brickwork for semi-circular arch in facings 215 mm wide & 440 mm on soffite & pointing both faces in cement lime mortar (1:1:6)
2/½/3 1/7/1.13
.22
Ddt Ex for fcgs
2/½/3 1/7/1.33
2/215
Fair curved cu
on facings

Fig. 40

*2ce instead of X2 used by some surveyors instead of writing 'Ddt. do' as a separate item.

Timesing	Dimensions	Description
2/	.44 1.60	Ex for fcgs a.b. (jambs
2/2/	1.50	Extra over facings for bullnose angle 60 mm radius
2/2/	1	Extra on last for stop brick
2/	1	Portland Stone keystone 200 x 150 x 300 mm twice sunk. {Arch not deducted
	1	Centre to semi-circular brick arch 440 mm on soffite & 900 mm clear span, notched for two key blocks.

CHAPTER 14

COMPOSITE JOINERY ITEMS

References to S.M.M.

A 5
N 17–27

Composite items are defined in the S.M.M. as items which may be fabricated off site and apart from door frames are enumerated and accompanied by drawn information. Traditionally these items were measured and priced in detail and adjusted if varied; with the introduction of the sixth edition of the S.M.M. this has given way to enumeration.

Windows and doors have been covered in the two preceding chapters and roof trusses would be measured with the roof construction described in Chapter 10. This leaves staircases, balustrades and fittings. The principle is that the item is described in sufficient detail to recognise it from the drawing. The drawing is intended to be the component detail or full working drawing to show all the information necessary for the manufacture of the component. The requirement is qualified however by stating that the method of jointing or form of construction can be at the discretion of the contractor if the designer so desires. In this case all that need be shown on the drawing is the size, the shape and the general appearance of the item, the designer leaving the detailed construction to the expert.

One problem that arises with fittings is to decide when the item is a composite item or when it is to be measured in detail. Shelving is a good example in that slatted shelving in a domestic linen cupboard is hardly likely to be fabricated off site, in which case it will be second fixings and measured in detail or possibly enumerated which could give more information than is required, a principle encouraged by S.M.M. A 1. Where the slatted shelving is a made up unit for say a Dry Store in a School Kitchen, however, it will in all probability be made up in the works and brought to the site in one or more pieces. In the latter case it would be a composite item and measured as such with the fixing taken separately. In measuring woodwork the first thing the taker off has to decide is into which of the four categories set out in section N of the S.M.M. does the item fall.

Unlike bill diagrams, which are usually incorporated within the bill of quantities the drawn information required for composite items will take the form of drawings accompanying the tender documents and sufficient copies must be obtained from the architect.

Having measured the composite item and, if necessary its fixing, any work in connection, plugging, grounds, decoration, etc., will then be taken, and any adjustments on finishings and the like made. It should be remembered that associated work is to be measured and given together with the composite item. If for instance the joint between a hardwood work bench and the wall is to be masked by a cover fillet in matching hardwood then the cover fillet, not being part of the shop made unit, will be a second fixing and measured accordingly, but billed with the fitting and not lost in the general second fixings section.

If drawn information is for any reason not available when the bill is prepared, S.M.M. N 26 requires the work to be covered by a provisional sum, such sum to include the fixing.

The examples that follow are for a simple staircase, a cupboard fitting and a small enquiry counter. In the case of the staircase the drawing is deemed to have been accompanied by a detailed specification from which the description has been made up. The cupboard drawing is complete in itself and the description therefore minimal; the counter drawing is indicative of what the architect requires, the detailed construction being left to the contractor.

EXAMPLE 28

STAIRCASE

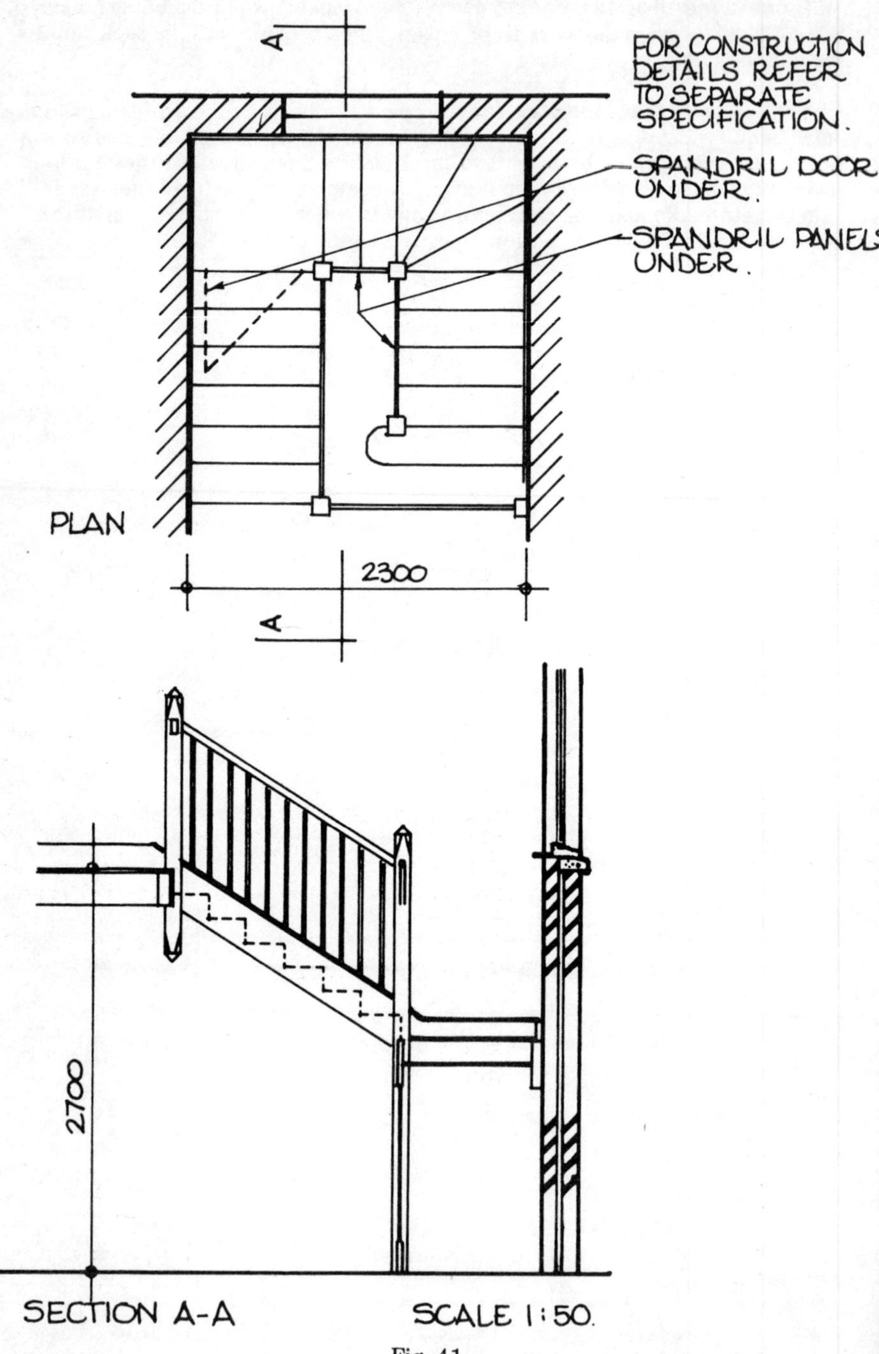

Fig. 41

	1		Staircase in softwood (unless otherwise stated) 900 mm wide & 2700 mm rise in three flights with 13 treads, 3 winders, 1 quarter space landing & 18 risers, with 250 mm going & 150 mm rise, of:- 32 mm Treads & winders with rounded nosing & small bedmould 25 mm Risers tongued & grooved with treads All glued blocked & bracketed to 50x100 mm sawn carriages 32 mm Landing with nosing & bedmould as above & 50x100 mm softwood bearers Semicircular end to bottom tread with circular riser 32x250 mm Moulded wall string plugged 38x250 mm Moulded outer string 32x125 mm Moulded skirting to landing Four balustrades, three raking & one level 100x100 mm Newels with cap & design, the bottoms dowelled or with drop to match cap 100x63 mm Half newels to match, plugged & screwed 25x38 mm Balusters 63x75 mm Mahogany fully moulded handrails 32 mm Moulded & square panelled spandrel framing under two flights (contd)

			(contd) 25x200 mm Moulded apron lining 25x75 mm Rounded nosing above top riser & apron lining all assembled & framed & wedged together as Drg 2	1600 2500 3000 1800 8900 1200 500 1700 3400
	3.40 .45		KPS & ③ on wood wkg	120 40 250 40 450 Outer string
	8.90 .40			Newels
11/8 /	.90 .40			Spandrils one side
11/8 /	.40 1.35			
	1.80		Do skirtings etc 150-300 mm girth	
2/	1.10			winders
	.60			
2/	.90			landing
	2.00			
	1.80		Do general surfaces 150-300 mm girth	Half newel
	1.30			apron
30/	.85		Do do not exceeding 150 mm girth	7 3 11 9 30 bals

Dimensions	Description
1.20	Wax polish hardwood handrail 150–300 mm girth
.50	
1.70	
1.30	

Door & frame to cupboard under stairs to take with doors

Dimensions	Description
1.20 .90	22 g. Expanded metal lathing to ceilings in staircases
.60 .90	&
.90 .90	Plaster, float & set on metal lathing (measured separately) to ceilings in staircases
1.80 .90	&
	Twice emulsion plastered ceilings
1.10 1.10	22 g. Eml. a.b. to flewing ceilings in staircases
	&
	P.f.&s. on eml. a.b. to flewing ceilings in staircases
	&
	Twice emulsion plas clgs
.90 .15	22 g Eml a.b. to clgs a.b. not exceeding 300 mm wide in staircase {at foot of bottom slope
	&
	Pf&s on eml ab to clgs n.e 300 mm wide in staircases

Dimensions	Description
.90 .15	Twice emulsion plas clgs a.b.
.90	Labour arris in staircases {at foot of top slope

EXAMPLE 29

WALL CUPBOARD

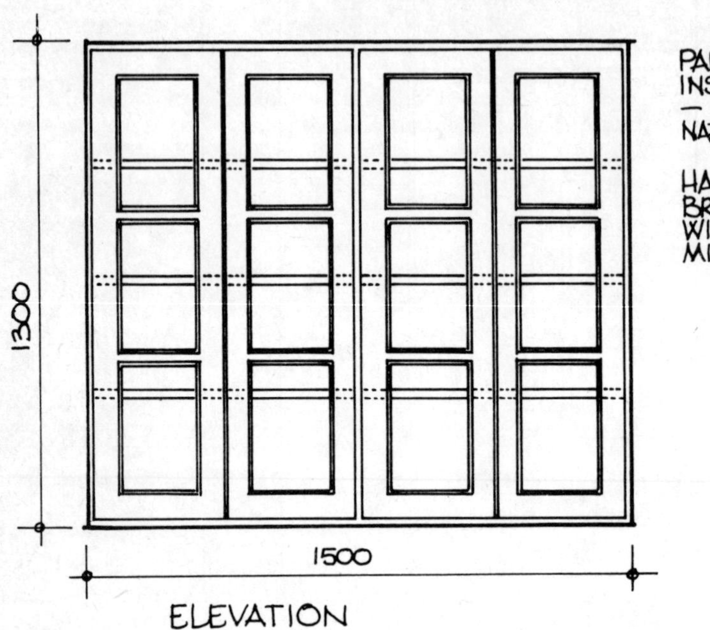
PAINT CUPBD. INSIDE & OUT — SHELVES LEFT NATURAL FINISH.
HANG UNIT TO BRICK WALLS WITH 3No BRASS MIRROR PLATES.
1300
1500
ELEVATION

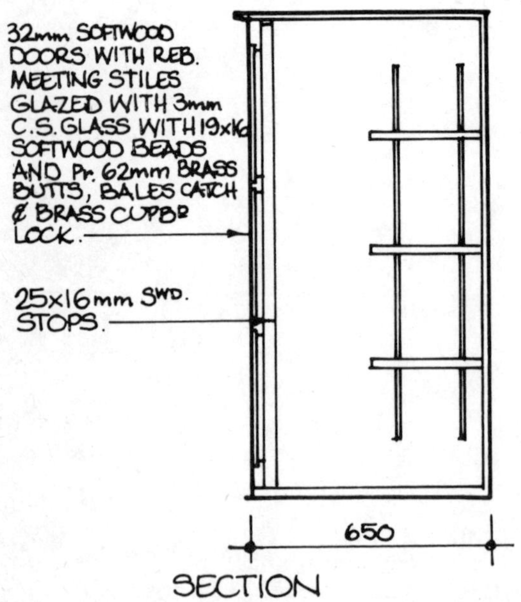
32mm SOFTWOOD DOORS WITH REB. MEETING STILES GLAZED WITH 3mm C.S. GLASS WITH 19x16 SOFTWOOD BEADS AND Pr. 62mm BRASS BUTTS, BALES CATCH & BRASS CUPBD LOCK.
25x16mm SWD. STOPS.
25mm BLOCKBOARD TOP, BOTTOM, ENDS & DIVISION WITH 32x19mm HARDWOOD LIPPINGS TO TOP & BOTTOM LEADING EDGES.
12mm PLY BACK SET IN REBATE IN BLOCKBOARD.
25mm BLOCKBD SHELVES 300mm WIDE HWD. LIPPED FRONT EDGES ON C.P. BOOKCASE STRIP.
650
SECTION
SCALE 1:20

Fig. 42

Timesing	Dimensions	Squaring	Description
	1		Supply wall cupboard 1500 x 650 x 1300 mm high with adjustable shelves and ironmongery all as Drawing X (glass & paint measured separately)
			&
			Fix wall cupboard 1500 x 650 x 1300 high including adjustable shelves, all as Drawing X on three 38 mm brass mirror plates plugged & screwed (glass & paint measured separately)
			650 / 25 / 675 650 / 40 / 25 / 40 / 755
	1.50 / .76		KPS & (3) utility general surfaces of woodwork { top outside
2/	.68 / 1.30		{ sides outside
2/	1.43 / .66		top inside 650 / 12 / 638 / 2/13 26 / 664 3/25 1500 / 75 / 1425 / 4/2/664 2656 / 4081
	4.08 / 1.25		bott inside 638 / 25 / 663 backs 1300 sides 2/25 50 inside 1250

Timesing	Dimensions	Squaring	Description
2/	1.43 / 1.25		KPs & (3) utility glazed doors in small panes Back 1300 Base 650 1950
	1.50 / 1.95		Prime only backs of joinery
12/	.22 / .33		3 mm Clear sheet glass & glazing to wood with beads (measured separately)

Alternative

Include the provisional sum of £______ for the supply of No 1 wall cupboard 1500 x 650 x 1300 mm high.

COUNTER

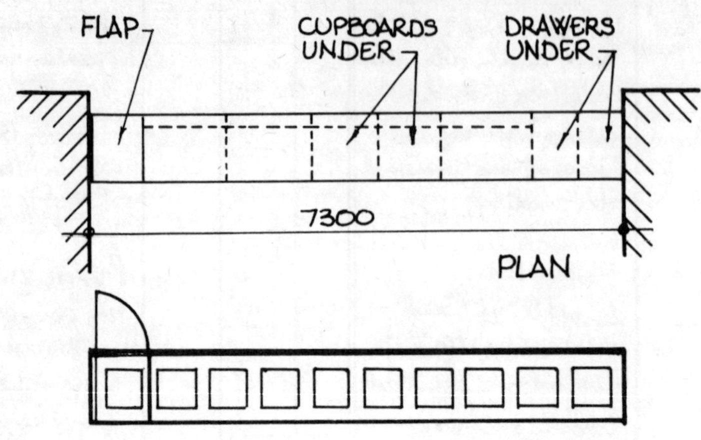

ELEVATION

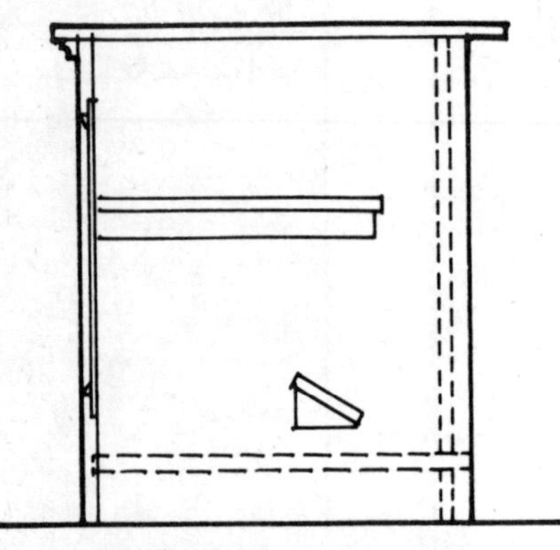

SECTION SHOWING CUPBOARDS DOTTED.

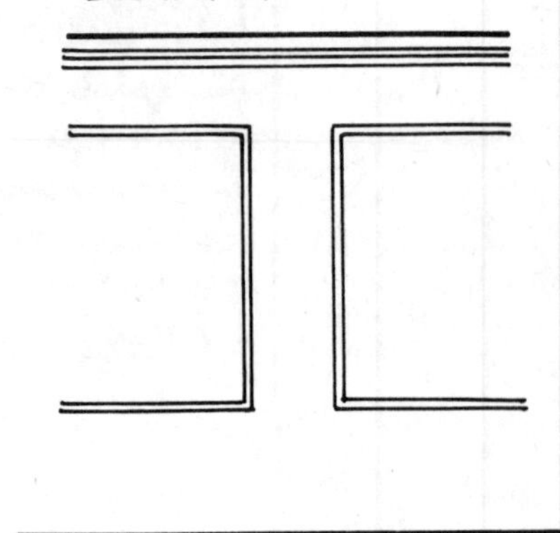

PART ELEVATION

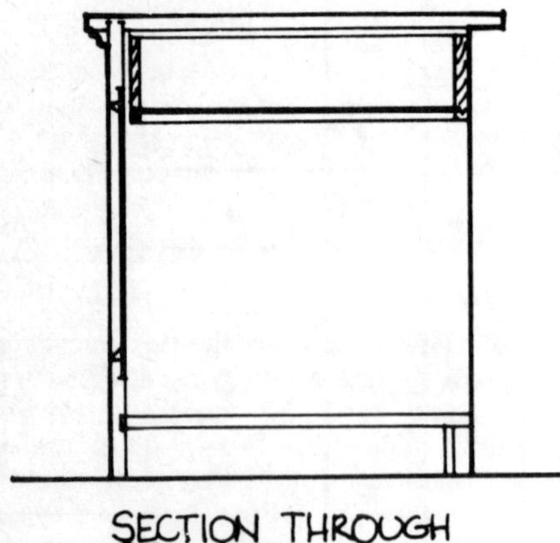

SECTION THROUGH DRAWER.

SCALES 1:100 & 1:20.

CONSTRUCTION NOTES.

1. THE TOP & FRONT TO BE 32mm ENGLISH OAK WITH 16mm PANELS MOULDING AROUND PANELS TO BE WORKED ON THE SOLID. OTHER MOULDS TO BE PLANTED.
2. THE SHELVING, BOTTOMS & CUPB DOORS TO BE 25mm BLOCKBOAR
3. FOOTRESTS TO BE 25mm OAK.
4. THE DRAWERS TO BE SOFTWOO WITH 32mm FRONT, 25mm SIDE & BACK & 4mm PLY BOTTOM.
5. OAK TO BE WAX POLISHED, S/W D TO BE PAINTED.
6. ALL IRONMONGERY TO BE BRA

Fig. 43

Timesing	Dimensions	Squaring	Description
	1		Supply counter 7300 x 900 x 950 mm high with 32 mm oak top with flap & backflap hinges, and 32 mm oak panelled front with doors with hinges & bales catch, three sections with shelf & 25 mm oak footrest, two sections with shelf, door, bottom & riser under the doors with bales catch & lock, two sections with drawer, bottom & riser, the drawers with runners & lock, 25 mm blockboard ends & divisions, top & front finished for polish, remainder for paint, all as Dwg Y
			&
			Fix counter 7300 x 900 x 950 mm high with oak top & front cupboards & drawers including plugging (polishing top & front & painting measured separately)
	7.30 1.00		Wax polish general surfaces of oak — 900 / 32 / 40 / 32 / 1004 {top
	.70 .92		950 / 32 / 918 {u/s flap
1 1/8/	7.30 .92		{front o.s.
1 1/8/	.70 .92		{door back

Timesing	Dimensions	Squaring	Description
3/ 1/4/	.75 .92		K.P.S. & (3) wood intly {under flap {where shelves
2/2/	.75 .60		1750 / 2/25 50 / 2)1700 / 850 / edge 25 / 825 {where drawers (not inside cupds)
2/2/	.88 .92		918 / 125 / 793 / 25 / 818 {doors
2/	.60		Do 150-300 mm girth {drawer front
2/	.85		Do skirting not exceeding 150 mm girth {risers
2/	.60		
			Shelves & bottoms left clean

CHAPTER 15

INTERNAL PLUMBING, HOT WATER AND GAS SERVICES

References to S.M.M.

D	13.8
F	9
G	12, 49, 51
N	29
R	1–5, 9–16, 22–29, 37
T	11, 19, 33
V	1–2, 7, 10

Subdivision.—The measurement of Internal Plumbing will be considerably simplified if it is dealt with in definite subsections. A logical method of measuring is to take the work in an order following the passage of water from the main in the road till it discharges into the drains, the sections required by the S.M.M. R 4.1b and c being subdivided thus:

Sanitary Installation

(a) Sanitary fittings.

(b) Waste, soil and vent pipes.

Cold Water Installation

(a) Connection to main and service up to boundary of site.

(b) Rising main.

(c) Branches from do. (i.e. drinking water services, hose points, etc.).

(d) Cistern and work in connection.

(e) Down services from cistern to the various fittings.

An early idea of the general lay-out is best obtained by starting with the sanitary fittings (a) above, followed by (b) continuing with water services (a), and completing the group at (e).

Preparing the Drawings.—It will be found a good plan if, before beginning to measure Internal Plumbing, all sanitary fittings are coloured with a coloured pencil or chalk, unless they are already coloured distinctively. They will then stand out and one is much less likely to miss a fitting, not a difficult thing to do when working on uncoloured drawings or drawings where a w.c. is coloured brown, the same colour as shelving and fittings. The sanitary fittings being thus marked, the position of the main storage cistern must be settled, if this is not marked. It should be placed as centrally as possible in relation to the fittings on plan, and in a convenient position for rising main and down services to run in an unobtrusive position on the wall faces under. Most important, it must have some walls or other supports strong enough to carry its weight and suitably placed to take the ends of cistern bearers. These may appear to be matters for the architect, but it sometimes happens that such points have not been considered. The cistern being placed, the lay-out of services should be drawn on the plans in pencil, or better still in coloured pen, the rising main and drinking services being represented by a different colour from the general down services. The Water Board's regulations should be obtained, as it will often be found that there are special requirements as to weights of pipes, stamping fittings, etc.

Fittings.—A schedule should first be made of all fittings classified by floors, special care being taken to see that it is complete, as the discovery of an additional fitting while measuring involves waste of time. If the p.c. for fittings is to be inserted as a lump sum, this schedule can be priced to arrive at that sum when there is no special estimate obtained. The fittings can either be dealt with by a lump sum followed by a list giving particulars of fixing, or each fitting can be numbered with a p.c. price and the fixing described with it unless fluctuations are being dealt with by using the Price Adjustment Formula which inhibits the p.c. in the description device. The measurement of the fittings should be followed by any work in connection with the fittings, such as backboards, paint, etc. Flush pipes to w.c.s, being a connection of two parts of the fitting, may be measured here, in the unlikely event of this not being supplied with the fitting.

Waste and Soil and Vent Pipes.—The fittings themselves being dealt with, the next section will be their wastes. These may be taken in groups, such as:

(1) Ground Floor sinks, basins, etc., having wastes discharging direct to gullies.

(2) Upper Floor sinks, basins, etc., with branch wastes and main stack pipes.

(3) Ground Floor w.c.s or other soil fittings connected direct to drain.

(4) Upper Floor do. with branch soil and main stack pipes.

Ground Floor w.c.s will probably only require an overflow pipe from the cistern, the cement joint to drain being taken with the Drains or included in the description of fixing, but it sometimes happens that such w.c.s are some distance above ground level; this must be watched, as the connection may have to be made with lead or iron pipe to the drain or to a main stack pipe. Except where w.c.s are connected direct to drain, the waste to gully or branch waste or soil pipe will be taken first with trap at one end (or joint only if trap is supplied with fitting, as is usual in the case of baths and w.c.s) and joint or other finish to the other end. The requirements of the S.M.M. as to bends, connectors, etc., must be borne in mind. The branch pipes being taken, the main stack pipe will follow, again taking pipe, finish to top, finish to bottom and any intermediate bends, branches, etc. Antisiphon or puff pipes will follow the waste and soil pipes, measured in the same way. In most modern fittings overflows are part of the fitting (except to flushing cisterns and baths), but separate overflow pipes required must be measured. An item to be looked for is the main vent pipe to the top of a drainage system, which may be purely a vent having no soil branches into it, and so possibly might be missed. It may be measured either with the Plumbing or Drains, but as probably similar pipes will be measured with the Plumbing it would be more convenient to measure it there.

Main Water Supply.—The provisional sum for Water Board's charges may be for tapping the main only or for the whole of the work up to the boundary of the property. In the former case the pipe laid in the road must be measured, but as in many districts the Local Authority would require to make good the damage to roadway themselves, and the Water Board may require to put in the main themselves up to their stop cock on the boundary, it is best either to ascertain exactly what the two Authorities will require or to include everything up to the boundary in the provisional sum. From here the service will be measured to the cistern, finishing with the ball valve and not forgetting stop cocks inside and outside the building, the latter probably with a stop cock box and brick pit. S.M.M. R 4.1c requires pipes carrying boosted cold water supply to be classified separately from ordinary distribution pipes. In the example following distinction is made between 'main service' and 'service' in the descriptions.

If no specification is supplied it should be ascertained whether the architect prefers or the local conditions require iron or copper services. In dealing with copper services it must be remembered that the brass or gunmetal fittings are the expensive part, and these must be accurately described. The correct terms with illustrations will be found in makers' lists.

Drinking Services.—Every habitable building, whether domestic or industrial, should have a supply of water direct from the main for drinking purposes. Unless a full specification is supplied it will probably be left to the surveyor to decide where these points are to be measured, the kitchen sink in a domestic building and the lavatories where there is no kitchen being usually the most convenient places. A separate stop cock should be measured on these branches in buildings of any size, so that the whole water supply need not be cut off to re-washer a tap. The branches will usually terminate with a bib cock and joint but these bib cocks are often included in the p.c. sum for sanitary fittings, as the architect may like to choose a particular type. In such a case the joint only will be measured, and any additional fixing described. For a kitchen sink the drinking supply will probably be connected to the normal cold tap, so that a separate tap will not be required. It may be that all the cold supply is direct from the main, the storage tank serving only as a feed tank to the hot-water installation.

Cistern, etc.—In taking the cistern the following must be considered in addition to the cistern itself:

(a) Bearers.

(b) Casing and/or cover.

(c) Overflow.

(d) Safe.

Down Services.—The down services must be followed systematically from the point where they leave the cistern to the end of each service, their course then being retraced and all branches measured, and the joint to the fitting measured with each branch. There will invariably be a stop cock on each separate down service close to the cistern, and additional stop cocks will be taken according to specification.

Pipes in Chases or Ducts.—Where pipes are to be fixed in chases or ducts they must be kept separate from those fixed on the surface, as extra labour is involved in the fixing (S.M.M. R 10.4).

Holes through Walls, etc.—With all services, wastes, overflows or other pipes must be measured all holes required through walls and the extra labour to finishings on each side. There is often a considerable difference in cost (especially in the case of large pipes) between a hole which the contractor can leave when he is building a wall and the hole he must cut out after the wall is built and which he must 'make good'.

This term 'making good' is apt to be used with two meanings. Strictly it means the repair of work that is damaged and its restoration to a good condition (e.g. where a hole is cut through an existing wall). It has also been used, rather loosely, to refer to such labour as working and finishing plaster around pipes already in position. The confusion is caused by the difficulty in knowing beforehand whether a given pipe will be in position before plastering is done. Factors such as delay in decisions on design, delay in delivery of materials or efficiency of the contractor's organisation may all affect the matter.

It is evident that the extent, and therefore value, of the labour will vary, but the surveyor cannot discriminate (except in the case of alterations necessarily made in existing work), and will measure the item of making good in all cases. It will be left to the contractor to decide whether he will risk pricing holes through walls as if they could be left, or whether he will price for cutting out after building. In the same way it is left to him to decide whether plaster or other finish can be worked round a pipe or whether it will have to be cut away and made good. He may choose to price at a rate between the two, having regard to the proportion he thinks he will have to cut out.

Where holes are definitely in existing walls or through existing plaster, &c., they should be clearly so defined, so that the contractor shall know that there is no question of his being able to leave the holes and work his normal plaster round the pipe.

Sundry Work.—The measurement of the 'Plumbing' section will conclude with sundry items in connection, such as:

(a) Paint on pipes.

(b) Wrapping pipes.

(c) Pipe casing.

(d) Draining boards.

(e) Glazed tiling behind fittings.

The first three might be measured with their respective pipes, but as they may apply to either main service, down service or wastes, the number of dimensions will be reduced if they can be measured together, thus saving work in the abstract. On the other hand, especially in an extensive scheme, the runs of pipes are more clearly in mind whilst they are being measured than at the end. Draining boards may have been measured with the 'Fittings' section and glazed tiling with 'Internal Finishings', though being so closely in connection with sanitary fittings it may be considered best for them to be measured with the 'Plumbing'.

Hot Water Services.—These may be measured at the end of the 'Plumbing' as a separate subsection, though when they are the subject of an estimate by a specialist firm, also probably carrying out a central heating installation, they would be dealt with in the section specially allotted to engineering services. The following divisions must be borne in mind in measuring:

(a) Cold feed from main cistern.

(b) Boiler and work in connection (base, etc.).

(c) Cylinder or tank and main flow and return from boiler.

(d) Secondary circulation (if any), expansion pipe and branch-services.

(e) Connections to fittings, possibly with a short length of pipe of a different material, with stop cocks to each if specified.

(f) Holes, paint, etc., as for cold services, the casing of pipes and sometimes of the boiler being especially important.

The hot water service dimensions should not be mixed up with other plumbing work, as this installation must be kept separate in the bill.

Gas Services.—These may form another subsection of the 'Plumbing' dimensions, but again should be kept distinct to form a separate section in the bill. It will usually be found that the Gas Authority require to do all work up to the meter, so the provisional sum should be arranged accordingly, the measurements beginning from this point. It may, however, be necessary for the builder to dig the trench inside the boundary of the property, in which case this must be measured. The necessary attendance on the Gas Authority's engineers must be provided for and any meter shelf, etc., measured. The runs of services should be laid out on the plans as a record of how the services were measured, a distinctive coloured pen being used to prevent confusion with water services. It must be ascertained whether fires, cookers, etc., and their fixing are to be included or whether they will be dealt with as furnishings outside the contract.

Example.—In the following example the incoming main is measured as in lead, the rising main and wastes in copper and the down service in galvanised steel. In practice the Water Authority may insist on the outside main being in lead or 'underground' copper, but the internal pipes are likely to be all in the same material, probably copper or plastic. Galvanised steel is only introduced here for the benefit of an example. Plastic pipes are measured in the same way as copper.

It will be seen from S.M.M. R 3.6 that pipes are to be kept separate according to background. In this example it has been assumed that all are fixed to plastered brick walls.

EXAMPLE 31

INTERNAL PLUMBING

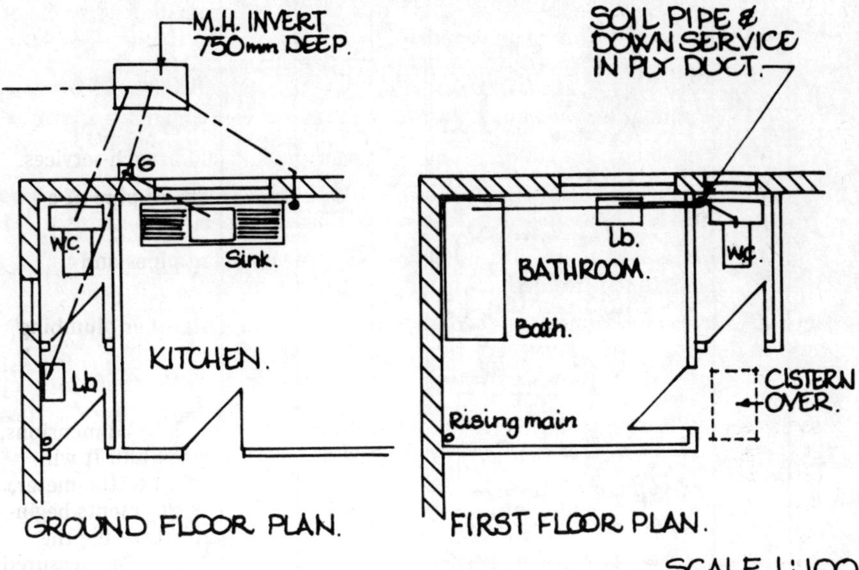

Fig. 44

		Provide the net pc sum of £ ___ for connection to water main & service up to boundary of site	1		12 mm Soldered joint to fitting {Water Co's sc
		Add for profit	1		12 mm Brass screw down stop cock with crutch handle & two soldered joints &
		Attend a.d.			Cast iron stop cock box with hinged locking cover &
		External Water Main			Stop cock pit 100×100 ×1000 mm deep in clear with 100 mm concrete base & half brick sides in foundation bricks in cement mortar, including excavation & disposal & holes for pipe.
18.50		12 mm lead main service to comply with BS. 602 table 1 weighing 7lb per yard lineal & laying in trench &			
		Excavate trench for 12mm lead service starting at ground level 750 mm deep including earthwork support filling & removing surplus			

	Dimension	Description
	1	Hole for small pipe through 1½B wall & making good.
		&
		Do through 150 mm concrete bed & do
		&
		Cut & fit quarry tile paving around pipe not exceeding ·30 m girth
		Rising Main
	1	12 mm Brass combined stop cock & drain cock with soldered joint to lead & union & joint to copper pipe
(Copper pipes etc have outside diameters)		GF - 1st F 2600 1st F 200 1st F - Clg 2600 5400
	5.40	15 mm Copper service to comply with B.S. 2871 Table X with capillary fittings & fixing to walls in tly
		&
		(2) copper pipe not exceeding 150 mm girth
		2.600 rnx 500 3100
	3.10	15 mm Copper service a.b. in roof space

Dimension	Description
3.10	Wrapping 15 mm copper pipe with glass wool strips a.d.
3	Made bend in 15 mm copper pipe
1	13 mm High pressure equilibrium ball valve to comply with BS1212 with brass stem, fly nu[t] & union & copper ball, with straight coupling with joint to copper & screwed joint to cistern
1	13 mm Brass stop cock & two joints to copper
2	Hole for pipe not exceeding ·30 m girth in plaster lat[h]
	&
	Making good plaste[r] around pipe not exceeding ·30 m gi[rth]
1	Hole for pipe throug[h] 25 mm softwood floor

Timesing	Dimension	Squaring	Description
			Branch to Cloaks basin & Kitchen sink
2/	1		Extra for 15mm square tee
			3200 2200 Rise to fitting 2/700 1400 6800
	6.80		15mm Copper service to walls ab & (2) copper pipe ne 150 mm gth
	1		Extra for 15 mm elbow {corner
2/	2		made bend in 15mm copper pipe {at fttgs
2/	1		13 mm Straight tap connector with screwed joint to fitting & joint to copper
	2		Hole for small pipe through 75 mm block partition & making good
2/	2		Make good plaster around pipe ab.
			Cistern
	1		Galvanised mild steel rivetted storage cistern 60 gallons capacity to water line, to BS417 type C9, holed for four pipes.

Timesing	Dimension	Squaring	Description
			(Bearers, casing etc follow here)
	1.50		28mm Copper overflow pipe & fixing in roof space
	2		made bend in 28 mm pipe
	1		28 mm Tank connector with screwed joint & joint to copper. & Splay cut end to 28 mm copper pipe with brass hinged flap & frame soldered in & Hole for small pipe through roof tiling & fixing lead slate supplied by Plumber & Code 5 lead slate 300 x 300mm holed for & soldered to 28 mm copper pipe, for fixing by Tiler (measured separately)
			Down Services
	1		Connect 25 mm steel tubing to cistern with nuts & washers & 25mm Stopcock with two joints to steel tubing.

Timesing	Dimension	Squaring	Description
	2.50		25 mm Galvanised steel tubing to BS 1387 medium weight with screwed joints in approved compound & fixing in roof space & Wrapping 25 mm steel pipe ab. to stg 2600 under bath 3000 5600
	5.60		25 mm Galvanised steel tubing ab. & fixing to walls with clips to keep pipe 12 mm clear of plaster face 5600 Less in duct 2600 3000
	3.00		(3) Dntly galvanised pipe not exceeding 150 mm girth 300 1700 2000
	2.00		13 mm Do (on to GF WC & (3) Dntly galv pipe ne 150 mm girth
	1		Extra for 25 mm square reducing tee (Bath
	2		(1st Fl Basin & Hx

Timesing	Dimension	Squaring	Description
	2		Extra for 25 mm elbow (Ente & lea du &
			Do 13 mm do (GFu
2/	.60		13 mm Galv tubing to walls ab (1 WC 1 Basin & (3) galv pipe ab
	.60		20 mm Galv tubing to walls (Bath inside csg
2/	2		Extra for 13 mm elbow
	2		Do for 20 mm do (Bath
3/	1		Join 13 mm tubing to fitting including connector (2 WC 1 Basin
	1		Do 20 mm do (Bath
	2		Hole for pipe not exceeding 30 m girth in plaster lath & Making good plaster around pipe not exceeding 30 mm girth
	1		Hole for pipe through 25 mm softwood floor & Hole for 20 mm pipe through 16 mm laminated plastic faced blockboard bath panel

	Quantity	Description
	1	Hole for s.p. thro 75 mm block ptn & m.g. (1st F WC
	2	m.g. plas. and pipe n.e. .30 m gth ab.
		Fittings
		Allow the p.c. sum of £ ____ for Sanitary Fittings
		Add for profit
		Fix the following including assembly (joints to services & wastes measured)
	1	Stainless steel sink & double drainer & setting on base unit
	1	Pair 12 mm chromium plated pillar valves
	2	White glazed vitreous china lavatory basin with waste fitting, two valves & pair of cantilever brackets (cutting & pinning measured separately)
	1	Rectangular top white porcelain enamelled cast iron bath with adjustable legs, waste fitting, two valves and brass trap

	Quantity	Description
	1	Low level WC suite with white glazed fireclay pan & trap plastic cistern with concealed brackets & chromium plated flush pipe including screwing pan to wood floor & plugging & screwing brackets to brickwork
	1	Do including plugging & screwing pan to concrete floor & do.
		W.C.s
2/	1	Mastic joint of W.C. pan to drain
	1	Cut & fit quarry tile paving around W.C. pan .30 - 1.00 m girth (G.F. only
2/	.60	22 mm Copper overflow pipe
2/	1	Made bend in 22 mm copper pipe & Hole for small pipe through 250 mm brick hollow wall & making good facings & Making good plaster around pipe not exceeding .30 m girth

Times	Dimension	Description
2/	1	22 mm Connector with screwed joint to cistern & joint to copper
		&
		Splay cut end to 22 mm copperpipe with brass hinged flap & frame soldered in
		Basins
2/	2	Cutting & pinning brackets to brickwork & making good
		&
		(3) Steel brackets
		&
		Making good plaster around bracket not exceeding 300 mm girth
		Bath
	1	16 mm Laminated plastic faced block-board bath panel with compensating veneer 1680 × 500 mm fixed with chromium plated screws with loose dome heads
	1	Do 700 × 500 mm do
	1	25×25×3 mm Black plastic angle 500 mm long countersunk holed & screwed with stainless steel screws

Times	Dimension	Description
2/	1.68	38×50 mm Wrot softwood bearers to bath panels
2/	.70	
1.3/	.50	
	.50	50×50 mm Do (angle)
	.35	35 mm Copper overflow pipe
	2	Made bend in 35 mm copper pipe
	2	35 mm Connector with screwed joint & joint to copper {connected to bath overflow & side of bath trap
		Soil Pipe GF 2600 1st F 2600 Roof 600 Above 450 6250
	6.25	100 mm Diameter cast iron socketted soil & vent pipe with molten lead joints & fix. to walls in duct internally with holderbats (measured separately)
	1	Cement joint to stoneware drain
	1	Extra for 89 mm branch with bolted access door {1st F WC

Timesing	Dimension	Description
	1	Extra for screwed boss to 100 mm pipe lapped 32 mm {1st F basin
		&
		Do lapped 38 mm {1st F bath
	4	Hinged holderbat to 100 mm pipe plugged & screwed to wall
	1	Galvanised wire balloon grating in top of 100 mm pipe
		&
		Hole for large pipe through roof tiling & fixing lead slate supplied by Plumber
		&
		Code 5 lead slate 450 x 450 mm with hole for & collar dressed up & around & into joint of 100 mm cast iron pipe, for fixing by Tiler (measured separately)
		<u>Wastes to Sink, Basins & Baths</u>
	2	32 mm Chromium plated brass bottle trap with black plastic base & joint to fitting. {Basins
	1	38 mm Do {sink {bath trap {w.p.c.

Timesing	Dimension	Description
	.60 1.50	35 mm Copper waste with capillary fitting & fixing to walls {GF basin {1st F do
		&
		(2) Ditto copper pipe not exceeding 150 mm length
	3.00 .80	42 mm Copper waste as last {Bath {Sink
2/	2	Made bend in 35 mm pipe
2/	2	Do in 42 mm do.
	1	54 x 35 mm Caulking bush with screwed joint to copper & caulked lead joint to cast iron drain {GF basin
	1	54 x 42 mm Do {sink
	2	Cut & fit quarry tile paving around pipe not exceeding .30 m girth
	1	35 mm Connector with screwed joint & joint to copper {basin to stack
	1	42 mm Do {bath to stack
	2	Hole for s.p. thro 75 mm block ptn at. {1st F WC
2/	2	Mg plas ard pipe ne .30 m gth at.
	1	Hole for 42 mm pipe thro 16 mm bath panel at.

{holes thro duct casing m'sd with ducts

Test all pipes & fittings in Cold Water Installation

Do in Sanitary Installation

(Here may follow glazed tiling behind fittings, Kitchen fittings & any other work conveniently taken with the plumbing)

(Hot water services assumed part of the central heating sub-contract. Show connections & other builders' work measured in the appropriate section)

CHAPTER 16

DRAINAGE

References to S.M.M.

B 11
W 1–9

Subdivision.—Drainage is naturally divided into:

(a) soil drains,

(b) rainwater drains,

where these are separate systems, as is often the case. The measurement of each system is then best kept distinct on a scheme of any size, even if the specification is the same in both cases, as this separation simplifies the tracing of any particular length of drain in the dimensions. Manholes, however, would usually be measured together whether on the rainwater or soil system, as indeed they often must be where adjoining manholes have a common wall. In each complete system the following subsections may be used:

(a) Main drains between manholes working from the top of the drain downwards.

(b) Branches in the same sequence.

(c) Gullies, shoes, etc., to top of branches.

(d) Manholes.

(e) Fresh air inlet and interceptor (if any).

(f) Vent to top of drains (if not measured with 'Plumbing').

(g) Connection to sewer and drain from last manhole to sewer.

A check should be made to see that every rainwater, soil or waste pipe measured has a drain for it on the plan, as one may quite easily be missed by the draughtsman.

Drain Pipes.—The measurement of the normal drain is in three parts:

(a) Excavation.

(b) Bed and flaunching or encasing.

(c) Pipe and joints.

Three separate items are required by the S.M.M., even though the lengths may be the same. There would probably be a difference between the lengths of pipes and the other two parts because certain lengths inside the building up to w.c.s, etc., are without excavation, though encased in concrete.

It often happens that two drains run close to each other and can be put in one trench, a treatment which may be either cheaper or dearer according to circumstances. If they can be put next to each other, the wider trench necessary for this will probably be narrower than the combined width of two trenches, thus saving digging, concrete, and earthwork support. If, however, the distance between drains is regulated by the fact that they have to pass through adjoining manholes, and therefore must be, say, 0.75 m centre to centre, the single trench will probably be wider than the sum of the widths of two normal trenches, thus involving additional cost, and, owing to the narrow strip of earth which would be left between two separate trenches, it may be practically necessary to make one such large trench.

In order to arrive at the average depths of digging for each length of drain it will be necessary to mark on the plan the levels of invert and adjoining ground at each manhole. The average depth of lengths between manholes can be arrived at from these levels, and that of lengths from gullies, etc., to manholes in a similar way, the digging at the gully end being assumed as about 500 mm deep from the ordinary type of gully. It must be remembered that allowance in depth of digging must be made for the thickness of concrete bed below invert levels. It will be noted that earthwork support is included with the item and not measured separately. It will be seen from S.M.M. W 3 that average depth of drain excavation is to be classified in stages of 2.00 m. The intention is that if, say, a length of drain runs from 0.50 to 2.50 m deep, that portion from 0.50 to 2.00 m shall be measured as average 1.25 m deep. The length from 2.00 to 2.50 m deep will be measured as average 2.25 m deep. It would not be correct to measure the whole length from 0.50 to 2.50 m deep together and describe it as average 1.50 m deep.

Bends.—There is sometimes some difficulty in deciding how many bends to take in a drain. In view of the face that bends of all types are usually classified together of whatever angle or length, it sometimes happens that what appears to be one bend on paper would require two 'easy' bends in practice. In the same way it may be found that the foreman on the works will try to impress on the surveyor how the particular type of gully used required two bends to get away from it, when only one had been measured to each gully. Where a gully is in two pieces the trap can be turned in the required direction whilst the upper part and grating are kept square with the building, and therefore one bend should be sufficient, and if the fall on the drain is slight, possibly none at all. On the other hand if the gully is in one piece and it is required to keep the grating square with the building, two bends may be needed, one for direction and the other for fall, although again if the direction happens to be right and the fall slight no bends may be used, the fall being obtained by making use of the play in the socket. The only rule is to anticipate the reasonable requirements, having regard to all the conditions, and measure accordingly.

Gullies.—Unless of ordinary type these are best referred to by makers' catalogue number, the catalogue being examined for any possible varieties of the same type of gully. For instance, the gully may be made in two sizes, and, if so, the description in the dimensions must specify which size, and gratings if galvanised must be so described. The number of inlets must be stated, but it is unnecessary to separate a gully with a back inlet from one with a side inlet, as the extra charge is normally the same in each case. There is, however, a slight difference in price between horizontal and vertical inlets, on which account it may be considered necessary to make a distinction. It must be remembered that specially heavy gratings are necessary where subject to traffic and that a yard gully with a drain inlet must have a raising piece varying in height according to the depth of the inlet.

Manholes.—A schedule of the manholes should be made on the dimension paper before measuring, giving reference number, size, depth to invert, particulars, etc. Sizes of manholes may not be shown or specified, and in such a case these must be decided. They should be of brick dimension and of sufficient size to accommodate the channels required. Extra size will also be necessary in deep manholes for access. One dimension, but not more, should be averaged, e.g. in the case of 6 manholes of the same size on plan the excavation for one manhole can be put down, using the average depth and timesed by 6. It may seem to simplify matters in measuring, say, six manholes to work out the average length, width and depth of the six, and then to measure as one (except as regards channels or other differences), timesing all dimensions by 6. This is, of course, not mathematically correct, and if there is any big divergence in actual sizes may lead to a not inconsiderable error*.

The work will be measured according to the general rules, except that the disposal of earth and earthwork support might be included with the item, as in the case of drain excavation. Main channels and branch channels will be numbered, no distinction being made for the angle at which the latter enter the manhole. The whole of the work should be taken under a heading, giving the total number of manholes, as the items will all be kept together in the bill.

Connection to Sewer.—As in the case of the water main it is probably best to cover all work up to the boundary of the property, or in this case the last manhole which will be near the boundary, by the provisional sum. Some Local Authorities will require to do the whole of this work themselves, others will only put in a saddle and expect the builder to do the rest, whilst some will expect the builder to do even that under their supervision. Definite information should be available as to the requirements of the case, but, if not, the boundary or last manhole makes a reasonable point from which to start the measured work.

Testing.—A clause to cover the cost of testing drains should be inserted in the bill, but being often written at the end it may be forgotten if not mentioned in the dimensions. A note written across the columns, 'Testing as Spec.' or 'Testing as usual', will prevent this clause being overlooked. Drains must usually be tested twice, once during the progress of the work and again on completion.

---

*See page 33.

EXAMPLE 32

DRAINAGE

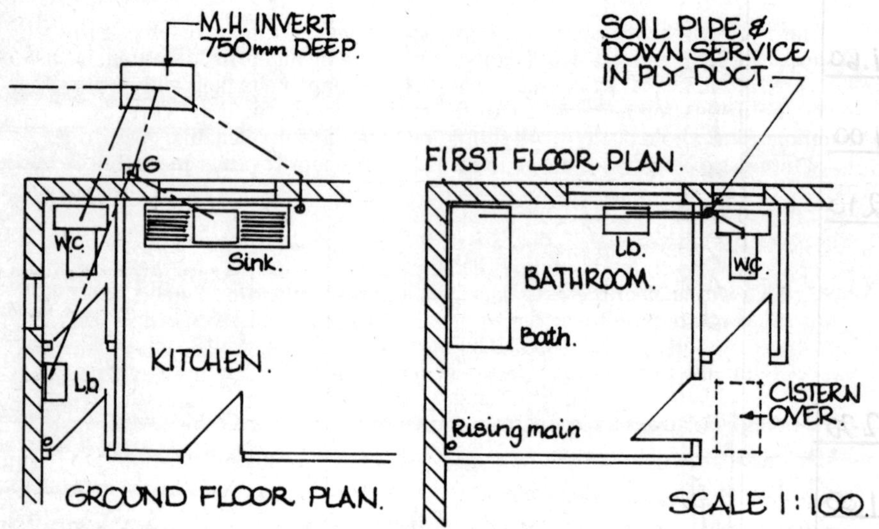

Fig. 44

		Prices for excavating trenches shall include for earthwork support, grading & compacting bottoms, filling in & compacting & removing surplus from site
		Branches into m.h. 750 / 450 / 2) 1200 / 600 / concrete 100 / 700
1.60 / 1.00 / 2.10		Excavate trench for drain not exceeding 200 mm diameter, not exceeding 2.00 m deep & average .75 m deep (WC / gulley / soil)
2.20 / 1.00 / 2.70		100 mm Stoneware drain laid & jointed as described in runs not exceeding 3.00 m (in No 3)
		100 mm = 125 / 2/150 300 / 425
1.60 / 1.00 / 2.10		425 × 100 mm Concrete (1:3:6) bed under 100 mm drain & 425 × average 65 mm Concrete (1:3:6) Benching to sides of 100 mm pipe

2/	.60	Conc (1:3:6) casing 100 mm thick all round 100 mm pipe (W.C. & soil pipe inside bldg)
3/	2	Extra for bend in 100 mm pipe
	1	Hole for large pipe through 1½ B wall & making good & Do through 150 mm concrete bed & do
	1	Stoneware trapped gulley with 100 mm outlet, 225 mm diameter raising piece 225 mm high with 100 mm back & side inlets, 100 × 50 mm reducing sockets set in inlets, & galvanised grating & setting in & surrounding with concrete, jointing to drain, & extra excavation
		Branches into gulley
	1.40 / 2.20	Excavate trench for drain not exceeding 200 mm diameter, not exceeding 2.00 m deep & average .25 m deep. (Sink / G F Basin)

Timesing	Dimensions	Description
	1.50 2.30	50 mm Cast iron drain laid & jointed a.d. in trench in run not exceeding 3.00 m (in No 2)
	1.40 2.20	375 × 100 mm Concrete (1:3:6) bed under 50 mm drain & 375 × average 40 mm Concrete (1:3:6) benching to sides of 50 mm pipe
2/	2	Extra for bend in 50 mm pipe
2/	1	Cement joint of 50 mm pipe to gulley
2/	1	Hole for small pipe through 1½B wall & making good & Do through 150 mm concrete bed a.b.

No 1 Manhole

(·90 × ·57 & ·75 m to invert)
(no spread)

	900 +	570
2/215	430	430
	1330	1000

	750
Bedding	25
Bottom	150
	925

Dimensions	Description
1.33 1.00 .93	Excavate starting at ground level & not exceeding 1.00 m deep & Remove excavated material from site 1330 1000 2/2330 4[illegible]
4.66 .93	Earth support to excavation not exceeding 1.00 m deep & not exceeding 2.00 m between opposite faces
1.33 1.00	Level & compact bottoms of excavation
1.33 1.00 .15	Concrete (1:3:6) bottom 100–150 mm thick 900 570 2/1470 294[illegible] 4/215 86[illegible] 380[illegible]
3.80 .60	1B wall in common bricks in cement mortar (1:3)
1	Benching to bottom 900 × 570 & average 190 mm thick in fine concrete 1:2:4 finished in cement & sand (1:[illegible]) trowelled smooth [illegible] steep falls to channel [illegible]

		600 190 410
2.94 .41		19 mm Rendering to walls in cement & sand (1:2) trowelled smooth
1		100 mm Salt-glazed half round curved main channel 1100 mm girth & bedding in cement mortar
2		100 mm Do three quarter section branch channel bend do
4		Hole for large pipe through one brick wall & making good
1		100 mm Fine precast concrete slab 1000 × 700 mm reinforced with steel fabric to BS 4483 ref A142 finished smooth on top & setting in cement mortar

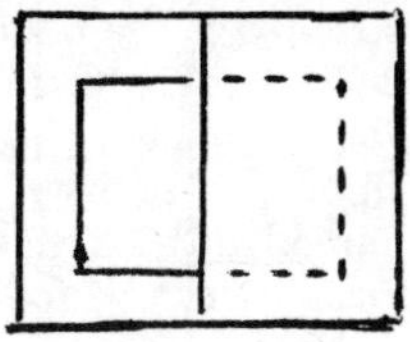

&

610 × 457 mm (Nominal) galvanised cast iron cover & frame & setting frame in cement & cover in grease

		2/485 970 2/215 430 570 1970
1.97 .10		Ddt one brick wall
1.54 .10		Ddt 19 mm rendering
		No step irons

(End of manhole)

Testing as usual.

Main drain vent }
Connection to sewer } to take

CHAPTER 17

ENGINEERING SERVICES AND SPECIALISTS' WORK

Reference to S.M.M.

B	9
F	6.19, 9
G	50–52
R	4, 9–40
S	25–27
T	11
V	1–2, 7, 10

Subdivision.—The following are the most usual engineering services to be dealt with in a simple type of building, but there is a great variety of other special services which would be dealt with in a similar way:

Heating and hot water services.
Electrical work.
Lifts.

Besides such engineering services, it often happens that the architect will nominate specialist firms to carry out special decorative work, such as fibrous plaster or terrazzo, or even work which might normally be left in the builder's hands to sublet as he chooses, e.g. plumbing, glazed tiling or block flooring. For the purpose of this book, where specialist firms are to be employed for these works, they are being considered as the subject of estimates to be included in the building contract as p.c. sums. There will, however, be in each case a certain amount of builder's work to be measured or otherwise provided for. In order to measure this accurately it is essential that the specialists' scheme and estimate should be obtained when the quantities are being prepared to give a basis for such measurements. Consultations with the specialists may also be necessary to ascertain their requirements as definitely as possible.

Where the specialists' work is such as terrazzo, glazed tiling, block flooring, etc., this work can be measured in the normal way by the taker-off, and as soon as all is measured a small bill of the work can be made and sent to several firms for competitive tenders. A p.c. lump sum based on these tenders should be given in the general bill of quantities to be included in the builder's tender (see Chapter 20). When work is treated in this way it is advisable for the taker-off to enter the item of the p.c. sum in his dimensions, making it clear that the work measured in this trade is for arriving at the amount of such sum. Otherwise, when the amounts are worked up, the p.c. sum might be missed. If the surveyor has to estimate the sum himself the same procedure can be followed, except that he can probably make up his figure on the abstract.

Specialists' Work Generally.—In all cases the estimates of specialists must be carefully examined. In some cases a number of conditions will be found in small print, easily overlooked, perhaps on the back of the estimate, and care must be taken to see that such conditions are not inconsistent with the contract. Apart from definite builder's work in cutting away and making good it may be found that the specialist requires a variety of services. A flooring contractor, for example, may require wood blocks to be unloaded and stacked by the builder, a roofing contractor or wall tile fixer may require cement and sand supplied without charge, a heating engineer may require fuel supplied to him for testing. Such items must all be mentioned to contractors tendering, or they will probably have a legitimate claim for an extra at a later stage. Besides these various requirements there will probably be clauses as to supply of water, use of scaffolding, etc., payment and other items. The contract (as in the case of the J.C.T. form) may make special provisions as to discounts, and it is necessary therefore to see that estimates include the required discount, otherwise the p.c. sum will be deficient.

Central Heating.—The following are the principal items to be measured in connection with this:

Boiler base and any special firebrick work to flue.
Bearers and casing to feed cistern and any safe under.
Cold supply to feed cistern with stop cock.
Holes through walls and floors.
Cutting and pinning of pipe brackets or holderbats.
Do. of radiator brackets and stays.
Paint on radiators and pipes.
Recesses for radiators or shelves over.

The feed cistern itself will normally be supplied and fixed complete with ball valve and overflow by the engineers, but the exact extent of the work included in the estimate must be ascertained in each case.

A point to remember in connection with Central Heating is that, once the installation is in working order, it will be necessary in winter to keep the heat on to dry out the building. In fact, it is dangerous to send good joinery to or lay block flooring in a building in winter unless it is thoroughly warmed. Who is to pay for the attendance and fuel? The heating engineer does not usually include it in his estimate, and the building contractor can hardly be expected to include for it unless it is specially mentioned, though it might be argued that it is he who wants it to complete his contract. Special provision should therefore be made in the contract for this item, thus removing any doubt. Fuel and water for testing must in any case be provided for.

Hot Water Services.—In this case the following are the principal items of builder's work:

Boiler base, etc., as for heating.
Bearers to cylinder or tank.
Cold supply from main cistern to boiler or cylinder with stop cock.
Connections to fittings with short length of pipe from engineers' service.
Holes through walls and floors.
Cutting and pinning of brackets or holderbats.
Paint on pipes.

The size of the cold service required should be definitely ascertained, as this, being usually a separate pipe from top to bottom of building, is an important item. If stop cocks are required to each fitting, it should be seen that these are included either by the engineer or in the builder's connections to the fittings. Fuel and water for testing will be required as for Heating.

Electrical Work.—The builder's work for this will chiefly consist in cutting away and making good. The normal work of this nature in a new building can be covered by a general clause giving the number of points, from which the estimator can gauge fairly accurately the work involved. Where steel conduit is used and this is to be chased in flush and bedded in brickwork, the chasing in and bedding is not measurable, but it must be stated that conduits are concealed (S.M.M. S 27.6).

Lifts.—Again consultation with the specialist is necessary for particulars of the following:

Size and depth of pit.
Base to motor.
Overhead steel supports.
Fixing blocks for guides, etc.
Doors or enclosures, if not provided for in the estimate.

It must also be seen that the lift engineer's requirements as to electric cable, etc., are included in the electrician's estimate.

Materials.—It may be that quotations will be required for specialists' goods to be fixed by the building contractor, for which prime cost prices must be inserted in the bill of quantities as is explained in Chapter 20. In such cases (e.g. sanitary fittings, ironmongery, etc.) prices may be based on actual costs in some previous job or preferably special quotations will be obtained. The surveyor may have to prepare a schedule of what is required on which the quotation will be based, and it is important that these schedules should be complete. The items can either be billed with individual p.c. prices to each (except when the Price Adjustment Formula is used), or the prices in each category can be collected into a lump sum. In the latter case fixing will be described separately (see sanitary fittings on page 165), no fuller description of the article being required than is necessary to price the fixing properly. Even if to be billed as a lump sum, it may be found more convenient to use individual fixing items in the taking off from which to build up the lump sum (as is done in the case of ironmongery on page 135; to use individual fixing items etc., above).

CHAPTER 18

ROADS, PATHS AND LAY-OUT OF GROUNDS

References to S.M.M.

As for building generally, and see especially:

D 5–9, 13, 27–44
F 6.8, 9, 12
Q 5
T 3–4, 8
X 1–14

This work may vary from a simple path or drive to a more formal garden. It would include work such as:

(a) Paths.

(b) Roads with channels, kerbs, etc. (if any).

(c) Surface water drainage.

(d) Paved spaces, garden steps, etc.

(e) Formation of flower-beds and lawns.

(f) Boundary walls and fences.

Preparatory Work.—Before measuring any garden work it is essential to have clearly established the levels of the existing ground and the finished levels of the various surfaces. The drawings must be examined to see that sufficient levels are given, as additional levels, though not shown, can sometimes be obtained from the architect's data. A visit to the site before measuring will be found of advantage, especially where existing lawns or paths are to be cut into or adapted. Such items of preparation as necessitate a visit to the site by the estimator to enable him to price them properly, e.g. felling trees, or removing existing steps, should be reserved for the 'Spot' bill, but straightforward items, such as stripping turf, breaking up gravel paths, etc., can quite well be put in this portion of the of the measured bill. Repointing of boundary walls is best kept for the 'Spot' bill, as the condition of the existing pointing will affect the price.

Divisions of the Work.—The actual measurement of the outside work will resolve itself into going over systematically the various finishes shown, the preparation and excavation having been first dealt with as a whole. The drainage work will probably be part of the general drainage system, but that portion which is due entirely to this work is best kept with it, so that a truer value of the cost of the outside work is obtained. The section will be concluded by making a circuit on the drawing of the boundaries shown, and dealing with any new walls, fences, etc., accordingly.

Fencing.—The measurement of fencing is covered by a special section of the S.M.M. which gives rules for each different type. Measurement of fences will be followed by the gates, post holes and foundations, also any painting.

EXAMPLE 33

ROADS AND PATHS

(Measurements are assumed)

Road

Road		3600	254
Kerbs	2/127	254	150
Spread	2/162	324	404
		4178	

Timesing	Dimensions	Description
	45.00 4.18 .40	Excavate to reduce levels not exceeding 1.00 m deep & Remove excavated material from site
	45.00 4.18	Trim & consolidate bottoms of excavations for road to falls & camber
		3600 spread 2/162 324 3276
	45.00 3.28	150 mm hardcore bed to falls & camber blinded with fine ashes & rolled with an 8 tonne roller
	45.00 3.60	Layer of waterproof building paper to BS 1521 Grade A1 lapped 225 mm at joints & laid on hardcore under concrete road (measured net, no allowance made for laps)
	45.00 3.60 .15	Reinforced concrete (1:2:4) road 100- 150 mm thick to fa & camber, in bay not exceeding 40 each, including formwork (between
	45.00 3.60	Steel fabric reinforcement t BS 4483 Ref C5 lapped 150 mm at joints & embedde in concrete ro
4/	3.60	Expansion joint in 150 mm concrete road with pre-moulded impregnated fibre board 35 mm wide the top 15 mm filled with approved sealing compound to BS 2499, including formwork & cutting fabric
2/	45.00 .40	Earthwork support exceeding 4.00 m between opposing faces & not exceeding 1.00 m deep

	Dimensions	Description
2/	45.00	127×254 mm Precast concrete (granite aggregate) Kerb to B.S. 340 Fig 7, bedded & jointed in cement mortar
		&
		455×150 mm Concrete (1:6) foundation to Kerb, including formwork to one edge, other edge against earth, & 152×150 mm triangular haunching to back of Kerb
2/	45.00 .16 .25	Ddt remove from site
		&
		Add back filling
		Path
	12.00 1.20	Excavate topsoil average 150 mm deep
		&
		Remove excavated material average 100 m & deposit in heaps X.15=
		&
		Trim & compact excavation for paths to falls
	12.00 1.00	Tar paving to BS 1242 to path to falls in two coats, the base 30 mm thick, the wearing course 20 mm thick rolled & blinded with grit
	12.00 1.00	100 mm Hardcore bed to falls, blinded with fine ashes for path
2/	12.00	51×152 mm Precast concrete edging to BS 340 Fig 10, bedded & jointed in cement mortar
		&
		150×75 mm Concrete (1:6) foundation to path edging, including formwork to one edge, the other against earth, & haunching to back of edging
	2	Extra for angle to edging
		&
		Extra for fair end to do.

Fencing

15.00	Sawn oak close boarded fencing 2.00 m high of 150×100 mm posts at approximately 2.50 m centres with tarred butts let 750 mm into ground, three arris rails (two out of 75×75 mm) housed & pinned to posts, 32×225 mm gravel board housed to posts & with 75×100 mm stiffeners with tarred butts let 500 mm into ground (one per bay) & 10×100 mm cleft boards lapped 10 mm & nailed with galvanised nails, finished with 38×75 mm saddleback capping housed over boards
7	Excavate post hole 400×400×750 mm deep, fill with concrete (1:6) around post & remove surplus soil from site

CHAPTER 19

'SPOT ITEMS'

References to S.M.M.

As for building generally, and see especially:

B 8
C 1–5
D 5–8

Definition.—'Spot items' (called more formally for the lack of a better term 'Works on Site') include all items to price which properly the estimator should see the existing premises or site. These are all kept together in a separate section of the bill, and would be measured either on the site or from notes made there, and the bill would probably be written by the taker-off. It is not proposed to go into detail here of the measurement of works of alteration generally, but only to deal with such items as would commonly occur in the connection of a new extension to an old building or in clearing a site, and which therefore might form part of the bill for a building of the simplest type. The chief types of item involved are:

(a) Building up openings.

(b) Cutting openings.

(c) Preparing old walls for connection to the new building.

(d) Connecting up existing roofs with the new building.

(e) Alterations to boundary walls or fences.

(f) Pulling down buildings.

The principles laid down, however, for such items will apply to the measurement of items of alteration generally, though in extensive alteration works, which are beyond the scope of this book, a more detailed analysis of the work involved will be made.

General Principles.—Descriptions should be as complete and precise as possible, though from the very nature of most 'spot items' the exact work involved cannot often be accurately judged, and it is for this reason, partly, that the estimator is expected to see the building and form his own opinion. Where definitely new work is involved in the alteration, e.g. lintel to an opening, new plastering, etc., this can be measured and dealt with in the same way as other new work, but the description of the 'spot item' must make clear what part (if any) of the item is measured elsewhere. It must also state how far the builder is to be responsible for making good existing work, though where any particular making good (e.g. decoration if this is measured) is not to be included this can be stated in a preamble to all the spot items. A preamble can also describe materials and workmanship to a certain extent to save repetition in a number of items. The materials generally can be specified to be as described under each trade (i.e. in the main portion of the bill) and a clause such as:

> 'All facing up of jambs is to be in solid brickwork in cement mortar properly cut toothed and bonded and pinned up to the existing work'

will help to shorten the descriptions of items of cutting openings in brickwork. A clause must also appear in the preamble to the 'spot items' to cover any shoring or strutting in connection with the works of alteration: this should meet the requirement of S.M.M. C 5. Another point which must be made clear is whether old materials may be reused, and if so to what extent. Any materials or articles reserved to the employer must be stated, otherwise all old materials will become the property of the contractor, and he will allow credit for them. Although many items will not be billed with quantities, all dimensions must, so far as practicable, be given which the estimator needs to make up his price. The items should eventually be arranged in the order most convenient to the estimator going round the site or existing building. A final visit to the premises with the draft bill, putting oneself in the place of the estimator, will often bring to notice something forgotten or information required for pricing and not given.

Building up Openings.—This type of work may either be described by a clause defining the position and size of the opening and describing the removal of any existing finishings and the building up and making out of plaster, skirting, etc., or the work in building up and making out can be measured separately. Where, however, in ordinary cases one or two openings only are being dealt with, the building up, etc., is best included with the spot item, as the large number of items involved do not seem justified. Examples of both methods are given at the end of this chapter.

Cutting Openings.—Cutting openings will be described by defining the position and size and describing the making good. Lintels, sills, joinery, etc., will be

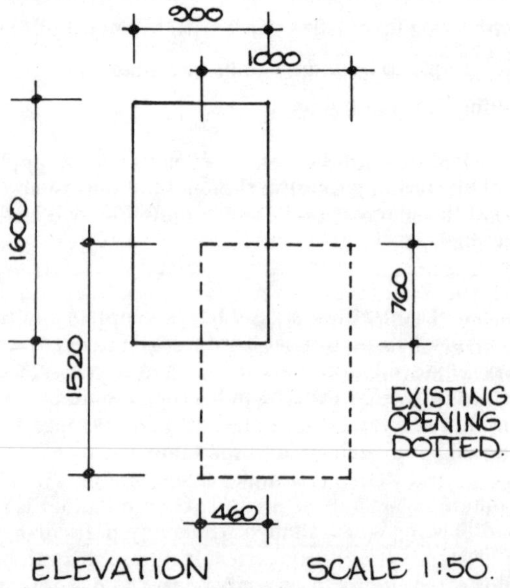

Fig. 45

measured. If there are reveals it must be made clear whether plaster to the reveals is measured elsewhere. The turning of an arch in facing bricks (possibly from the bricks removed) is probably best included in the spot item, though a concrete or stone lintel should be measured, the cutting out for it alone being included in the spot item. It sometimes happens that an existing opening is to be enlarged or altered, or that the cutting of a new opening overlaps one existing. An outline elevation of the two openings, superimposed on each other and drawn in the margin of the bill, is the best indication to the estimator of the extent of the overlap, as shown in Fig. 45 on page 184.

Preparing Old Walls.—The preparation of old walls to form part of a new building involves the cutting away of any projecting string courses, removal of copings, etc., which should be given in metres in the 'Spot' bill. Bonding of the walls will be measured as already described in Chapter 6. Any hacking off of roughcast or other external rendering must be measured, and an item taken for hacking face and raking out joints of old wall as key for new plaster. The latter will probably be measured when the plaster in the new building is taken and appear in the measured bill, it not being usually necessary for the estimator to see the building to price this item. An item will also be necessary for levelling up the top of the old wall where to be raised.

Connection of Roofs.—In many cases when a new building is to be built against an existing one some connection of the roofs will have to be made. Projecting eaves must be stripped and rafters cut back to suit the formation of a gutter, or a verge must be stripped and bonded to the new roof and any barge boards removed. The removal of rainwater pipes will also be included, together with any shortening of gutters and grubbing up or diversion of drains. All these will be described in detail with measurements where possible.

Alterations to Boundary Walls, etc.—Even though no existing building is involved it may be necessary to have a 'Spot' bill in connection with such items as alterations or repairs to fences, formation of pavement crossings, alterations to paths or drives, etc. The measurement of these will follow the general principles already suggested.

Pulling Down.—The entire demolition of existing buildings must be so described as to define its extent, and it must be remembered that demolition is generally taken to be to ground level only. For all ordinary purposes complete demolition can be described in one all-embracing item giving the principal dimensions of the building, though theoretically to arrive at an accurate estimate it should be measured by giving detail of areas of roof to be stripped, walls pulled down, etc. Such labour is, however, generally wasted, as estimators experienced in pricing demolition work will look at the building, note its size and estimate a lump sum for the work. Grubbing up of the foundations and hacking up of concrete beds must be measured in addition. A general clause should specify well watering whilst pulling down, and where adjoining buildings are close by this is important. Where buildings are to be partially pulled down, the extent of the pulling down must be accurately described and measurements given.

Credits.—It is not often necessary in work of the size under consideration to make a credit bill, but if there is doubt as to what materials, fittings, etc., will be retained by the building owner, it may be advisable. The 'Spot' bill is in such cases written on paper with double cash columns, one being headed 'Value of Works' and the other 'Amount of Credits'. A clause will appear in the preamble instructing the contractor to price the works at their full value and price the credits separately, and stating that the building owner reserves the right to retain any of the items credited at the prices allowed in the estimate (perhaps with a percentage addition).

Metrication.—Following metrication surveyors are faced with the problem when measuring 'spot items' of joining metric to imperial dimensioned buildings: the balance will have to be struck between recording exactly converted dimensions and reasonable metric equivalents. Fig. 45 shows dimensions of 0.90 m and 1.00 m, whereas an imperial measure tape would have shown 3′0″ (0.91 m) and 3′3″ (0.99 m) a difference in both cases of 10 millimetres or less than half an inch.

EXAMPLE 34

'SPOT ITEMS'

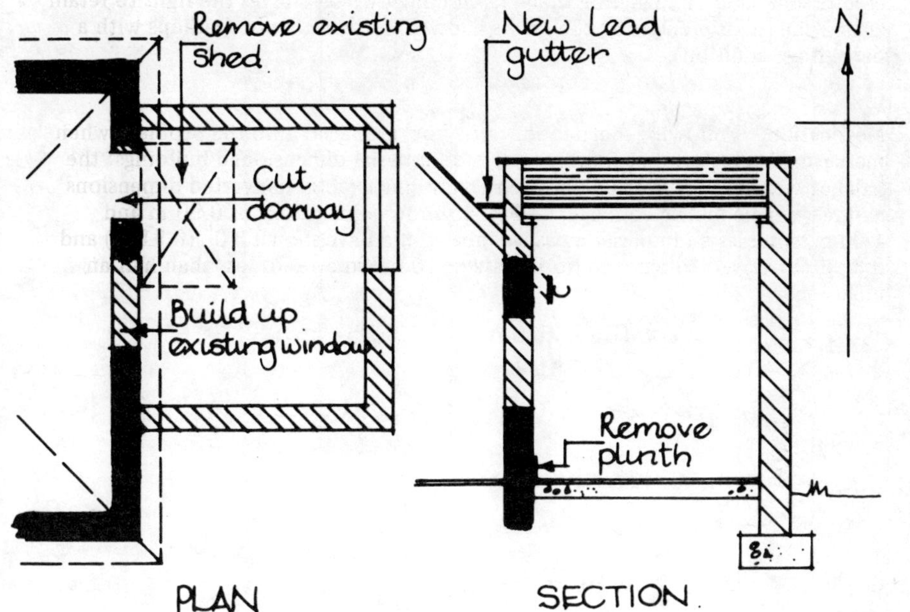

Fig. 46

			Pull down & clear away to ground level the shed against the East wall of Kitchen approximately 1.90 × 1.30 × 2.10 m high & make good remaining brickwork & facings
	1.90 1.30		Break up & clear away 150 mm concrete floor with hardcore bed under
			Take out & clear away the window 1.20 × 1.20 m in East wall of Kitchen, with stone sill

			1200 sill 150 1350
	1.20 1.35		1½ B wall in common bricks in cement mortar in building up openings
	1.20		Form level bed on old 1½ B wall for raising & Pin up 1½ B wall to old soffite with slates in cement mortar

2/	1.35	Labour & material cutting toothing & bonding new 1½B wall to old
	1.20 1.35	Plaster & set wall in built up opening
		1200 1350 2/2550 5100
	5.10	Make good joint of new & old plaster

(Redecoration of whole room to take)

Cut opening .85 × 2.05 m in 1½B wall adjoining window in East wall for door, cut out for & insert concrete lintol (measured) face up jambs, make out tile floor & skirting into opening & make good plaster up to new door linings

Door	750
Frame 2/50	100
Bearing 2/150	300
	1150

	1	327 × 140 mm Precast concrete (1:2:4) lintol 1.15 m long with three 12 mm mild steel bars

(New door & finishings to take)

Cut back the projecting brick plinth 25 × 300 mm on East elevation for a length of approximately 4.40 m & make good both ends up to new wall

Take down eaves gutter & fascia for a length of approximately 4.40 m & make good both ends, including providing stop ends to gutter

(Rainwater outlets to check on site)

Strip roof covering & cut back projecting rafters for a length of approximately 4.40 m & prepare 1½ B wall for raising, & make good roof up to new gutter.

(Eaves filler & gutter to take)

CHAPTER 20

PROCEDURE IN TAKING OFF A COMPLETE BUILDING

It is proposed in this chapter to make various suggestions, chiefly as to procedure, for the guidance of the taker-off in dealing with a complete building. It must not be forgotten that the methods of different individuals and the customs of different offices vary in the organisation and carrying out of the work. The fact that a particular suggestion is made here does not mean that it is universally adopted, nor does it preclude the use of an alternative.

Preliminary Study of Drawings.—Before any dimensions are written at all the taker-off should look over the drawings and study the general character of the building. He must, so to speak, get his bearings by seeing how each elevation drawn is related to the plans and where section lines are taken. The position of the latter should have been marked on one of the plans, but if this has not been done he should mark his plans so that he can see at a glance to which section he must refer if he wants some particular information. He may find it of use where there is more than one storey to mark the section lines on all floor plans.

The taker-off should also see that the drawings are properly figured up. If overall dimensions are not already figured, he should calculate them and mark them on the drawing, and see that all projections on external walls are also figured. If this is done the calculation of the perimeter of the external walls will be simplified. He should also see that he has all the information necessary to calculate the dimensions of every room, and it is an advantage to figure every room on the plans except where a series of rooms are obviously all of the same dimension in one direction. A little time spent in this preliminary figuring of the drawings obviates the possibility of inconsistency in dimensions. Where more than one taker-off is employed the result of this work must be communicated to each, and their drawings marked accordingly. Figured dimensions must always be followed in preference to scale, and any dimensions which can be calculated from those figured should be so worked out. A larger scale will usually supersede a smaller scale drawing, except in so far as the smaller is figured where the larger is not.

Where to Start.—If all drawings are completed and available the taker-off will follow the order of sections given in Chapter 4, or such other order as may be the custom of his office. This order will be seen to follow more or less logically the order of erection of the building, except that certain special work and services are dealt with at the end. It may however be that the design of, say, reinforced concrete foundations is not completed, and therefore measurement cannot begin as usual with foundations. In such a case a point such as Ground Floor or damp-proof course level must be selected from which to measure the structure, the work below that level being measured at a later stage when the necessary information is available. It may be that 1:100 scale drawings have been received, but 1:20 details are to follow. In such a case floor finishings and internal plaster could probably be taken first, as the measurement of these is generally dependent on the figured dimensions given on the 1:100 scale, which is to be presumed will not be altered. Moreover, these sections give the taker-off a good idea of the plan and general nature of the building.

Accuracy.—There may be a temptation, especially to those not sure of their ground, to take measurements on the full side, and so cover themselves against possible claims for deficiency. Such measurements are very definitely to be deprecated, as it will be realised that, if measurements were on an average $2\frac{1}{2}$ per cent or perhaps 5 per cent full, a very substantial amount would be added to the tender. Where figured dimensions are the basis the measurements taken should be exact, but where they are scaled there is some excuse for measurements slightly full, as there may be some shrinkage of the paper and the lines on the drawing are not usually drawn sufficiently precisely to scale nearer than, say, 75 mm on an 1:100 scale plan with any certainty. It will be seen therefore that the care with which the architect's drawings are prepared may affect the quantities, and that measurement from fully figured drawings must necessarily be more accurate. Furthermore, if a surveyor makes a practice of measuring full, this will be realised by contractors, who will count on this fullness to the disadvantage of any firm tendering and ignorant of the facts and to their own sorrow if circumstances should force a remeasurement of the work as carried out.

When working from figured drawings it may be found that three places of decimals are in some cases indicated. In setting down the dimensions the figures should normally be taken to the nearest two places*, the excess measurement thus obtained being usually very slight in proportion to the whole. Three places may, however, be necessary in setting down side casts.

In short, the surveyor must aim at giving in his bill a representation as accurate as possible under the circumstances of the building work in question.

Numbering the Dimension Sheets.—All dimension sheets should be numbered as soon as possible. For those in traditional form some surveyors number each column, others each page, this being a matter of individual preference. If the numbering is done at the earliest opportunity, it will minimise the risk of a page being mislaid and overlooked. If sheets are inserted after numbering, they can be numbered with the last number and a suffix a, b, c, etc., but it is essential that if, say, a sheet numbered 31a, 31b, 31c, and 31d is inserted that a note should be put against the number 31 '31a—d follow', otherwise the inserted sheet might be lost and not missed.

In any case it will be found of value if the taker-off numbers his pages at the top, according to the section they represent, e.g. Floors 1, Roofs 6, Plumbing 9, etc., irrespective of any other system of numbering. He can thus at any time make cross-references without leaving the page number blank, possibly never to be filled in. This method of heading the sheets may be seen in the dimensions given for abstracting in Example 36 below. It is further of value in that on opening the dimensions at any page one has immediate indication of what they refer to.

The method of numbering 'cut and shuffle' sheets is explained in Chapter 21.

---

*See S.M.M. A 3.2.

Cross-References.—The taker-off should do all he can to make his dimensions clear to others besides himself, as it is quite possible that, when variations on the contract have to be adjusted, someone else will be entrusted with the work, and will have to find his way about the dimensions. If the taker-off finds that he has not room for something in its proper place and is forced to put it down elsewhere, a reference should be made on the dimensions in the proper place so that the item can be found. Any further cross-referencing should also be made which may be of use later. It has been known for jobs to be postponed for a year or two after tenders were received, and even the taker-off will then need some references and notes to refresh his memory. If the final numbering of dimension sheets has not been made, references should be to such sectional numbering as the taker-off has adopted, and the column or page number referred to should not be left blank.

Clearness of the Dimensions.—Besides the use of cross-references, a good deal can be done to make the dimensions clear by the manner in which they are set down. It has already been pointed out that a regular order of length, width and depth (or height) should be maintained in writing down the dimensions, and even when it may be difficult to determine which is length or width a consistent order should be kept. In measuring areas of floor finishings, for instance, the dimensions horizontal on the plan could be put first regularly, always followed by the vertical ones. Collections should be made wherever possible on waste and not in the head, and timesing should be made consistently. For instance, in measuring six doors each with four squares of glass all timesed for two floors the dimensions should be timesed thus:

2/ 6/	1		50 mm S.w. Four panel door etc.
2/ 6/ 4/	0.23 0.45		6 mm glass to wood.

the last item *not* being written:

2/ 4/ 6/	0.23 0.45		6 mm glass to wood.

It will be realised that when timesing becomes complicated it will help considerably in tracing items if the method of timesing is consistent. In the example above, the outer timesing represents the floors and the next the number of doors, and if the order is reversed in the middle of a series there is apt to be confusion, All timesing in connection with a single door should be on the right of that representing the number of doors, and that in turn on the right of timesing representing number of floors. The use of coloured pens in timesing or dotting on to represent different floors or sections of the work will be found to help considerably in tracing dimensions later.

Sequence of Measurement.—It is advisable when measuring to follow the same sequence in different parts of the work. For example, in collecting up the girth of the external walls of a building it is a good plan, as was suggested above, to work clockwise, starting, say, from the top left-hand corner of the plan. If this is done consistently it will assist in reference later, when perhaps the length of a particular section of wall has to be extracted from a long collection. If a particular sequence of rooms has been adopted in measuring ceilings, the same sequence should be used for wall finish, skirtings, cornices, etc. In this way, if all the finishings of a particular room are to be traced, it will be known in which part of each group the relative dimensions are to be found.

Headings.—The use of headings in the dimensions will further help in future reference. Apart from the section heading already suggested for each page, subheadings should be clearly written wherever possible, and these will stand out if underlined. The sequence of measurement in the section will then easily be followed by a glance at the subheadings. Special subheadings will also be necessary where it is required that a group of dimensions are to be billed together, as, for instance, in the detail measurement of manholes or joinery fittings, and the end of any such work to be grouped together must be clearly defined by a note such as 'End of manholes'.

Notes.—The making of notes by the taker-off on his dimensions is of the utmost value. Such notes are usually of one of three kinds.

(1) Explanatory for use in writing the specification or adjusting variations.

(2) For reference before the taking off is finished, e.g. notes of items to measure, or queries to be settled.

(3) Instructions to the worker-up.

The explanatory type of note should include memoranda for the specification, such as the rules followed in measurement of lintel reinforcement, or, say, in the case of a plate bolted down to brickwork, the spacing of bolts assumed. Such notes will save the specification writer from spending time trying to see on what principle reinforcement is measured or how far apart bolts were taken, and even if the taker-off himself writes the specification he will find such notes of value, writing a month or two after he finished the taking off. They will also be found of value in adjusting variations, especially if this is done by someone else. This type of note should be written at the side of the description column on 'waste', and is best marked off by a line or bracket to prevent confusion with descriptions. All this assumes that a full specification is not available to work on.

The second type of note, made for reference before the taking off is finished, is necessary when perhaps some point must be referred to the architect, or for other reasons something cannot be finally measured. A list should be made of all queries to be answered on a separate sheet of paper, ruled down the middle so that answers can be written opposite and kept as a record. This record is often useful as evidence of verbal instructions which at a later stage may be queried. Memoranda, too, should be made at the end of the day's work of anything unfinished which, the train of thought being broken, might be forgotten. It is much safer to make notes of such matters on the dimensions than to trust to memory, and these notes enable the work to be carried on in the case of unexpected absence. Such notes as these are sometimes written in pencil to be rubbed out when dealt with, or they may be written in ink across the description column in such a way that they cannot be missed. It is a well-known fact that the subconscious mind continues to work long after the conscious mind has turned to something else, and the subconscious thoughts have a way of pushing themselves forward suddenly at most unexpected times. If anything of importance should occur to the taker-off in this way during leisure hours — something forgotten or something which could be improved — he should make a point of writing it down, or the thought will vanish as quickly as it came.

The third type of note is that which is an instruction to the worker-up, used generally where a correction or alteration can be more easily made by a general instruction than by writing down new dimensions. These notes, too, must be written in such a way that they will not be missed by the worker-up. An example of this type of note would be such an instruction as 'Alter all 25 mm shelving to 32 mm'. How such notes are to be dealt with is explained in Chapter 22*.

The Specification.—If a specification is supplied, it should be read through cursorily first, not with the idea of mastering it in detail, but rather with a view to getting a general idea of its contents and knowing one's way about it. One would then normally study the Excavation, Concrete Work and Brickwork more closely before beginning the taking off of the foundations. It is useful when the taking off is well forward to go through the specification and run through in pencil all parts that have been dealt with, not of course such paragraphs as will form preambles to the bill or such descriptions as have not been repeated in the dimensions. If this is done it is not likely that anything specified will be missed. The specification is not, under the usual J.C.T. form of contract,† a contract document, but if the two documents both form part of the contract they will have to be read together, and differences in wording may lead to uncertainty and difficulties. In such cases care must be taken to see that the wording in the dimensions corresponds exactly with that in the specification, or a note must be made of any differences so that the draft specification can be altered.

More often than not, however, no formal specification is available. Brief specification notes may be supplied, and further notes must be made of verbal instructions which will be given by the architect and which will form the nucleus of the specification, to be added to from time to time as queries are raised with him. These notes must be supplemented by the surveyor's own knowledge of the architect's usual practice or by his own ideas of what is reasonably required. In making decisions on matters of specification the surveyor should bear in mind that what is theoretically correct is not necessarily the most practicable or economical solution. In the case of timber, for instance, he must not only bear in mind the difference between basic and finished sizes referred to in Chapter 9, but he should where possible specify sizes which are customary sizes in the market. The multiplication, too, of minor varieties of the same article does not tend to economy, especially in items of joinery where machines have to be reset for each different moulding, in fact the S.M.M. in the case of door frames calls for the incidence of repetition of identical items to be referred to. (N 20)

P.C. Items and Provisional Sums.—For various reasons it is not always possible to define finally, when quantities are being prepared, everything necessary for the completion of the building. It will be necessary for the architect to select

---

*See page 216. †See footnote to page 32.

certain articles such as sanitary fittings, ironmongery, etc., in consultation with his client, and the details of these are not considered at the early stage when tenders are being obtained. It is usual therefore to put in the bill 'prime cost' ('p.c.') sums for these items which the estimator will include in his tender for goods to be obtained from a supplier, but which are subject to adjustment against the actual cost of the articles selected.

Further, it will be necessary to employ on the works certain specialist firms to carry out work which the builder does not in his normal course of business do, such as electrical work, heating and hot water services, lifts, etc. If possible, estimates for these works will be obtained from specialist firms and p.c. sums included in the bill of quantities, which the estimator will include in his tender. The firms eventually employed for these works will be subcontractors of the general contractor, who retains general control and responsibility.

A provisional sum is usually included for general contingencies or to cover something to be done by the general contractor which is at the moment uncertain. Whilst the bill of quantities gives the tenderer an opportunity of adding for his profit to the p.c. sums referred to above, such provisional sums include for profit and any incidental work which will be added in the final account.

A definition of p.c. and provisional sums will be found in S.M.M. A 8. In regard to p.c. sums, as the J.C.T. form of contract allows different cash discounts for subcontractors and suppliers, it is important to keep them quite distinct. The matter of discounts will be dealt with in Chapter 25.

Attendance.—In the case of p.c. sums for subcontractors, provision is made in the bill of quantities for the estimator to price both general and special attendance on the subcontractor. A definition of general attendance is given in S.M.M. B 9.2: this can be covered by a general preamble and reference to it following the p.c. sum.

Special attendance referred to in S.M.M. B 9.3 will differ according to the nature of the work and must be considered for each item. The conditions accompanying the quotation (often small print on the back) can be helpful in drafting this item.*

Provisional Quantities.—Work to be carried out by the general contractor, which may be uncertain in extent, can also be provided for by means of provisional quantities, i.e. by measuring work in the normal way, but keeping it separate in the bill and marking it 'provisional'. For instance, the foundations of a building, where the nature of the soil in uncertain, may be measured all as shown on the drawings, and additional excavation, brickwork, etc., measured separately and marked 'provisional' to cover any extra depth to which it may be necessary to take the foundations. It is thus made clear that adjustment of these quantities on completion of the work is anticipated.

Diagrams.—In certain circumstances the S.M.M. calls for line diagrams to be included as an adjunct to the written description. These line diagrams are defined in S.M.M. A 5.1c. Line diagrams will be either extracts from the drawings or

---

*See page 238.

specially prepared for incorporation with the written description. Alternatively the diagrams are collected together and printed on one or more sheets at the end of the bill, each diagram being given a number and being referred to by that number in the body of the bill. Diagrams should be marked Plan, Section, etc., and be drawn to scale, the scale being indicated or the dimensions figured.

Apart from the above, diagrams will be made in the dimensions or on separate sheets to work out points of construction not detailed or to supplement the architect's details. If possible, these should be made on the dimension sheets where the particular work is measured, or if made on separate sheets they should be carefully preserved. They may be drawn sometimes on any spare space on the drawings to ensure their being preserved with them. Any of importance should be confirmed with the architect.

Materials.—The taker-off must have a thorough knowledge of the materials with which he is dealing, and should, where possible, if a material is unknown to him make a point of seeing samples and studying the manufacturers' catalogue or leaflet, so that he is conversant with the limits and (perhaps optimistically stated) capabilities of the material. The handling of the material and study of any literature will often assist in the measurement of the work or in the framing of a proper description.

Insertion of Items.—It quite often happens that the taker-off must go back on his work and make alterations or insert additional items, either because he has forgotten something or because he has received some altered instructions. Such alterations and additions should wherever possible be made in the proper place in the dimensions, so that when the dimensions are referred to at a later stage everything can be found where expected. Once more the importance of plenty of space must be emphasised, and on work of any size it will be found of advantage to start each section of the taking off on a new sheet, leaving any odd blank columns for later use if necessary. Further, if the dimensions are kept in subsections or groups with a definite gap between, these gaps will also be found of use to insert in their proper place any dimensions which may be an afterthought. If it is found impossible to insert an item or group of items in its proper place, a place must be found for it elsewhere and proper cross-references made in both places.

Decision on Doubtful Points.—A thorough knowledge of the *Standard Method of Measurement*, the *Practice Manual* and a study of all the published textbooks will still leave occasions when the taker-off must make decisions for himself on the method of measurement or extent of descriptions. In doing so he should have one consideration only, viz. what will best enable the estimator to understand (not merely guess) the work involved and help him to price it *quickly* and *accurately*.

WORKING UP

The chapters that follow describe working up, the traditional term for the process whereby the measured dimensions and descriptions are converted into the finished bill of quantities. Chapter 21 deals with cut and shuffle, the process most common today, Chapters 22 and 23 deal with abstracting and Chapter 24 with writing the bill.

CHAPTER 21

CUT AND SHUFFLE

Paper and Rulings.—Several systems of cut and shuffle are in use which, though differing little in principle, differ in detail. A sheet of foolscap or A4 size can be divided into four, as shown on page 199, the sections of which can be separated by perforations or the cutting can be done with a guillotine. Some use larger paper divided into, perhaps, five sections. The important thing is that the taker-off should do his writing on a reasonable size piece of paper, though for sorting purposes smaller pieces are more convenient.

Obviously, if every item is to be on a separate sheet many sheets will have only one or two dimensions on each. There will, however, be cases where there are so many dimensions for an item that they will need two or more sheets. The first sheet used is called the 'master sheet'. This is the one from which the bill will be written or typed. Additional sheets for the same item, the use of which is referred to below, are known as 'slave sheets'.

The normal dimension paper ruling needed some modification if the sheets were to serve as a draft bill. The item number, description and worked-out quantity must be together in a prominent place where the typist can find them without confusion with other matter on the sheet. Several 'boxes' are therefore provided as shown on page 199, on one section of the reproduction they have been numbered for reference.

1. Is for the bill item number where the quantity surveyor numbers his bill items serially. This will be entered immediately before sending to the printers. If identification of items is by serial letters on each page, this will be left blank.
2. This space is for the description which must be written carefully and in full by the taker-off on master sheets, remembering that in doing so he is writing the final draft bill.
3. When calculations are complete, this space on the master sheet will have the quantity to be inserted in the bill with its unit of measurement: it will be left blank on other sheets.

These three boxes will be the only ones to be looked at by the printer and only the material to be printed must be put in them. If the description is a long one it can overflow into the top of the three dimension columns, but not into box 3. The remaining numbers are

4. The normal dimension paper ruling the right-hand column being only used for waste collections, location notes and location headings.
5. Reference to job number, taking-off section and dimension column number, e.g. 20/A/43 (job 20, foundations, column 43). A suggested table of taking-off sections with their references is given on page 203. Each taking-off section should start at 1, the columns being prenumbered or numbered as used.
6. Cast off the squared dimensions.

		Description			Description				Description
		Excavate surface soil average 150mm deep.			Remove vegetable soil a.b. (A 25).				
	6.08 6.08		4.00 w/s 2/440. 0.88 w/e space 2/600 1.20 6.08	6.08 6.08 0.15					
		20/A/45.			20/A/46.				

1. 2. 3. 4. 5. 6. 7. 8.

7. In this box should be put C, S or L (cube, square or lineal), only when, as shown later, the category is sometimes not obvious. Each of the four sections is holed in the top left hand corner so that after cutting they can be filed in batches as convenient with long string tags enabling them to be easily turned over.
8. This is a spare box which can be used for elemental references if preparing a bill of this kind.

Rules for Taking-Off.—There are some rules that the taker-off must follow:

1. Descriptions must be written in full as in a bill — no abbreviations, except as in 6 and 7 below.
2. Deductions must be on a separate set of columns and 'Ddt' must be written in box 2 and repeated in box 6 to come against the total. This insertion in box 6 is very important, and after completion of a section the taker-off, when looking through his dimensions, must check that all 'Ddts' are so inserted. Otherwise, the machine operator doing the casting and who is only required to look at this bottom line may make a serious mistake.
3. Two descriptions can be coupled to a single set of dimensions by '&' by writing the second description in full on the new column and by putting '&' in the dimension column with the box 5 reference referred to. This is a case where C, S or L must be put in box 7.
4. Instead of marking paint as ÷ 8 it must be timesed by $1\frac{1}{8}$.
5. Cube items should be set down as cubes, not lineal to be cubed up later.
6. The word 'ditto' should never be used in descriptions, since when the sheets are cut there would be no indication of what is referred to. Instead on slave sheets a reference should be given to the column number, e.g. '25 x 100 mm. s.w. skirting a.b. as I/67' and normal abbreviations are then allowable. The description must be full enough to leave no doubt when sorting the separated dimensions: 'skirting a.b.' is not enough, as the sorter would not have I/67 in front of him and he might think it was tile, granolithic or something else.
7. As many slave sheets as necessary for each item may be used. Normal abbreviated descriptions can be used for such sheets, provided that the item is clearly identified, remembering that the sheets will be separated after shuffling. Slave sheets will eventually be pinned to the master sheet in such a way that the printer can turn over the whole batch, as he only has to copy from the master sheet. Some surveyors prefer to detach the slave sheets, sending to the printer only those from which he has to copy.
8. If a whole column is nilled, 'nil' should be written in the item number box (1) and the quantity box (3) as well as against the dimensions. It could also be written across any description.
9. Columns which are left blank, e.g. at the end of a section to provide for possible other items, must have their serial number in box 5. They will be set aside in shuffling.
10. Specialists' work measured to obtain a basis for a p.c. sum should be measured together, so that these sheets can be taken out, photographed, cut and shuffled in advance of the main bill.
11. Items which are to be grouped together (i.e. those that would have been billed direct under the traditional method) in the bill could be marked with

a distinguishing letter, perhaps the taking-off section letter and another. For instance, when measuring drains all manhole dimensions could be marked XA, then, perhaps, drainage from last manhole to sewer XB. A list of the letters used and their meaning should be kept. A special set of rubber stamp letters will be required for this purpose. The shuffling of these sheets is the equivalent of the former billing direct.

Taking off will proceed in the normal way apart from the restriction of a new column for each new description. Dimension headings can be written as usual across the dimension columns. It will be an advantage to have standardised section and letter references for sections of the taking off (see page 208), and the taker-off must see that before parting with his dimensions they are marked in box 5 as described above. The two specimen columns on page 199 are at the stage of leaving the taker-off.

It will be found that good use can be made of schedules instead of making long collections on waste. These can be set out on abstract paper and should, of course, be preserved as a record of measurements which will be required for adjustment of variations. Such schedules should indicate clearly by room number or otherwise the position of all measurements. They should be numbered serially so that they can be referred to in side notes on the dimension sheets.

Squaring and Casting.—Squaring and casting are invariably done with a calculating machine, either checked mentally or by another machine and operator. The most useful type of machine is one which gives the figures on a band of paper and keeps a running cast which is transferred to the paper when wanted. Squaring and casting and their checking can be done on the whole sheets before cutting, but in some offices the whole is left to be done in one operation with the reducing after the editing referred to below. If all is so done in one operation, the final answer only will appear on the master sheet in box 3.

If the machine is not one that can deal with deductions in the running cast, the total of squaring will appear on every sheet. The cast of the adds will then be made and entered on the master sheet and the cast of deducts entered below it, the deduction will be made and the result reduced and entered in box 3. This method might also be adopted because staff is available to do the squaring at the earlier stage and so get the work forward. With this procedure space must be left at the bottom of the waste column of box 4 on the master sheet for the calculation to be entered.

There will not normally be need for squaring to be entered against each measurement if done by a machine that will make a running cast. Such figures are only of value for adjustment of variations and could quite well be worked out again if and when required.

Duplicate Dimensions.—A duplicate of the dimensions is almost essential; this is retained uncut, the dimensions remaining in the order of taking off. It is naturally easier then to follow the taker-off's mind. A copy can be made with carbon paper, but this is not very satisfactory. A photographic copy of each sheet is much better. There is a variety of copying machines on the market, but one of the 'dye line' print type which needs a fairly translucent paper is probably the most economical. The casting done and checked, the sheets can be photographed.

Cutting and Shuffling.—The copy taken, before any cutting is done the sheets to be cut must be listed, so that there is a record of the number of columns under each dimension classification. The sheets will then be torn up on the perforations, or cut by guillotine, checked with the photo copies and sorted into pigeon holes, each of which represents a section of the final bill. For this a special fitting will be required with, say, 36 pigeon holes made to suit the size of the cut slips. Wasted slips whether blanks or nilled will be filed together (not destroyed).

The contents of each pigeon hole will then be taken out in turn and sorted into bill order. Slave sheets will be collected and pinned to their master sheets (deduction sheets being put at the end) and each bill section threaded on a string tag. The sheets are then ready for editing. A check should be made at this stage by listing the number of cut sheets in each section of the bill, adding the wasted sheets and checking the total with the number of original sheets in the uncut copy.

Editing.—Although the abstract is saved, the work of editing is probably heavier under this system than the traditional method in which much co-ordination was done by the biller. The editor must check the descriptions and order of items, amend descriptions to 'do.' where necessary and insert group headings. These are written on blank pieces of paper preferably coloured, of the same size as the cut sheets and inserted in their proper places. He will also write the bill section headings and preambles on normal bill paper and will see that items to be written short are given a distinctive mark. The editor will do all his work in red or other distinctive colour and will insert in box 3 'Lin.M' (or 'M Lin.' or just 'M'), 'Nr.', &c. as required to be printed in the bill, leaving room for the quantity to be inserted later. Again a special set of rubber stamps is useful for this purpose.

If extra items are found necessary in editing, they should be written on a blank sheet, also on the blank photographed copy of the same reference number. Similarly if a sheet is nilled, it should be nilled on the photo copy.

P.c. and provisional sums will appear on dimension sheets in the normal way, but the editor may like to write the bill of these items in the traditional way, together with the Preliminary Bill, Spot Bill and Summary.

Reducing Quantities and Numbering Items.—The editor has then finished his work and the bill is ready for the printer, except for the insertion of the quantities and item numbers. The collection of totals on each master and its slave sheets is best done on a calculating machine which gives cumulative totals, the result being entered in the lower part of the waste column of the master sheet. The total will be reduced to the unit marked and entered in box 3 of the master sheet. Both processes must, of course, be checked. Finally items will be serially numbered through the bill if that method of numbering is adopted. Some surveyors prefer a method of using letters serially from A on each page, which can only be done by the typist. It does seem an advantage to have all the resulting small pieces of paper (sometimes thousands) serially numbered, and, if there is any cross-referencing to be done, e.g. with spot items, this numbering is useful as the references can be inserted before typing.

Standard Lists of Sections.—There is appended on page 203 a suggested list of taking-off sections.

Checking.—It will be found that special care is necessary in checking the proof. It is not so easy to spot mistakes in the cut and shuffle dimensions as in a draft bill written in the traditional form (though that is difficult enough!).

Instructions to Printers.—Instructions to printers must be precise, particularly as to the system adopted for marking headings, the extent of their continuation and the grouping of items. It may be found helpful to number all sheets to be typed (including preambles, headings, etc.) serially by numbering machine before sending to the printers. This gives a certain check if a sheet goes astray and helps the printers if they want to divide up between typists and afterwards reassemble.

Progress Schedule.—A progress schedule will be found useful, so that at any time the stage reached by each section of the taking off can be seen. A specimen schedule follows this page. The sections are taking-off sections, not elemental or bill sections. For instance, foundations, frame and suspended floors are all together, as they were measured from one set of engineer's drawings and in this case there was no need to separate them.

Filing.—Cardboard boxes are probably best for keeping the papers together during the progress of the contract, making them easily portable. If foolscap paper is used for the uncut sheets, a standard box will probably be found suitable. If not, boxes can be made to special design economically if 50 or more are ordered at a time.

TAKING-OFF SECTIONS

A Foundations.
B Frame.
C Brickwork.
D Facings.
E Roofs.
F Ground Floors.
G Suspended Floors.
H Internal Partitions.
I Internal Finishings.
J Windows.
K Internal Doors.
L External Doors.
M Blank openings.
N Fires and Vents.
P Stairs and Lifts.
Q Builder's Work in connection with Engineering Services.
S Plumbing and Engineering.
X Drains.
Y External Works.
Z Fittings.

There are spare letters for sections not listed, if any should be needed.

JOB - SOUTHTOWN SCHOOL

JOB No. 13.

PROGRESS SCHEDULE

DIM. COLUMN NUMBERS.	T.O. INITIAL	TAKING-OFF SECTIONS.	SQUARED	CHKD.		DIMS COPIED	No. CUT SHEETS	PHOTO COPIES CHKD.
A1-144.	CJW.	FOUNDATIONS & R.C. FRAME	✓	✓		✓	144	✓
C1-164	JAK.	BRICKWORK & FACINGS	✓	✓		✓	164	✓
E1-80	MDC.	ROOF COVERINGS	✓	✓		✓	80	✓
I1-260	MDC	INTERNAL FINISHINGS.	✓	✓		✓	260	✓
J.1-116	RPP.	WINDOWS.	✓	✓		✓	116	✓
K1-80	RPP.	INTERNAL DOORS.	✓	✓		✓	80	✓
L1-100	RPP.	EXTERNAL DOORS.	✓	✓		✓	100	✓
O 1-128	R.W.	FITTINGS & DUCT CASINGS	✓	✓		✓	128	✓
P. 1-20.	CJW.	EXTERNAL SERVICES.	✓	✓		✓	20	✓
Q1-64	CJW.	B.W.I.C.	✓	✓		✓	64	✓
S1-224	CJW.	PLUMBING.	✓	✓		✓	224	✓
Y1-96.	RW.	EXTERNAL WORKS.	✓	✓		✓	96.	✓
X1-128.	RW.	DRAINAGE.	✓	✓		✓	128	✓
							1604	

DATE - JANUARY 1978.

SHEET No. 1.

CUT	INITIAL SHUFFLE TO SECTIONS	BILL SECTIONS.	FINAL SHUFFLE & PREAMBLES & HEADING SLIPS DRAFTED	DRAFT BILL EDITED	QUANTS CHECKED	QUANTS CHKD	No. OF CUT SHEETS IN SECTION	ITEMS NUMBERED		SENT FOR TYPING
✓	✓	PRELIMINARIES.	✓	✓	✓	✓	–	✓		✓
✓	✓	P.C. & PROVISIONAL SUMS	✓	✓	✓	✓	20	✓		✓
✓	✓	WORKS ON SITE.	✓	✓	✓	✓	–	✓		✓
✓	✓	EXCAVATION & EARTHWORK	✓	✓	✓	✓	25	✓		✓
✓	✓	CONCRETE WORK	✓	✓	✓	✓	147	✓		✓
✓	✓	BRICKWORK	✓	✓	✓	✓	195.	✓		✓
✓	✓	WOODWORK.	✓	✓	✓	✓	218	✓		✓
✓	✓	METALWORK	✓	✓	✓	✓	68.	✓		✓
✓	✓	PLUMBING.	✓	✓	✓	✓	180	✓		✓
✓	✓	PLASTERWORK ETC.	✓	✓	✓	✓	75	✓		✓
✓	✓	GLAZING.	✓	✓	✓	✓	29	✓		✓
✓	✓	PAINTING & DECORATING.	✓	✓	✓	✓	233	✓		✓
✓	✓	BWIC ENGINEERING SERVICES.	✓	✓	✓	✓	120	✓		✓
✓	✓	DRAINAGE.	✓	✓	✓	✓	118	✓		✓
✓	✓	EXTERNAL SERVICES	✓	✓	✓	✓	20	✓		✓
✓	✓	SITE LAYOUT.	✓	✓	✓	✓	96	✓		✓
							1544			
–	–	SPARES.	–	–	–	–	60	–		–
							1604			

CHAPTER 22

PREPARING THE ABSTRACT

Object and Nature of the Abstract.—In splitting up the building into its constituent parts the taker-off follows a systematic method, but his method must normally be such that he has to repeat the same item in different parts of his dimensions. Moreover, he will measure at the same time items that will appear in different sections of the bill, which will be divided either according to the sections of the S.M.M. or more strictly into trades. The function of the abstract is to collect similar items together and to classify them primarily into their sections and subsequently according to certain accepted rules of order and arrangement, with a view to their being in a suitable order for the writing of the bill.

This classification is done by copying the items from the dimension sheets in a tabulated form on large sheets of paper, arranging them, as nearly as practicable, in the order of the eventual bill.

As stated in the previous chapter the need for any abstract is eliminated by use of the 'cut and shuffle' system. In that system the principles behind the abstract are retained, but the sorting is effected by having each item on a separate piece of paper and 'shuffling' them into the correct order.

There are offices that have not adopted that system, and in any case there may be in any office occasional need for an abstract for a small job or for some special purpose.

This chapter assumes the preparation of an abstract in the traditional form.

Numbering the Dimension Sheets.—The dimension sheets being received from the taker-off, they should be examined to see that the pages or columns are numbered as described in Chapter 20, and that no sheets are missing. If sheets have only been temporarily numbered, they should now be given the permanent numbering which will be used for reference on the abstract.

Squaring the Dimensions.—The dimensions must then be 'squared', a term used in a wide sense to mean the calculating of volumes, areas, etc. contained in the dimensions column. The mathematics of the decimal system should be familiar to all, so the detailed instruction on squaring that was found necessary with duodecimals can be dispensed with.

It is most important in writing down the results to be careful that the digits are properly under each other. If this is not done, not only is the time spent in adding up considerably increased, but mistakes are likely to be made of such a nature that they are repeated by a second person checking the cast. It is equally important that all figures are clear and definite, and any tendency to scribble figures must be avoided.

The squaring, as well as casts and mathematical calculations generally, is now done by machine operators, so relieving the technical staff of the drudgery of mental calculation which afflicted the last generation. One must, however, remember that such operators are not technical and may have no idea of the meaning of what they are doing. It is easy for somebody working mechanically to add instead of deducting, and for such a slip to be checked as correct. Clear indication to the operator of what is required is essential, particular attention being given to any unusual requirement which might not be realised.

Checking of Waste Collections.—When the dimensions are squared, all collections and calculations on 'waste', i.e. on the righthand side of the description column, must be checked, each calculation being marked by a tick to indicate that this has been done. If any mistakes are found they should be corrected, and, as collections are sometimes reused several times, the taker-off should be asked to alter such dimensions as are affected by the mistake.

Checking the Squaring.—The dimensions having been squared, the results set down must be checked by a different person, each result being ticked, preferably in red or other coloured ink. Care must be taken not to hurry a series of what appear simple calculations, as it is easy in such cases to overlook a mistake. Where necessary, corrections will be made in a coloured ink, and all such corrections must be cross-checked. Ticks should in all checking be made as closely as possible to the figure checked, as it often happens that dimensions and the resultant squaring are altered. If the tick is placed high and the altered figure is placed above that deleted, it may appear that the corrected figure has been checked.

A special warning should, perhaps, be given of the danger in checking a cubic item, where the person squaring has multiplied two of the dimensions and forgotten to multiply by the third. The checker, having multiplied the two, sees that the result corresponds with what he is checking and, if not fully on the alert, automatically ticks it.

Casting up the Dimensions.—The squaring being checked, the result will now be cast up in groups where necessary as shown by the brackets, which should have been made by the taker-off, thus:

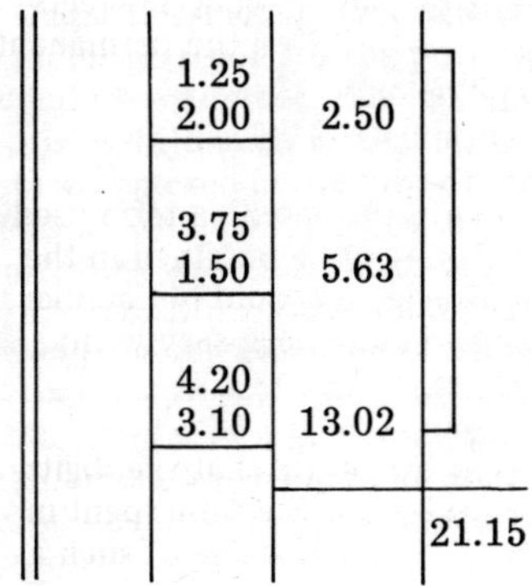

1.25 2.00	2.50	
3.75 1.50	5.63	
4.20 3.10	13.02	
		21.15

Where a deduction immediately follows an item it should, where possible, be made on the dimension sheet, so that only one entry need be made on the abstract, e.g.:

	20.00		
	3.00	60.00	Dist. walls.
	10.00		
	2.00	20.00	
			80.00
4/	1.00		
	2.25	9.00	Ddt.
	1.00		
	2.75	2.75	11.75
			68.25
	2.25		
	3.00	6.75	Add.
	1.25		
	1.00	1.25	8.00
			76.25

It will be noticed that the cast, where it is to be deducted from or added to a previous cast, is put above the line, leaving the space under the line for the result. Casts should not, however, be carried over the end of a column; if an item is broken at the end of a column, it will be entered in two parts on the abstract, and the casts must be prepared accordingly.

Some surveyors are accustomed to entering the cast in the squaring column, but it helps to keep it distinct from the squaring if the totalling line is carried out into the description column and the total written there. It further helps to keep the figures distinct if the casts are made in a different-coloured ink.

Where a number of dimensions are bracketed as described above for casting up together, it may not in some cases be necessary to make any entry in the squaring column. For instance, the following group can be totalled direct from the dimension column:

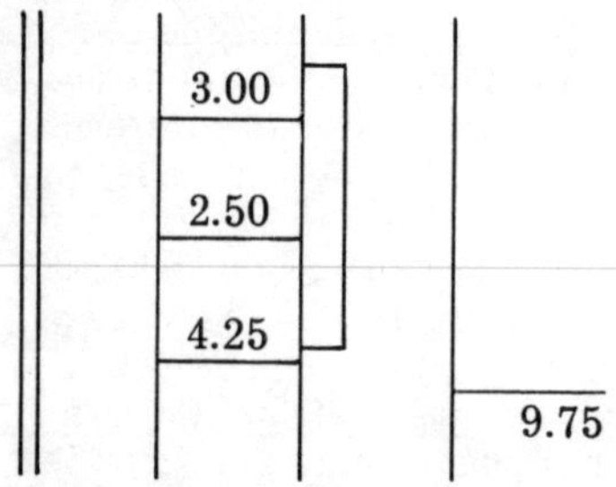

If, however, one or more of the items in the group is timesed, it is safer to enter all in the squaring column (timesed where necessary) before making the cast. Very little extra time is involved by so doing, and the chance of a mistake is lessened.

The dimensions being squared, checked and cast, they are now ready for abstracting.

Abstract Paper.—The abstract paper is usually a double sheet ruled in columns about an inch wide. It should not be torn in half, but the double sheet should be opened flat and used on both sides, first on the face and then on the back, in each case working from the extreme left of the double page towards the right. Sometimes the columns are subdivided with an additional line to separate the main figures from the references. Every sheet should be headed with the name of the job either written or stamped on. The heading of the section and subsection would appear on each page, and as soon as is possible sheets would be numbered consecutively. All headings, numbering, etc., should be in the same relative position in each case, the left-hand top corner being probably the most usual position for the section heading, and the right-hand top corner for the numbering, the name of the job occupying the centre.

Paper printed on one side only can be used, which saves the constant turning over, but, of course, means twice the number of sheets to be handled.

Order in the Abstract.—The following general rules of order are suggested:

(A) Trades or Sections are divided into subsections.

(B) Within each subsection the order followed is cube, square, lineal, numbers.

(C) Labour items precede labour and material items within each subdivision of Rule B.

(D) Timber is classified within each subdivision of Rule B, in order of thickness, the thinnest first.

(E) Except as mentioned in Rules C and D, items within each subdivision of Rule B are placed in their approximate order of value, the cheapest first.

(F) Provisional sums come last in the subsection to which they apply or are cognate, or alternatively form a separate section of their own.

Setting out the Abstract.—Before setting out the abstract an attempt should be made so far as is possible to visualise the form of the bill. To do this the dimensions available should be looked through, and the taker-off consulted as to the general nature of the work. It should also help the abstractor to visualise his work if he looks over the drawings, and so forms an idea of the general character of the building. The actual spacing out of the sheets to suit the various sections is largely a matter of experience. The beginner can help himself to gain this experience by taking one subsection of the abstract at a time, and going through the whole available dimensions, picking out the items which belong to this subsection. This is naturally slower than going straight through the dimensions in the order in which they are written and entering them on the appropriate pages of the abstract. This latter method, which the experienced abstractor will follow, has also the advantage that an abstractor who is thinking of the meaning of his work might be able to point out an omission or error on the part of the taker-off. If a worker-up suspects the possibility of a mistake in the taking off, he should not be afraid to raise the point, as no taker-off is infallible. Even though in nine cases out of ten there may be some proper explanation, the tenth may be of importance.

Placing the Items.—Let it be assumed for a simple case that the abstractor is dealing with the numbers of general brickwork to which he allots two pages (one sheet). Looking through the dimensions he sees a number of items which are practically speaking 'labour only' items, such as holes through walls, ends of iron bars cut and pinned, and he knows that these should in the abstract come before such items as air bricks, soot doors and the like, which are quite definitely labour and material. He may think that one page should be allotted to each group, or half a page to one group and a page and a half to the other, and will space them accordingly. Within the space allotted he will group similar items together, but otherwise he will place them so far as he can judge in order of cost from cheapest to dearest. The chief difficulty of the beginner, even when he has reduced down to a definite empty page the position of an item, is to know exactly where to put it on that page. The knowledge of this comes largely by experience. Knowing that he must leave room in front of it for any likely items which would precede it in the bill, and after it for any items which would follow, he should be reduced to a limited space. As each item is entered the space for subsequent items is more narrowly defined. If items are slightly out of order on the same page the abstractor need not be concerned, as the biller will always look ahead a little, but the abstractor should avoid putting items on the wrong page or section, thus involving transfer by the biller.

Writing Down the Items.—The process of writing down the items, taking the same case, will be as follows: the first item of the section which the abstractor meets on the dimensions may be:

	6		Form opg. 230 x 75 mm for air bricks in 1B wall rendd. around in ct.

Having decided whereabouts on the abstract allotted to Bricklayer's numbers this item will be placed, he will write it down as follows:

Form opg. 230 x 75 mm for air bricks in 1B wall rendd. around in ct.				
6 2				

Each item will be written down in the same way, a line being drawn under the description which is usually written across two or even more columns. Every item will also be referenced to the dimensions, the figure 2 in the above example indicating that the item will be found in column 2 of the dimensions. If each taker-off's dimensions have been numbered separately, the items on Mr. X's sheets may be referenced X 1 or X 2, etc., to indicate column (or page) 1 or 2 of Mr. X's dimensions.

If at a later stage in column 6 in the dimensions the following are met with:

	3		Opg. 230 x 75 mm for air bks. in 1B a.b. & Do. 230 x 75 mm in o.w. inc. cutting out & m.g.

these would be entered on the abstract as follows:

Form opg. 230 x 75 mm for air bricks in 1B wall rendd. around in ct.				
6 / 3	2 / 6 Do. 230 x 75 mm in o.w. inc. cutting out & m.g.			
	3 6			

The second description being written as shown under the underlining of the first, a group is formed, and this grouping can be continued by repeating the process thus:

Form opg. 230 x 75 mm for air bricks in 1B wall rendd. around in ct.				
6 / 3	2 / 6 Do. 230 x 75 mm in o.w. inc. cutting out & m.g.			
	3	6 Do. 230 x 150 mm as first.		
		7	10 Do. 230 x 150 mm in o.w. a.b.	
			2 14	

Each item is put down in the group in the order in which it is met with, irrespective of whether it is exactly the correct order to be followed in the bill. The object of the group is to help in gathering together items which will be grouped together in the bill, it being much easier to pick out the items correctly for a bill in a page of abstract having 6 to 12 groups of this nature than if the items were all set out individually. The biller can settle the order of the groups first, and then deal with the order of individual items within the group. In some cases a group of similar items can be anticipated and the space better utilised accordingly. For instance, the abstractor receiving a batch of dimensions for copper service pipes may find scattered through them a number of unions of various sizes. He can prepare for these by putting a heading in the appropriate space as shown below, covering as many columns as he thinks will be necessary, and write in the size of the various unions in the order in which he comes to them.

Unions w. scr. jt to iron & jt. to copper		
22 mm	35 mm	15 mm
10 74	2 75	8 76

Tees would be dealt with in the same way. Other items which lend themselves to this treatment are timber in floors or partitions, holes through walls, ends cut and pinned, etc.

It is sometimes required to bill an item with two units of measurement, e.g. glass in panes not exceeding 0.10 m^2, but it is also necessary to give the total number of panes in the bill. The taker-off will probably put '(In Nr. 1 each)' at the end of his description of the superficial measurement, as explained on page 30, and the items would be abstracted as square items in the ordinary way, each area being preceded by the number, thus:

6 mm c.s. glass n.e. 0.10 m^2				
12 = 1.00 14 18 = 1.50 16 6 = .50 17				

When these are eventually totalled both the areas and number will be added up, giving a result in the above case: 36 = 3.00, i.e. 3 square metres in Nr. 36 panes.

Deductions.—Certain items in the dimensions will practically always have deductions, e.g. facings or wall plastering which will be deducted for windows, doors, etc., and space will therefore be left to provide for this. If the following item is met with

20.00 3.00	60.00	F & S walls.

and later on the following

3/	1.25 2.00	7.50	Ddt. F & S walls.

this would be set down thus:

F & S walls.			
60.00 17	Ddt.		
	7.50 21		

If it was found necessary to group items having deductions this can be done by extending the first underlining, thus:

F & S walls.			
60.00 17	Ddt.	Do. on o.w.	
	7.50 21	70.00 23	Ddt.
			25.50 25

If an unexpected deduction appears, for which space cannot be provided in the group, it can be written below in the same column as the add, after allowing sufficient space, but there must be no doubt as to which description the ddt. refers to, thus:

Opgs. 230 × 75 mm in 1B for air bks.			
Do. 230 × 75 mm do. in o.w. inc. cuttg. out & m.g.	15 24	Do. 230 × 150 mm do.	
		10 25	Do. 230 × 230 mm do.
4 27			2 27
	Ddt.	Ddt.	
	2 28	2 28	

Writing Short.—It is often convenient for pricing purposes to keep together items in the bill which would under normal rules of order be separated. For example, it is simpler for an estimator to price the fittings on a gutter while he is thinking about the gutter, even though it means dealing with a number in the middle of the lineal items. Items so placed out of their proper category and attached to another are called 'written short' from the way they are written in the bill, which was explained in Chapter 20. In the abstract they are placed as follows:

100 mm H.R. gutter			
140.0 45	S.E.		
	20 45	75 mm outlet	
		10 45	

These items written short are usually confined to numbered items, but some surveyors also write short a lineal item which refers closely to a square one, such as a labour rounded edge to a superficial quantity of shelving. In any case there must be such a close connection between the two items that it would be more convenient for the estimator to price the items in that order.

It sometimes happens that it is more convenient not to write short items which one might think should be so dealt with. For instance, in the case of copper pipes in which there may be six different sizes from 12 mm to 50 mm, each with bends, it is usually best to abstract all the lineal items of pipes and then deal with the bends, unions, etc., in the ordinary way with the numbered items. How far the writing short should be done is largely a matter of personal taste or custom.

Running through the Dimensions.—As each item is entered on the abstract it is run through with a vertical line, the top and bottom of which should be clearly defined. This enables the abstractor to pick out items from the dimensions in any order he likes, and at the same time leave no doubt as to which items he has dealt with and which he has not. As will be seen from the example below, items not dealt with are made to stand out by the break in the vertical line.

	20.00 3.00	60.00	F & S bk. walls & Dist. walls.
2/	2.40	4.80	Extnl. Angle

Some surveyors prefer to draw their line through the squaring column, but this is apt to confuse the figures. It seems better to draw the line through the description, as normally each description involves one entry on the abstract, whereas each figure or group of figures in the squaring column may involve several entries. Another way of running through used by some surveyors and of especial value when descriptions are cramped is this:—

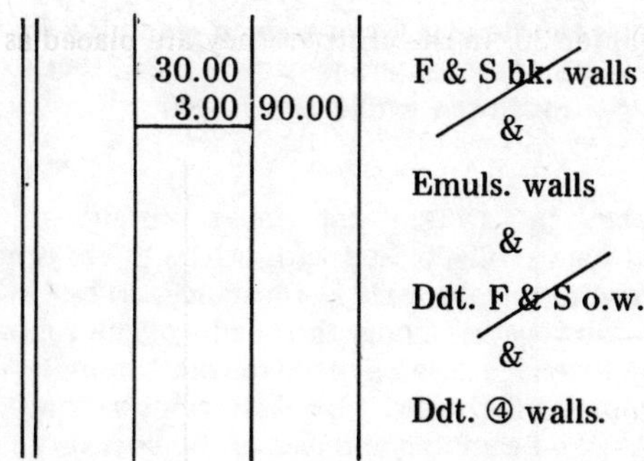

30.00
3.00
90.00
F & S bk. walls
&
Emuls. walls
&
Ddt. F & S o.w.
&
Ddt. ④ walls.

The items entered are marked with a diagonal line, the vertical line being drawn through all four items at once when the whole batch has been dealt with.

Taker-off's Notes.—The subject of notes made by the taker-off is dealt with in Chapter 24. The abstractor should be careful that all instructions to the worker-up are dealt with by being entered in a suitable place on the abstract. For instance, a note such as 'All brickwork is in ct.' would be entered at the head of the Brickwork abstract, or 'Take ④ on all r.w. goods' on the Painting abstract. In each case the dimension sheet would be run through in the ordinary way. On the other hand, care should be taken not to run through a note which the taker-off may have put for his further attention, or it may be missed.

Abbreviations.—It has already been pointed out that descriptions on the dimensions are considerably abbreviated, and the same abbreviations are used in writing the abstract. Although words should be abbreviated wherever possible consistent with clearness, the descriptions should not generally be curtailed, but copied as written on the dimensions, the abstract being really a rearranged and simplified form of the worked-out dimensions. If, however, any description is particularly long it can be merely referred to with a reference sufficiently clear for its identification, so that when billing, the original dimension sheet can be looked up and the description copied. This method should be reserved for very long descriptions only, as the necessity for constant reference to the dimension sheets in billing may waste more time than is saved in abstracting.

Advantage of Space.—The abstractor should always err by taking too much space rather than too little. A crowded abstract wastes a lot of time in billing, time which is much more valuable than the extra paper used to space the work well out. It is even better to waste a little time in copying out portions of the abstract which have become too crowded than to risk the chance of confusion from items getting mixed up. The abstractor should be looking out for the red light ahead and decide as early as possible if any part is to be rewritten. It is very dangerous to do this after it has been partly checked, unless the checking is again very carefully done.

Essentials of a Good Abstract.—A good abstract must have figures neatly and carefully written and with digits properly set out under each other so that no confusion will arise in casting up totals. Items should be well spaced out and arranged where possible in groups so that the biller can easily see his way about. References to the dimensions must be accurate. A careless mistake in writing down the reference sometimes involves waste of a lot of time in searching for the item on the dimensions when adjusting variations, and may even mean that the item cannot be traced without going through the whole dimensions.

Items Billed Direct.—Where items occur in a group in the dimensions and will be grouped together in the bill without being collected up with others, there is no necessity to copy them out *in extenso* in the abstract. For instance, all the work in manholes will probably be measured together under the heading 'The following in No. 10 manholes'. A note can in such a case be made on the Drains abstract in the proper position, 'Manholes B.D. cols. 146—148 inclusive' or 'Manholes B.D. cols. 40—43 A to A' (the beginning and end of the portion to be billed direct being clearly defined by identifying letters written on the dimensions). When the biller reaches this point on the abstract he will look up the reference and write his bill direct from the dimension sheets. It may be even that the whole of the drains can be billed direct. It is most important that the necessary reference should appear on the abstract, otherwise the portion to be billed direct might be forgotten.

Alterations 'en bloc'.—It sometimes happens that the abstractor will find on the dimensions an instruction such as 'Alter all 25 mm shelving to 32 mm' or 'Alter all ④ on iron to ③'. In such cases he has probably abstracted a number of the items as originally described. He should in the first case alter his description to 32 mm and note the reference against the alteration. In the second case he would probably copy out the instructions as written at the top of the page of ④, again with the reference. Unless the alteration and reference are clearly shown, the person checking the abstract will not understand what has happened. If the alteration means that the description becomes duplicated (i.e. if there was some 32 mm shelving or ③ on iron already) the two totals can be easily collected together when the abstract is cast up. It will be seen that an alteration can be made by a taker-off much more simply in this way than by going back and altering all the appropriate dimensions which have been abstracted and possibly checked.

Inserted Items.—Care must be taken to deal with any items inserted or altered in the dimensions after the page in question has been abstracted. If an alteration is made to something already abstracted, the abstract should be altered at once before it is overlooked. In any case, when the abstract is completed the whole of the dimensions should be looked through carefully to see that all calculations are checked and everything dealt with, and at the same time the numbering should be checked to ensure that no pages have been missed.

Abstracting on Dimension Sheets.—It is sometimes possible to prepare the equivalent of an abstract on the dimension sheets, when, perhaps, some simple plumbing can be billed direct, or where measurements are being taken trade by trade. Such collections of similar items will be done in the same way as on the larger abstract, and references to the columns from which transfers are made are equally important to save time when tracing them in the future. These minor abstracts can either be done on any suitable space available on the dimension sheets, or the subsequent figures for each item can be transferred and added to or deducted from the first measurement of the same item.

Example.—For example see end of Chapter 23.

CHAPTER 23

CHECKING AND COMPLETING THE ABSTRACT

Procedure in Checking.—Before the checking of the abstract is begun it should be examined to see that the sheets are properly numbered in sequence to prevent any chance of a sheet being missed. If the writing of the abstract is still in progress the sheets should be numbered through in pencil. In the process of checking, each item on the abstract will be ticked, preferably in red, the tick being placed between the item and the reference. As each item is ticked a red line will be run through the dimensions parallel to the line made by the abstractor and with its ends similarly defined. The process is in fact a repetition of the abstracting, but instead of its being rewritten the abstract as already prepared is ticked or altered where necessary. As in the dimensions so in the abstract figures should not be altered by superimposing, but should be neatly crossed out and rewritten in such a way as to be perfectly clear. Alterations to descriptions should similarly have such part as may be necessary rewritten, the placing of any insertion being clearly marked. All alterations must be cross-checked to avoid the possibility of a mistaken correction. Care should be taken to watch descriptions as well as figures, especially sizes which may be given in the description. It sometimes happens that in an abstract done too hurriedly, say, 45 mm is written as 40 mm or may be misread as such, or other clerical errors are made, sometimes of considerable importance. References, too, should be watched and any omission to give a reference rectified. When the abstract has been completely checked it should be looked through to see that all the items have been ticked. It may happen that the checker has been unable to find an item on the abstract which has not been put where he would expect it. If after looking in any other possible places he cannot find it, he should write it down again in red ink. If the item has already been entered, the final examination of the abstract will reveal it as unticked, and either the original or the rewritten entry can then be deleted.

Casting Up.—When checked the abstract will be cast up, and special care is necessary where long casts are involved. If the casting is done in a coloured ink the confusion which might arise on a crowded sheet will be to a great extent avoided. After casting, all deductions will be transferred to the addition column and the subtraction made, the deduction column being run through (to indicate that this is now finished with), thus:

F & S walls					
1432.00	16	Ddt.			
723.00	17				
212.60	19	94.00	24		
103.00	21	12.00	25		
2470.60		10.60	27		
116.60		116.60			
2354.00					

All casts will of course be checked and ticked. If the casts are long, it is best to defer the transfer of deductions till after the casts are checked, and so avoid unnecessary corrections. The transfer of deductions will also be checked, the transferred entry being ticked and the deduction column run through as before, but this time in red.

Reducing.—The abstract having reached a stage where all casts are made and checked, it is necessary in some cases to 'reduce' totals to the recognised units of measurement used in the bill. For instance, when the unit of billing is the tonne, the weight is obtained by multiplying the number of metres by the weight per metre.

— Dia. steel bars in fdns.			
12 mm		10 mm	
95.00	4	152.00	4
210.00	6	200.00	6
16.00	9	352.00	
321.00			
		352.00 x 0.617 kg = 217 kg = 0.22 Tonne	
321.00 x 0.888 kg = 285 kg = 0.29 Tonne			

Where the weight per metre is not given or known, as for steel joists, etc., it must be ascertained from tables which will be found in the appropriate reference books or the manufacturers' lists.

Example.—In the following example all items in other sections than plumbing with which the dimensions would normally be interspersed, such as holes through walls, paint, &c., have been omitted, as they are not required for the purpose of the example. The crossing out referred to above has also been omitted in both dimensions and abstract for clearness.

A somewhat larger building is here dealt with than the domestic or small industrial building contemplated in the study of taking off, as the beginner in taking off may be expected to have a wider knowledge of working up.

The student is advised to work through the example by ticking each item of the dimensions on the abstract and running it through in the dimensions as explained in Chapter 22.

EXAMPLE 35

TYPICAL PORTION OF AN ABSTRACT WITH ITS DIMENSIONS

Plumbing 1			Down Services
			All pipes are cold water services internally
			The sizes of copper pipes & fittings are outside diameters
			Joints in copper pipes & fittings shall be capillary type
			From Cistern
	1		Extra for 54 mm tank connector with joint to cistern
	2.00		54 mm Copper pipe & fixing to brick or concrete
	2		Made bend to 54 mm pipe
	1		Extra for 54 mm Corner tee
	2		Do for 54 mm reducing coupling
	15.00		42 mm Copper pipe & fixing to brick or concrete
	3		Extra for 42 mm elbow
			1

	1		42 mm Brass screw down stop cock to BS1010 with unions for copper
	1		Extra for 42 mm square reducing tee
	2		Made bend to 42 mm pipe
	1		Made offset 50 mm projection to 42 mm pipe
	1		28 mm Stop cock ab.
	2.00		22 mm Copper pipe ab.
	6.00		
	4.50	12.50	
	3		Extra for 22 mm elbow
	4		Do 22 mm square tee
2•	3	5	Do 22 mm square reducing tee
	3		Made bend to 22 mm pipe
			2

Plumbing 2

Dimension	Total	Description
		Branches to First Floor Fittings (from tee above)
2.00		22 mm Copper pipe ar
4.25		
6.50	12.75	
4.50		15 mm Do
2.50		
7.25	14.25	
7.00		22 mm Copper pipe & fixing in chase
4.50		15 mm Do
6		Ex for 22 mm elbow
4		Do 15 mm do
10		made bend to 22 mm pipe
6		Do to 15 mm do
6		Ex for 22 mm square reducing tee
6		Ex for 15 mm straight tap connector with screwed joint
6		15 mm S.c.ab. with unions for copper

3

Dimension	Total	Description
		Branches to GF Fittings (from tee above)
16.00		22 mm Copper pipe ar
4.00		15 mm Do
3.50		
2.75	10.25	
5.00		22 mm Do in chase
4.50	9.50	
10.00		22 mm Do & embedding in screed
6		Ex for 22 mm elbow
6		Do 15 mm do
4		Made bend to 22 mm pipe
4		Do to 15 mm do
4		Ex for 22 mm square tee
2		Do for 22 mm reducing tee
4		Do for 15 mm tap connector ar
2		Do for 22 mm do

4

			Plumbing 3
	1		Ex for 15 mm bent tap connector with screwed joint
1 ·	4	5	15 mm S.c. a.b. with unions for copper
	2		22 mm Do
			Branch to W.C.s & Urinals (from coupling on col 1)
	10.50		35 mm Copper pipe a.b.
	4.75		35 mm Do in chase
	2		Ex for 35 mm square reducing tee
	8		Do for 35 mm elbow
	6		Made bend to 35 mm pipe
2/	2.50	5.00	15 mm Copper pipe to walls a.b. (urinals
2/	2	4	Made bend to 15 mm pipe
	2		Ex for 15 mm tank connector a.b.
	2		15 mm S.c. a.b. with unions for copper
	3.50		22 mm Copper pipe a.b.
	2.75	6.25	

5

	1.50		22 mm Copper pipe in chase
	2.50	4.00	
	2		22 mm S.c. a.b.
3 ·	2	5	Ex for 22 mm square reducing tee
	1		Do for 22 mm square tee
3/	1.50	4.50	15 mm Copper pipe a.b.
	3		Ex for 15 mm elbow
	3		Made bend to 15 mm pipe
	3		Ex for 15 mm bent tank connector with joint to plastic cistern
	3		15 mm S.c. a.b.
			Branches to Bath Fittings
	11.00		28 mm Copper pipe
	5.00		28 mm Do & embedding in screed
	1		28 mm S.c. a.b.
	6		Made bend to 28 mm pipe
	1		Ex for 28 mm square reducing tee

6

Plumbing 4

	10.50		22 mm Copper pipe to walls
	6.50	17.00	
	3.00		22 mm Do in chase
2	·4	6	Ex for 22 mm elbow
5	·3	8	Made bend to 22 mm pipe
1	·4	10	Ex for 22 mm square reducing tee
2/	5	10	Ex for 15 mm straight tap connector at & 15 mm SC at.

Plumbing Internally – Brass Fittings for Copper Pipes

Extra for elbow

42 mm	22 mm	35 mm	15 mm
3 1	3 2	8 5	4 3
	6 3		6 4
	6 4		3 6
	6 7		
	21		13

Extra for reducing coupling

54 mm
2 1

Extra for straight tap connector with screwed joint

15 mm	22 mm	15 mm bent
6 3	2 4	1 5
4 4		
10 7		
20		

Extra for straight tank connector with screwed joint to plastic cistern

15 mm	54 mm	15 mm bent
2 5	1 1	3 6

Extra for square tee

22 mm	54 mm corner tee
4 2	1 1
4 4	
1 6	
9	

Extra for square reducing tee

42 mm	22 mm	35 mm	28 mm
1 2	5 2	2 5	1 6
	6 3		
	2 4		
	5 6		
	10 7		
	28		

Screwdown stop cock to BS 1010 with unions for copper

42 mm	28 mm	15 mm	22 mm
1 2	1 2	6 3	2 5
	1 6	5 5	2 6
		2 5	
	2	3 6	4
		10 1	
		26	

Plumbing Internally – Cold Water Service Pipes

Preamble Notes on CoC 1

Pipes fixed to brickwork or concrete

54 mm	42 mm	22 mm	15 mm	35 mm	28 mm
2.00 1	15.00 1	12.50 2	14.25 3	10.50 5	11.00 6
		12.75 3	10.25 4		
		16.00 4	5.00 5		
		6.25 5	4.50 6		
		17.00 7			
		64.50	34.00		

Pipes fixed to brickwork or concrete in chase

22 mm	15 mm	35 mm
7.00 3	4.50 3	4.75 5
9.50 4		
4.00 6		
3.00 7		
23.50		

Pipes & embedding in screed

22 mm	28 mm
10.00 4	5.00 6

Made bends

54 mm	42 mm	22 mm	15 mm	35 mm	28 mm
2 1	2 2	3 2	6 3	6 5	6 6
		10 3	4 4		
		4 4	4 5		
		8 7	3 6		
		25	17		

Made offset 50 mm projection

42 mm
1 2

CHAPTER 24

WRITING THE BILL

The writing of the bill is theoretically copying out the quantities and descriptions from the abstract in the form of a schedule or list on paper ruled with money columns for pricing, but in practice it is a good deal more than this. The taker-off may only briefly describe an item in general use, and leave it to the biller to write the full and proper description. Moreover, where several takers-off are working on the same job, their descriptions must be co-ordinated. They cannot always be asking each other the exact wording of the description of a particular item, and so different men will sometimes describe the same thing differently. The biller must therefore understand what he is writing about, and see where different descriptions approach each other so closely as to mean in effect the same thing.

Division into Sections.—The bill of quantities is usually divided up into trades or sections as already explained in the case of the abstract. In certain parts of the country separate tenders are still invited for each trade, but in London and most of England it is usual to invite tenders from a general contractor only. Where separate tenders are invited, the need for separate bills for each trade is obvious, but even where tenders are obtained from a general contractor the division into sections is of assistance in pricing, and simplifies the contractor's work if he wants to sublet any particular trade. Moreover, it is the first step in that subdivision of the bill which enables items to be so classified that they can be easily traced. The sections into which the S.M.M. is divided depart comparatively little from trade classification, and the departures, such as the transfer of block floors and plywood to the general 'Finishings' section, are now well known.

Besides the items actually on the dimensions and abstract, the normal bill has a series of preliminary items, and each trade has a preamble describing the materials and workmanship. These will be more fully dealt with in Chapter 25.

Elemental Bills.—A development has been the elemental bill, in which the sections are elements or constituent parts of the building, e.g. foundations, floor construction, windows, etc., irrespective of the trade or section of the S.M.M. to which they belong. The main purpose of such a bill is to assist a standardised system of cost analysis which may be adopted, particularly where buildings of a similar nature may be repeated. The list of elements will be supplied to the taker-off, who will take off in sections accordingly, and each such section will form a separate bill, the normal order of trades or bill sections being retained within each such bill.

General Principles.—The rules of order given for the abstract will be followed in the bill, and it should therefore be possible to go through the abstract systematically, taking the items practically in the order already written. In the bill no abbreviations will be used in descriptions. The biller must remember that he is preparing what is in most cases a contract document, and he must therefore be absolutely clear. He must have sufficient knowledge of construction to understand the description he writes, and if any appear to him to be vague or in any way not clear he should consult the taker-off as to his exact meaning, and have the description altered if necessary. The draft bill should be written on one side of the paper only, the back being used for any items which may have to be inserted after the main portion is written, such items being clearly referenced to the exact position to which they are to be typed. As each item is written on the draft bill the corresponding item on the abstract will be run through with the pen, thus:

1B. Wall		Deduct.	
		1B.	
18.00	1		
22.00	2		
5.50	2	15.00	4
67.50	3	2.50	4
11.25	3	1.25	4
124.25		18.75	
18.75			
105.50			
= 106 m²			

It will then be clear at any stage what has been billed and what still remains to be dealt with. It will be seen in the above examples that a loop has been formed on lines indicating a transfer of totals, a straight line being reserved for the columns actually billed, so that by looking at any column on the abstract it can be seen at once whether it has been billed or transferred to some other column. The bill of each trade should be begun on a new sheet of paper, the ruling of the paper and typical heading being shown below:

	Description	Unit	Quantity	Rate	£
	BILL No. 4				
	BRICKWORK				
	The bricks to be sound, hard, square, well-burnt local wire-cut bricks, free from stones, cracks and other defects, and equal to a sample to be deposited with and approved by the Architect.				£
	(Here follow the remaining preambles.)				
38	Half brick wall in gauged mortar	m²	682		
	Etc., etc.				

Use of the Columns.—The first (left-hand) column is for item serial references and binding margin. If preferred, a separate line could be ruled to separate binding margin from reference column. The main wide column is for descriptions. Then follow columns for unit of billing, quantity, rate per unit and extension to

£. It is advisable for the unit of billing to be repeated with each item, though some surveyors in the following example would put two dots under 'm^2' and 'm' to indicate repetition.

38	Half brick wall in gauged mortar.	m^2	682		
39	Extra for fair internal face and raking out and pointing with a neat flush joint in cement mortar.	m^2	40		

Very great care must be taken when a change is made from cube to square or square to lineal, as a mistake, easily made when billing in a hurry, may raise a doubt as to the intention. For example, two consecutive items might be:

Concrete in bed not exceeding 100 mm thick	m^3	10		
Labour trowelling top surface smooth.	m^2	8		

If in the second item two dots were put instead of 'm^2' an important difference in price would be involved if the estimator did not realise the misprint. Such errors are very apt to arise where, say, a lineal item is inserted between two square items after the bill is written. Care must be taken in such a case that 'm^2' is written again in the item immediately following that inserted. Enumerated items are usually written thus:

Ends iron bar cut and pinned in cement and making good	Nr.	10		
Ends small rolled steel joists do.	Nr.	5		

When the estimator has put his rate per unit, the money columns can be completed. Where totals are to be carried over, 'Continued £' may be written at the bottom of the pages thus:

Continued	£	

the end of each section being ruled off thus:

Carried to Summary	£	

As it is often considered more convenient to cast up the prices in the bill page by page instead of carrying forward totals, the bill may, if preferred, be prepared accordingly. In such a case each page would have the cash columns headed £, and finished at the foot as above but with the words 'To Collection' instead of 'Continued', space being provided at the end of the trade for a collection to be made, the total of which will be carried to the summary, thus:

		£
Page	1	
,,	2	
,,	3	
,,	4	
Carried to Summary	£	

Or the collection may be made independently, thus:

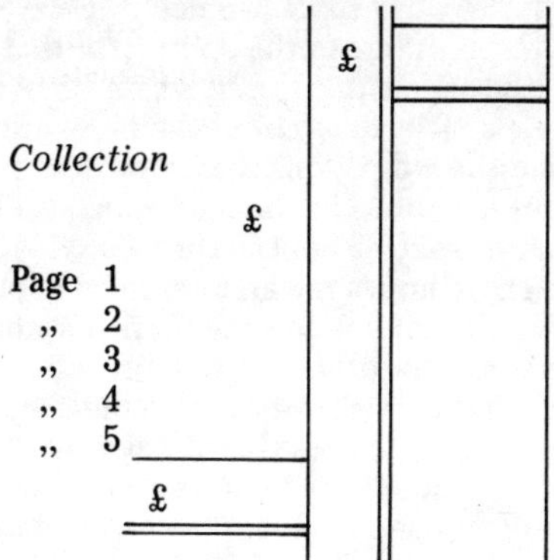

Writing Short.—The meaning and object of writing short has been explained in Chapter 22*. In order not to break the sequence of runs and to identify the item particularly with that immediately preceding, items written short are billed as follows:

Description	Unit	Quantity		
100 mm Half round gutter fixed with and including standard brackets plugged and screwed.	m	140		
Stopped end.	Nr.	20		
75 mm outlet.	Nr.	10		
150 mm Do.	m	125		
Stopped ends.	Nr.	12		
100 mm outlet.	Nr.	6		

From the above it will be seen that the items written short are well inset. For the purpose of the description of the next item, those written short can be ignored, the 'Do.' in the above case referring to the first item. It will also be noticed that these items refer automatically to the item to which they belong without any need to repeat it or refer to it with a ditto.

---

*Page 213.

Unit of Billing.—It will be seen that the S.M.M. lays down the general unit of billing (for other than enumerated items). Steel bar reinforcement and structural steel to be billed by weight are the only exceptions to the general rule that the unit of billing is a metre.

Framing of Descriptions.—Descriptions must be so framed as to leave no doubt as to their meaning. They should in their opening phrase indicate the principal part of the item, and not make it necessary for the estimator to read the whole description before he realises what it is about. However short the description, the horse must come before the cart.

The word 'approved' is a word to be avoided if it leaves a doubt as to price. Its sole justification is to point out to the contractor that he should obtain the architect's approval to the article to be used where there may be a choice of several types of the same article all at about the same price. If some particular material is described and the words 'or other approved' are added to the description, a gambling element is at once introduced which is directly contrary to the purpose of a bill of quantities. One contractor would look round for some cheaper alternative which he hopes the architect will approve, whereas another may think that the architect will require the particular material specified and price accordingly. The words 'or other equal approved' are sometimes inserted by public authorities after the specification of some proprietary article for protection against complaint by critics that A has been specified, when B could have met the requirements equally well and at a lower price, so economising in the expenditure of public money.

The long-winded description, too, must be avoided. Such descriptions as these are found with beginners (the italics indicate the superfluous words):

> *Small* 19 x 19 mm cover fillet.
> *Labour and Material* plugging walls for fixing joinery.
> Bottom and bearers *under*.
> 75 x 100 mm *framed* frame.

There is not normally any reason to describe timber in carcassing work as 'spiked on'. All items include nails and fixing, and if the item is not described as 'framed' or 'plugged' it is to be assumed that nothing further than spiking is required. The same applies to the term 'planted on' in the case of joinery mouldings, etc. Where the two terms are used it should be noted that the former is strictly a carpenter's term, implying the use of spikes or large nails, whereas 'planted on' refers to the fixing with panel pins or small nails.

A description such as the following, which has actually been met with, can be considerably curtailed without loss of anything essential:

> Extra labour and material dubbing out to form plain projecting band 75 mm wide and 7 mm projection circular on plan and continuous round circular opening 0.75 m diameter in ceiling, including two arrises and one narrow return.

This could be more concisely expressed thus:

> Extra for 75 x 7 mm plain projecting band circular continuous round opening 0.75 m diameter, including arrises and one return and dubbing.

Consistency must be observed in the language used even if the difference in terms appears to be unimportant. For instance two consecutive items have been known to be written:

Raking cutting *on* 25 mm boarding.

Circular cutting *to* do.

when the same word should have been used in each case. Although there may be no actual difference in meaning in this case there might be in others, e.g. 'Hole in concrete floor for iron bar' might be read to mean something different from 'Hole through concrete floor for iron bar', or it might be thought that the difference in wording was intended to convey a distinction when in fact it was not.

Two extreme examples of verbosity taken from actual examination papers may be given to emphasise what should *not* be done. In the first the candidate, having measured a two-course external tile sill to a window, took a separate item of the same dimensions as follows:

> 'Fair cutting on bevel to one course of bricks (see sketch), to provide for giving tile sill a slight fall in the direction of its width to throw off rainwater quickly'.

This was accompanied by an isometric sketch. All that was necessary under the S.M.M. of the time was an item of 'Rough-cut splay 5″ wide', or better still an addition to the description of tile sill of 'including rough splay cutting to brickwork under'.

In the second the candidate described a cupboard top as follows:

> '1″ thick wrot deal cupboard top, planed top and undersides and squared ends, crosstongued lengthwise and screwed on to bearers at ends'.

A sufficient description would have been '1″ crosstongued cupboard top screwed', possibly with the addition of 'wrot', though items of composite units may be assumed to be 'wrot' unless otherwise stated.

There is a very definite art to be cultivated by the quantity surveyor of making his descriptions concise but at the same time omitting nothing essential to the estimator in pricing.

Care is necessary in the use of words, which are often found used in a wrong sense. Steel beams or filler joists should not be referred to as reinforcement; they are the structure and the concrete casing is only a clothing, whereas 'reinforcement' is a component part of the structure which is not designed to stand by itself without the help of the concrete. Another common fault in the use of words is the confusion between 'splay' and 'raking'. A little thought would show in any particular case which was the right word to use.

A common fault in descriptions is the use of the architectural designations of mouldings, e.g. torus, ovolo, scotia, etc. These are not normally necessary in the bill of quantities, as the actual contour of the moulding should not materially affect the price. This detail should be left to the architect. For example, a skirting may be described as '25 x 175 mm moulded skirting', a door as '50 mm deal four panel moulded both sides (or moulded on solid both sides) door'.

There is no obligation to adopt the exact terms used by the S.M.M., though to do so naturally relates the item more closely to the appropriate clause of the

S.M.M. So long as the meaning is clearly expressed, the choice of words is a matter for the surveyor.

Ditto.—The word 'ditto' (often abbreviated to 'do.') is one commonly used to abbreviate descriptions, but every effort must be made to make it quite clear to the estimator exactly what is covered by the word. One ditto may be quite sufficient to cover the repetition of a long description, whereas a shorter description may sometimes need two or three. A good rule is to assume that the word ditto covers everything in the preceding description except another ditto and such portion of that description as is obviously superseded by the second description. For instance:

Float and set walls.

Ditto circular on plan.

where ditto refers to the whole description 'Float and set walls'.

Float and set soffite of concrete floors.

Ditto brick walls.

the word 'ditto' quite evidently means no more than 'Float and set' because the term 'brick walls' obviously supersedes 'soffite of concrete floors'. There is sometimes a key word which indicates the limit of the ditto, as for example:

40 x 63 mm Moulded picture rail including 19 mm twice splayed grounds.

40 x 63 mm Ditto including ditto plugged.

In this case the word 'including' is the key word, being repeated in the second example. The first ditto refers to everything in the first description preceding 'including' (except the size, which is repeated), and the second ditto refers to everything after the word 'including'. It is advisable, though not perhaps absolutely necessary, to repeat the size in such cases and not leave it to be covered by the ditto. The word 'ditto' should not be used in the first item on a page, but the description should either be repeated in full or abbreviated by such a phrase as 'all as last described' or 'all as item 234'.

Order of Scantlings.—In describing such an item as a concrete lintel 230 x 150 mm would mean 230 mm on bed and 150 mm high, and this order should be maintained for such items. This is especially important where one of the dimensions applies to a special labour. For example, a 230 x 150 mm moulded stone string course would involve a different amount of labour from a 150 x 230 mm string course. It is therefore in such a case necessary to keep the recognised order of the sizes.

'Making Good'.*—Where several different trades or trade sections are affected by an item of making good the item should be subdivided, e.g. if a hole is cut in a wall with tile hanging one side and plaster the other, the making good should appear in three places:

(a) *General brickwork.*

Cut holes in one brick wall for small pipe and make good.

---

*See page 159 under 'Holes through Walls, etc.'

(b) *Tile hanging.*
Make good vertical tiling around small pipe.

(c) *Plastering.*
Make good plaster around small pipe.

In the same way items of making good terrazzo, glazed tiling, asphalt, etc., may be transferred to their portion of the bill. In the case of fibre board or similar linings the item might be described as 'hole in fibre board for small pipe'. It is well to remember that where pipes pass through a stud partition there is no such thing as 'hole in stud partition' (for the pipes would not normally pass through the studs, but between them): there would be two holes through the covering only. The same applies to floors of wood construction, where a hole in wood flooring and making good of plaster ceiling are alone required.

Where holes are cut or alterations made in existing work, it is essential that the making good to these should be billed separately from that in new construction.

Use of Headings.—A generous use of headings in the bill will help the estimator considerably in finding his way about, and will indicate more clearly the general arrangement of the document. They are generally one of three kinds:

(a) Sectional headings, e.g. Brickwork, Woodwork, etc.

(b) Subsection headings, such as Facings, Windows in Softwood, etc.

(c) Headings which are necessary for the proper explanation of a number of items grouped together, as where manholes or joinery fittings are measured out in detail.

Except the sectional headings, headings should be repeated on each page, so that on opening any particular page it can be seen at once what is being dealt with, instead of having to turn back two or three pages to see this. Where such items as manholes, joinery fittings, etc., are billed together under a heading, it should be quite clear where the items covered by the heading end, and if there is any doubt a note should be put across the description column '(End of . . .)'.

Numbering of Items.—Items in the bill should be marked with a reference for easy identification. The most satisfactory way is to number the items serially right through the draft bill with a numbering machine before the bill is sent for duplicating. This facilitates cross-references within the bill, useful when similar items repeat in different subdivisions, or to refer spot items to each other.

Another way is to use for references serial letters beginning with A on each page. This has the disadvantage that it cannot be done till the duplicating stage, so necessitating blanks for cross-references to be filled in later. Admittedly, slips may be made in machine numbering and new items may be inserted or alterations made after the numbering of the draft has been completed, but these difficulties are easily met by adding a, b, c and so on, e.g. 256a for an inserted item following item 256. Where superfluous numbers arise, they will be inserted in the series with 'not used' typed against them. The great value to the estimator of cross-references overrides such minor irregularities in form.

Abbreviation of Descriptions.—It may happen that the estimate is to be subdivided, e.g. by the need of a separate estimate for a garage or for outside paths, etc. In such cases the description in the bills for the later sections may be abbreviated, a general clause being put at their head as follows:

> The preambles to each section and descriptions of labour and material as set out in the foregoing bills are to apply equally to the following, so far as they are not inconsistent herewith, and the contractor is referred thereto for full descriptions.

Instead of a full description of, say, hardcore the item could be:

Bed of hardcore 150 mm thick.

Where items are numbered serially long descriptions can be avoided by referring to the item number in the previous bills, e.g. 'Eaves corbels as item 146.'

EXAMPLE 36

BILL OF THE ABSTRACT IN EXAMPLE 35

Description	Quantity	£	
Copper Cold Water Service Pipes and Brass Fittings			
The copper tubing shall be light gauge to comply with B.S. 659, Table A. The sizes are outside diameters.			
No bend or curve shall be made in any pipe in such a way as to diminish the waterway.			
Brass fittings shall be capillary type to comply with B.S. 864.			
Prices for copper pipes shall include for fixing with approved pattern unpolished brass strip pipe brackets plugged and screwed with brass screws.			
22 mm Pipes and embedding in cement screed.	10 m		
28 mm Do	5 m		
15 mm Pipes and fixing to brick or concrete.	34 m		
22 mm Do.	65 m		
28 mm Do.	11 m		
35 mm Do.	11 m		
42 mm Do.	15 m		
54 mm Do.	2 m		
15 mm Do. and fixing to brick or concrete in chase.	5 m		
22 mm Do. do.	24 m		
35 mm Do. do.	5 m		
Made bends to 15 mm pipe.	17 Nr.		
Do. to 22 mm do.	25 Nr.		
Do. to 28 mm do.	6 Nr.		
Do. to 35 mm do.	6 Nr.		
Do. to 42 mm do.	2 Nr.		
Do. to 54 mm do.	2 Nr.		
1	To Collection £		

Copper Cold Water Service Pipes and Brass Fittings (contd.)

Description	Quantity		£	
Made offset 50 mm projection to 42 mm pipe.	1 Nr.			
Extra for elbow to 15 mm pipe.	13 Nr.			
Do. to 22 mm do.	21 Nr.			
Do. to 35 mm do.	8 Nr.			
Do. to 42 mm do.	3 Nr.			
Extra for reducing coupling to 54 mm pipe.	2 Nr.			
Extra for 15 mm straight tap connector with screwed joint.	20 Nr.			
Do. for 22 mm do.	2 Nr.			
Do. for 15 mm bent do.	1 Nr.			
Extra for 15 mm straight tank connector with screwed joint to plastic cistern.	2 Nr.			
Do. for 54 mm do.	1 Nr.			
Do. for 15 mm bent do.	3 Nr.			
Extra for 22 mm square tee.	9 Nr.			
Extra for 54 mm corner tee.	1 Nr.			
Extra for 22 mm square reducing tee.	28 Nr.			
Do. for 28 mm do.	1 Nr.			
Do. for 35 mm do.	2 Nr.			
Do. for 42 mm do.	1 Nr.			
15 mm screwdown Stopcocks to BS 1010 with unions to copper.	26 Nr.			
22 mm do.	4 Nr.			
28 mm do.	2 Nr.			
42 mm do.	1 Nr.			
		£		
		Page 1		
Carried to Summary		£		

CHAPTER 25

PRELIMINARY ITEMS, PREAMBLES TO THE TRADES, SUMMARY, ETC.

Reference to S.M.M.

A 8
B 1–14

These portions of the bill are here discussed after the general billing of each trade, as in actual practice they are usually last to be drafted, or they are at any rate left to a late stage. Where a full specification is supplied this will form the basis of these clauses, and if the work measured has been run through in the specification as previously suggested, the clauses not yet dealt with will stand out clearly.

Constitution of Preliminary Bill.—It must be remembered that the bill of quantities must set out all circumstances and conditions which may affect the estimator's price. Such items as are of a general nature and not referring to any particular trade will be set out in a 'Preliminary' bill. A full list of the most usual items will be found in the S.M.M., but the special requirements of each job must not be overlooked. A number of the items referred to in the S.M.M. will be fully described in the Conditions of Contract, and therefore need not be described again in full in the bill of quantities, if reference is made to the form of contract in a clause stating that it is to be read as incorporated in the bill, and the titles of the clauses set out in schedule form. The form of contract must, of course, be available for inspection by the estimator, and the decision as to what clauses require pricing must be left to him.

Modification of Conditions of Contract.—Special clauses may sometimes have to be added to the conditions of contract in the case of public work to comply with the standing orders of the local authority or other body concerned, e.g. as to employment of local labour. Any modifications of a specified form of contract which are contemplated should be made clear in the bill of quantities for the contractor to note at the time of tendering. Such modifications, however, should also be made in the contract itself which is being signed, as it is not advisable to rely on a clause in the bill of quantities alone (even though it may be one of the contract documents) on a matter which properly belongs to the conditions of contract. Clause 12(1) of the J.C.T. form emphasises that the bills of quantities are only concerned with the quality and quantity of the work, and the end of that paragraph makes it clear that the bill cannot override the contract.

P.C. Items and Provisional Sums.—A special note may be made as to these, their definition being important. The extent to which they are defined in the form of contract should be examined, as some supplementary definition may be necessary. It will be seen that S.M.M. A 8 gives a definition to apply unless otherwise provided.

There must be no doubt as to what cash discount the contractor can reckon on as included in the p.c. items in the bill of quantities. If he knows he will receive 5 per cent cash discount he may add little or no profit, but if he is to receive no discount at all he must add in his tender the whole sum that he requires over and above what he has to pay out. It will be seen therefore that tenders are substantially affected by any doubt as to the discount. The conditions of Contract in the J.C.T. form make it clear that the p.c. sums for work to be carried out on the site by 'nominated subcontractors' referred to in clause 27 are to include a cash discount of 2½ per cent, and p.c. sums for goods to be supplied by 'nominated suppliers' referred to in clause 28 (and fixed by the contractor) are to include a cash discount of 5 per cent. One cannot but think that the position would have been considerably simplified if the same percentage had been fixed in both cases. As it is, the architect every time he asks for an estimate must think whether he should ask for it as subject to 2½ per cent or 5 per cent, and the estimator every time he prices a p.c. item in the bill of quantities has to ask himself the same question, possibly sometimes getting the wrong answer. The type of clause, unfortunately still seen in some contracts, which says that the contractor may retain a cash discount not exceeding 2½ (or 5) per cent, if allowed, is to be strongly deprecated, as introducing an unnecessary gambling element.

Where a provisional sum is intended for work to be carried out by the contractor himself, either as a general contingency or as a lump sum to cover something indefinite, that provision would include no discount, but would include the contractor's profit on any work to be set against it. This is best conveyed by carrying the amount out to the cash column, without any clause asking the contractor to add profit to that item, so indicating that the work to be set against it will be valued to include contractor's profit.

Further, it must be made clear to the estimator whether p.c. prices for materials include for delivery to station or to site. Railway carriage on the goods should be included in the p.c. price, as the estimator cannot be expected to price carriage from an unknown source. The cost of returning empties need not be mentioned (S.M.M. B 10.2); though the estimator cannot price it accurately, he usually can do so within a reasonable margin. Where the site is near a large town, so that merchants would usually deliver by lorry direct to the site, p.c. prices should include delivery to the site, and if any are actually delivered to station the cartage from station to site can afterwards be allowed to the contractor and set against the p.c. price.

Preambles to Each Section.—The bill of each section and sometimes separate subsections will be preceded by clauses applying to the section or subsection generally. These are usually in the nature of a specification of materials and workmanship, which by being put at the head of the section or subsection helps to curtail descriptions in the body of the bill. For instance, the Brickwork bill will have clauses as to type and quality of bricks, composition and mixing of mortar, etc., so that a reference to cement mortar or lime mortar in the body of the bill will be fully understood without further description. The example on page 235 shows the items relative to the copper services there billed.

Drafting from Previous Bills.—In practice the 'Preliminary' bill and trade preambles are often drafted from a proof or spare copy of a previous bill, and in such cases special care is necessary to see that the items previously used really apply to the work in hand. Each item should be considered in turn and where necessary adapted. Further, if, as sometimes happens, an item is forgotten in the Preliminary Bill, the danger of its being forgotten again, when that bill is used as a draft for another, must be guarded against.

The Summary.—It is usual to bring the bills of each section to separate totals to be carried to a general summary. This summary will set out the titles of the sectional bills with a cash column for totalling. Space should be provided below the total for the pricing of Water, Fire, etc., Third Party, Employer's Liability Insurances, etc., which, being based on the cost of the works, are more conveniently priced here. The following may also be provided for in this position:

Holidays with Pay contributions
Guaranteed weekly minimum wage

A total will again be made, and if it is required to show separately any credit for old materials, the total will again be made and space provided for a deduction of the amount of credit, the final result being marked as 'Carried to Form of Tender'.

Cover, Endorsement and Index.—Front cover sheet must be drafted to suit the circumstances: it should have title of the work, date and architect's name and address as well as surveyor's name and address. If the volume is a portion only of a larger bill, the portion should be clearly defined. An index on a separate sheet bound inside the front cover is useful, especially in the case of a large bill or where the bills for a number of different estimates are bound together.

CHAPTER 26

CHECKING THE BILL

The Process of Checking.—The bill being written, it must be very carefully checked from the abstract, each item being ticked in red ink on the left of the draft bill or against the quantities, and the item in the abstract being at the same time run through in red. The various points to be looked for are:

(a) In each item—

(1) Correctness of figures.

(2) Do. of unit for pricing, watching particularly changes from one unit to another, i.e. from cube to square, square to lineal, etc., properly indicated.

(3) Correctness of descriptions, especially as to figures.

(b) Generally—

(1) Sections and subsections of the bill properly headed and headings carried over where necessary.

(2) Order of the items.

(3) Proper provision for page totals and their carrying forward or collection.

These may sound fairly simple, but it is extremely easy in the rush to finish a bill, which is quite usual, for some inaccuracy to be overlooked. A 40 mm fascia on the abstract may be billed as 45 mm, especially if the abstractor's figures are at all slovenly. Special care is necessary in checking items transferred or inserted from the back of the sheet, to see that such insertion does not disturb the sequence of descriptions, perhaps making meaningless a 'ditto' or 'as last' in the item following the insertion.

Numbering Pages and Items.—It is important to see that pages of the draft bill are numbered in sequence before checking is begun, as a missing page lost after checking might not be noticed, as it must be when the bill is being checked. If one of the later sections has to be checked before the earlier, the pages should be given temporary numbering and the complete section pinned up or fastened with a string-tag so that parts cannot be separated or mislaid.

When the bill is complete it should be all fastened together and finally looked through to see that all pages are in sequence, and covers, index, summary, etc., provided for. The numbering of items has been referred to on page 233.

Printer's Proof.—A word may perhaps be said as to the checking of a proof, which should always be obtained from the reproducing firm, as this is a further stage in checking the final product. Besides the actual comparing of words and figures, which is of course important, and in which special care should be taken to see that figures are correct and in the right unit, special attention should be given to the reproduction of headings and the first items on each page, as the pages will probably be broken at a different place in the printed bill from the draft. A slip may also be made where two or more similar items follow each other. In one case in actual practice a building was so designed that it had certain steel beams at each floor level (at a time when it was required to bill steelwork at each level separately), the weight at each level being the same. These were billed as successive items, the only distinction being the mention of the particular floor level. The quantities were the same for three successive items, one of which was missed by the printers and not noticed in the proof. The result might have been much worse than it was.

General Final Check.—The whole of the dimensions and abstract should be examined carefully to see that all processes have been ticked as checked and all items run through in the proper way. Any queries or notes apparently not dealt with should be brought to the notice of the taker-off or other person concerned. An opportunity should be given to the taker-off to look through the bill, as he may find that his intentions have been misinterpreted by the worker-up, and errors in descriptions will sometimes stand out to his eyes where they would otherwise pass unnoticed. An approximate check of the main items can also be made by himself or an independent taker-off by taking approximate measurements on the following lines:

(1) Compare strip surface and floor areas, making allowance for the external walls and projection of strip surface outside.

(2) Check total of cube excavation with total cube of disposal of soil measured.

(3) Measure total floor area of the building on all floors inside external walls (ignoring internal walls), and compare with a collection of all floor finishings in the bill.

(4) Make an approximate measurement of brickwork, deducting all openings.

(5) Count up windows and doors and see that the total number of each compares with the numbers billed. Ironmongery, too, could be compared with the totals.

(6) Check over sanitary fittings with those billed.

(7) Measure approximate area of roof tiling, slating or flat roofing and check with bill.

(8) Check approximately any important items which lend themselves to this, e.g. length of copings, cornices and eaves gutters, number of stoves, chimneypieces, cupboards, etc.

(9) Compare the Painting bill with the corresponding items in other sections so far as possible, e.g. take total area of all types of plaster and compare with total area of all types of decoration on plaster. Similarly compare quantity of gutters and rainwater pipes, heads and other ironwork with the painting items, and look through the Metalwork bill for any ironwork items on which paint may have been missed.

The check must not be expected to produce an exact comparison. It is principally to ensure that the quantities are not wildly out through some serious mistake, and if it gives figures reasonably near those in the bill it will serve its purpose. Other items besides those mentioned above will occur to one on looking through any individual bill. If this checking cannot be done before the bills are sent out, it can be done during the period before tenders are delivered, any corrections to the printed bill being circulated to contractors. A large number of items, cannot, of course, be checked at all without a good deal of labour which is not usually undertaken, unless there is some doubt or nervousness about the taker-off's ability. It cannot be emphasised too clearly that a surveyor must be able to feel that confidence in his takers-off that a general should feel in his subordinate commanders in battle, and that in the case of a large building once the attack is launched the surveyor can in the same way do little but exercise general supervision and control, and must rely on the tactics and skill of his subordinates for success or failure.

APPENDICES

APPENDIX 1

ABBREVIATIONS

The abbreviations here given are those in most common use and must be supplemented by others which may be customary in any office. Contractions of words are very commonly made by the omission of several letters, and, their meaning being usually obvious from the context, they are not included in this list, except in one or two cases of words very frequently met with. In some cases, as will be seen, the same abbreviations may have two or more meanings according to the context.

a.b.	as before.
a.d.	as described.
a.f.	after fixing. angle fillet.
ard.	around.
asp.	asphalt.
av.	average.
b. & p.	bed and point.
b.b.	blue brick.
b.c.	bib cock.
b.d.	bill direct.
b.e.	both edges. bossed ends.
b.f.	before fixing.
b.i.	built in.
b.m.	birdsmouth.
b.n.	bullnosed.
b.o.e.	brick on edge.
b.s.	both sides.
bal.	baluster.
bast.	basement.
bdd.	beaded. boarded.
bdg.	boarding.
bkk. bwk.	brickwork
bkt.	bracket.
blbd.	blockboard.
bldg.	building.
brrs.	bearers.
c. & f.	cut and fit.
c. & p.	cut and pin.
c. & s.	cups and screws.
c. & w.	cutting and waste.
c.b.	common brickwork.
c.c.	curved (or circular) cutting.
c.c.n.	close copper nailing.
c.i.	cast iron.
c.j.	ceiling joist. close jointed.
c.l.	centre line.
c.n.	copper nailing.
c.o.e.	curved (or circular) on elevation.
c.o.p.	curved (or circular) on plan.
c.p.	chromium plated.
c.s.	clear sheet (glass)
chfd.	chamfered.
chy.	chimney.
clg.	ceiling.
cos.	course.
csk.	countersunk.
ct.	cement
cupd.	cupboard.
d.b.	direct to bill.
d.c.	dormer cheek.
d.p.c.	damp-proof course.
ddt. ded.	deduct.
dp.	deep.
e.g.	eaves gutter.
e.m.l.	expanded metal lathing.
emul.	emulsion.
e.o.	extra only. extra over.
e.s.	edges shot.
e.w.m.	elsewhere measured.

ea.	each.
exc.s.t.	excavate surface trench.
f.a.i.	fresh air inlet.
f.c.c.	fair curved cutting.
f.e.	fitted end ('fair end' best written in full to distinguish). feather edged.
f.f.	fair face.
f.l. & b.	framed ledged and braced.
f.o.	fixing only.
f.s.	flat sweep.
f. & s.	float and set.
fcgs.	facings.
fdns.	foundations.
fin.	finished.
flg.	flooring.
fr.	frame.
frd.	framed.
fwk.	formwork.
g.b. & b.	glued, blocked and bracketed.
g.i.	galvanised iron.
g.m.	gunmetal.
gth.	girth.
h.b.s.	herring bone strutting.
h.b.w.	half-brick wall.
h.c. h.d.c.	hardcore.
h.j.	heading joint.
h.m.s.f.	hand-made sand faced.
h.n. & w.	head, nut and washers.
h.p.	high pressure.
h.r.	half round. hand rail. heat resisting.
hsed.	housed.
ht.	height.
hth.	hearth.
h.w.	hardwood. hollow wall.
impreg.	impregnated.
inc.	including.
intl.	internal.
jst.	joist.

jt.	joint.
k.p.s. & p.	knot, prime, stop and paint.
l. lab.	labour.
l. & b.	ledged and braced.
l. & m.	labour and materials.
l. & p.	lath and plaster.
l. & r.	level and ram.
l.c. & w.	labour cutting and waste.
l.p.f. & s.	lath, plaster, float and set.
l.s.	lead service.
la.	large.
lt.	light.
m.c.	metal casement.
m.e.	match existing.
m.g.	make good.
m.h.	manhole.
m.l.	mortice lock.
m.s.	measured separately. meeting stiles. mild steel.
mis.	mitres.
mo.	moulded.
msd.	measured.
n.e.	not exceeding.
n.w.	narrow widths.
o.e.	one edge. other edge. one end. other end.
o.s.	one side. one stile.
o.w.	old wall.
opg.	opening.
③	three oils.
p. & c.	parge and core.
p. & s.	planking and strutting.
p.b.	plinth block. plaster board.
p.c.	prime cost.

P.ct.	Portland cement.
p.f.	plain face.
p.m.	purpose made.
p.o.	planted on.
p.p.	polished plate.
p.r.	picture rail.
P.s.	Portland stone.
p.s.	pressed steel.
plas.	plaster.
ppt.	parapet.
pr.	pair.
pt.	point.
ptn.	partition.
q.t.	quarry tile.
r. & g.	rubbed and gauged.
r. & s.	render and set.
r.c. & w.	raking cutting and waste.
r.c.	reinforced concrete. rough cut. raking cutting.
r.f. & r.	return, fill and ram.
r.f. & s.	render, float and set.
r.l.j.	red lead joint.
r.m.e.	returned mitred end.
r.o.j.	rake out joints.
r.r.e.	returned rounded end.
r.s.j.	rolled steel joist.
r.w.p.	rainwater pipe.
reb.	rebated.
rem.	remove.
retd.	returned.
ro.	rough.
rodd.	rounded.
s.b.j.	soldered branch joint.
s.c.	stop cock.
s.e.	stopped end. soldered end.
s.f.	stepped flashing.
s.g.	salt glazed.
s.j.	soldered joint.
s.l.	short length.
s.n.	swan neck.
s.o.	setting only.
s.p.	small pipe.
s.q.	small quantities.
s.t.	surface trench.
s.w.	stoneware. softwood.
sk.	sunk.
sktg.	skirting.
sq.	square.
t. & g.	tongued and grooved.
t. & r.	treads and risers.
t.c.	terra-cotta.
t.p.	turning piece.
w.	with
w. & f.	wrot and framed.
w.g.	white glazed.
w.i.	wrot iron.
w.l.	wash leather.
w.p.	wax polish.
w.p.e.	white porcelain enamelled.
w.s. & ③	wash, stop and three oils.
w.w.p.	water waste preventer.
wdw.	window.
wt.	weight. wrot.
x grain.	cross grain.
x tgd.	crosstongued.
xtg.	existing.
xtl.	external.
Y.s.	York stone.

APPENDIX 2

TYPICAL SCHEDULE OF WINDOWS

D.H. Sash

First Floor	Size of Opg.		1½B	H.w.	Sqs. ea.	Walls	Glass
2	0.90 x 1.50 m		1	1	12	Emul.	1/Ob.
1	0.75 x 1.40 m		—	1	8	Gloss.	
2	1.40 x 1.50 m	2 lt.	1	1	16	Emul.	
5							
Ground Floor							
2	0.90 x 1.70 m		2	—	12	Emul.	
1	0.75 x 1.50 m		1	—	8	Gloss.	
2	1.80 x 1.70 m	2 lt.	2	—	24	Emul.	
5							

Casement

First Floor	Size of Opg.		1½B	H.w.	Sqs. ea.	Walls	Glass
1	1.80 x 2.00 m	2 lt. T*	—	1	20	Emul.	Ob.
1	1.20 x 1.20 m	2 lt.	1	—	12	Emul.	
2							
Ground Floor							
1	0.75 x 1.20 m		1	—	6	Emul.	Ob.
1							

Metal

First Floor	Size of Opg.		1½B	H.w.	Sqs. ea.	Walls	Glass
1	0.30 x 0.60		1	—	2	Gloss	
1							
Ground Floor							
1	0.30 x 0.90 m		1	—	3	F.F. & Emul.	
1							
15			11	4			

In the above schedule the sizes given will be those of the brick opening from which the size of casements, etc., must be calculated. Thicknesses and internal finish of walls are given for deductions, the number of squares in *each* window for calculating glass, and those windows to be glazed with obscure glass are so marked.

---

*T = with transome.

INDEX